TH
BKS
TH
4571
G85
046443 CIV
MW00657893

Guidelines for Seismic Evaluation and Design of Petrochemical Facilities

Prepared by the
TASK COMMITTEE ON SEISMIC EVALUATION AND DESIGN OF PETROCHEMICAL FACILITIES
of the
PETROCHEMICAL COMMITTEE of the
ENERGY DIVISION of the
AMERICAN SOCIETY OF CIVIL ENGINEERS

BKS TH/4571/G85
American Society of Civil Engineers . Task Committee
Guidelines for seismic evaluation and design of petrochemical facilities
046443 CIV

Rec'd 94605

Published by
ASCE American Society of Civil Engineers
345 East 47th Street
New York, New York 10017-2398

Abstract:

These guidelines are intended to provide practical recommendations on several areas which affect the safety of a petrochemical facility during and following an earthquake. In the area of new design, these guidelines emphasize interpretations of the intent of building codes as applied to petrochemical facilities, and practical guidance on design details and considerations which are not included in building codes. For existing facilities, these guidelines provide evaluation methodologies which rely heavily on experience from past earthquakes, coupled with focused analyses. The guidelines emphasize methods to address seismic vulnerabilities which are not covered by building codes, but which can be identified by experienced engineers. This document also provides background information and recommendations in several areas related to seismic safety where the civil engineer may be interacting with other disciplines and with plant operations. These areas include seismic hazards, contingency planning, and post-earthquake damage assessment.

Library of Congress Cataloging-in-Publication Data

Guidelines for seismic evaluation and design of petrochemical facilities / prepared by the Task Committee on Seismic Evaluation and Design of Petrochemical Facilities of the Petrochemical Committee of the Energy Division of the American Society of Civil Engineers.

p. cm.

ISBN 0-7844-0264-7

1. Petroleum refineries--Design and construction. 2. Earthquake engineering. I. American Society of Civil Engineers. Task Committee on Seismic Evaluation and Design of Petrochemical Facilities.

TH4571.G85 1997 97-20918

693.8'52--dc21 CIP

The material presented in this publication has been prepared in accordance with generally recognized engineering principles and practices, and is for general information only. This information should not be used without first securing competent advice with respect to its suitability for any general or specific application.

The contents of this publication are not intended to be and should not be construed to be a standard of the American Society of Civil Engineers (ASCE) and are not intended for use as a reference in purchase specifications, contracts, regulations, statutes, or any other legal document.

No reference made in this publication to any specific method, product, process or service constitutes or implies an endorsement, recommendation, or warranty thereof by ASCE.

ASCE makes no representation or warranty of any kind, whether express or implied, concerning the accuracy, completeness, suitability, or utility of any information, apparatus, product, or process discussed in this publication, and assumes no liability therefore.

Anyone utilizing this information assumes all liability arising from such use, including but not limited to infringement of any patent or patents.

Photocopies. Authorization to photocopy material for internal or personal use under circumstances not falling within the fair use provisions of the Copyright Act is granted by ASCE to libraries and other users registered with the Copyright Clearance Center (CCC) Transactional Reporting Service, provided that the base fee of $4.00 per article plus $.25 per page is paid directly to CCC, 222 Rosewood Drive, Danvers, MA 01923. The identification for ASCE Books is 0-7844-0264-7/97/$4.00 + $.25 per page. Requests for special permission or bulk copying should be addressed to Permissions & Copyright Dept., ASCE.

Copyright © 1997 by the American Society of Civil Engineers,
All Rights Reserved.
Library of Congress Catalog Card No: 97-20918
ISBN 0-7844-0264-7
Manufactured in the United States of America.

ASCE Petrochemical Energy Committee

This publication is one of five state-of-the-practice engineering reports produced, to date, by the ASCE Petrochemical Energy Committee. These engineering reports are intended to be a summary of current engineering knowledge and design practice, and present guidelines for the design of petrochemical facilities. They represent a consensus opinion of task committee members active in their development. These five ASCE engineering reports are:

1) *Design of Anchor Bolts in Petrochemical Facilities*

2) *Design of Blast Resistant Buildings in Petrochemical Facilities*

3) *Design of Secondary Containment in Petrochemical Facilities*

4) *Guidelines for Seismic Evaluation and Design of Petrochemical Facilities*

5) *Wind Loads on Petrochemical Facilities*

The ASCE Petrochemical Energy Committee was organized by A. K. Gupta in 1991 and initially chaired by Curley Turner. Under their leadership the five task committees were formed. More recently, the Committee has been chaired by Joseph A. Bohinsky and Frank J. Hsiu.

Frank J. Hsiu Chevron Research and Technology Company chairman	J. Marcell Hunt Hudson Engineering Corporation secretary

Joseph A. Bohinsky	Brown & Root, Inc.
William Bounds	Fluor Daniel, Inc.
Clay Flint	Bechtel, Inc.
John Geigel	Exxon Chemical Company
Ajaya K. Gupta	North Carolina State University
Magdy H. Hanna	Jacobs Engineering Group
Steven R. Hemler	Eastman Chemical Co.
Gayle S. Johnson	EQE International, Inc.
James Maple	J. A. Maple & Associates
Douglas J. Nyman	D. J. Nyman & Associates
Norman C. Rennalls	BASF Corporation
Curley Turner	Fluor Daniel, Inc.

THE ASCE TASK COMMITTEE ON SEISMIC EVALUATION AND DESIGN OF PETROCHEMICAL FACILITIES

This document was prepared to provide guidance in the seismic design of new petrochemical facilities and the seismic evaluation of existing facilities. Though the makeup of the committee and the writing of this document are directed at petrochemical facilities, these guidelines are applicable to similar situations in other industries. The intended audience for this document includes structural design engineers, operating company personnel responsible for establishing seismic design and construction standards, and local building authorities.

The task committee was established because of a significant interest in the petrochemical industry in addressing the wide variation of design and construction practices and standards that are applied throughout the country with regards to the petrochemical industry. Another primary purpose was to address the need for consistent evaluation methodologies and standards for existing facilities. Most governing building codes and design standards address only new design, and it is recognized that it would be prohibitively expensive to retrofit existing facilities to meet current standards. It is also recognized that standards for new design do not address all of the conditions that may be found in existing facilities.

These guidelines are intended to provide practical recommendations on several areas which affect the safety of a petrochemical facility during and following an earthquake.

In the area of new design, these guidelines emphasize interpretations of the intent of building codes as applied to petrochemical facilities, and practical guidance on design details and considerations which are not included in building codes.

For existing facilities, these guidelines provide evaluation methodologies which rely heavily on experience from past earthquakes, coupled with focused analyses. The guidelines emphasize methods to address seismic vulnerabilities which are not covered by building codes, but which can be identified by experienced engineers.

This document also provides background information and recommendations in several areas related to seismic safety where the civil engineer may be interacting with other disciplines and with plant operations. These areas include seismic hazards, contingency planning, and post-earthquake damage assessment.

In helping to create a consensus set of guidelines, a number of key individuals dedicated significant amounts of time to formulating, writing, and reviewing in detail specific sections of this document. Those members are identified below.

The ASCE Task Committee on Seismic Evaluation and Design of Petrochemical Facilities

Gayle S. Johnson EQE International, Inc. Chairman	Frank J. Hsiu Chevron Research & Technology Co. Vice-Chairman

Leo Bragagnolo	EQE International, Inc.
Sohrab Esfandiari	ENOVA Engineering Services
Martin L. Eskijian	California State Lands Commission
Orhan Gurbuz	Bechtel Corporation
Ron Haupt	Pressure Piping Engineering
Pete Hults	Chevron Research & Technology Co.
Makis Manetas	PMB Engineering
Bill McCarron	Amoco Worldwide Engineering and Construction
Tom Miller	Unocal Corporation
Rudy Mulia	Vectra Technologies
Ahmed Nisar	Dames & Moore
Douglas J. Nyman	D. J. Nyman & Associates
Phil Richter	Fluor Daniel, Inc.
Mufid Samara	Brown and Root, Inc.
Tim Sheckler	Chevron Research & Technology Co.
Paul B. Summers	Dames & Moore
Mike Whitten	Fluor Daniel, Inc.
Sheng Wu	Bechtel Corporation

The committee would like to thank the following individuals for their reviews and other contributions.

Reviewers and Other Contributors

Nguyen Ai	Jacobs Engineering
Junius Allen	Arco Exploration and Production Technology / Gas Processors Association
Bob Bachman	Fluor Daniel, Inc.
Joe Bohinsky	Brown and Root, Inc.
Michael Craig	Unocal Corporation
Del Forbes	Exxon Research and Engineering
Khurram Gaba	Esso Engineering, Europe
Vernon Greggerson	El Paso Natural Gas / Gas Processors Association
Timothy K. Hasselman	ACTA Inc.
Mark R. Legg	ACTA Inc.
Al Wussler	El Paso Natural Gas / Gas Processors Association

CONTENTS

CONTENTS (Cont.)

CONTENTS (Cont.)

Chapter 1
INTRODUCTION

1.1 OBJECTIVE

Many different codes and standards are used in the structural and seismic design and assessment of petrochemical facilities. Many of these codes have been developed primarily for use in the design of buildings, and generally offer insufficiently detailed guidelines for complete design and evaluation of structures commonly found in petrochemical facilities. The engineer is often forced to rely on broad subjective interpretation of the intent of these codes to develop detailed design criteria and procedures as they apply to items found in petrochemical facilities. Consequently, these facilities may be designed and built with inconsistent degrees of conservatism and design margins.

There are also no widely accepted standards for the seismic evaluation of existing facilities. As the public and regulators become more aware of environmental and safety issues associated with such facilities, regulators, owners, and engineers have an ever increasing need for a consistent approach and a technically sound, practical basis for performing evaluations.

Recognizing the need for design and evaluation guidelines in several technical areas specifically applicable to petrochemical facilities, the American Society of Civil Engineers (ASCE) Energy Division set up the Petrochemical Energy Committee to undertake the effort to fill the existing gap in establishing criteria and guidance for practical application. The Seismic Task Committee of the Petrochemical Energy Committee was charged with development of this document.

This document has been developed to provide practical guidance to engineers involved in the seismic design and evaluation of petrochemical facilities. It is intended to serve several objectives:

a. to help practicing engineers better understand the intent behind certain provisions of seismic design codes, so that the codes and provisions can be more properly and uniformly applied to structures and systems typically found in petrochemical facilities.

b. to provide guidance for seismic engineering practice beyond that covered in the building codes.

c. to provide background information on technical areas that are related to the seismic evaluation of petrochemical facilities, but not always well understood by civil engineers.

d. to provide guidance specific to the seismic evaluation of existing petrochemical facilities.

e. to provide practical analytical guidance specifically applicable to petrochemical facilities.

f. to alert engineers and operations personnel to areas other than structural where earthquakes might affect the safety of petrochemical facilities, such as contingency planning, post-earthquake damage inspection, and operational issues.

The topics included in this document address seismic design and related construction of new structures and components as well as evaluation and retrofit design of existing structures and systems in petrochemical facilities. The scope generally emphasizes work that is commonly under the direction of an engineer.

Despite the attempt to make this a comprehensive document, it is recognized that there will be applicable topics not fully covered. In all instances, it is ultimately the responsibility of engineers involved in the design or evaluation process to use their professional judgment to ensure that applicable safety objectives, criteria and other performance goals are met.

1.2 RELATED INDUSTRY CODES, STANDARDS AND SPECIFICATIONS

A number of available industry codes, standards and specifications are normally used for the design of structures and components at petrochemical facilities. These may include, but are not limited to the following:

a. *Uniform Building Code* (UBC)
b. *National Building Code* (BOCA)
c. *Standard Building Code* (SBC)
d. *API Standard 650, Welded Steel Tanks for Oil Storage*
e. *AISC Manual of Steel Construction, Allowable Stress Design*
f. *AISC Manual of Steel Construction, Load and Resistance Factor Design*
g. *ACI 318, Building Code Requirements for Reinforced Concrete*

h. *ACI 530, Building Code Requirements for Masonry Structures*
i. *ASCE-7, Minimum Design Loads for Buildings and Other Structures*
j. *ASME Boiler and Pressure Vessel Code*
k. *ASME B31.3, Code for Chemical Plant and Petroleum Refinery Piping*

A matrix indicating typical use of these codes, standards and specifications for different structures and components of petrochemical facilities is presented in Table 1.1.

TABLE 1.1: Codes and Standards Commonly Used for Petrochemical Facilities

	UBC	*BOCA*	*SBC*	*ASCE 7*(1)	*AISC*	*ACI 318*	*ACI 530*	*API 650*	*ASME BPV*	*ASME B31.3*
Steel Design	X	X	X	X	X					
Concrete Design	X	X	X	X		X				
Masonry Design	X	X	X	X			X			
Tanks	X(2)	X(2)	X(2)	X(2)				X		
Pressure Vessels & Piping	X(2)	X(2)	X(2)	X(2)					X	X

(1) Primarily used in practice for wind loads.
(2) Primarily used only for determining seismic loads and support design.

With respect to code provisions, the guidelines presented throughout this document refer often to the *Uniform Building Code* (*UBC*). This was done because most of the effort in seismic design code development in the last two decades has been related to the *UBC*. Furthermore, the *UBC* is the most widely used design code in highly seismic regions of the United States.

It is recognized that other codes and standards, such as from *BOCA* and *SBC*, may be in effect in a particular locale. Rather than attempt to thoroughly address all applicable provisions in all governing codes, this committee has focused discussion of specific provisions and examples to those codes and standards which have been demonstrated to be the most commonly used in current practice. However, it is intended that sufficient background and intent be provided such that the guidelines are applicable over a wide range of design standards, and the use of this document with standards other than the *UBC* should result in comparable designs.

It is also recognized that ongoing efforts in code development and refinement related to the *UBC* and other codes may at one time or another make some of the specific guidance provided in this document obsolete, especially where related to particular building code provisions. However, the intent and philosophy of much of the guidance provided herein is expected, for the most part, to remain directly applicable to petrochemical applications. Much of the design philosophy, analytical techniques, analytical tools, and specific guidance provided in this document is appropriate across a wide range of design criteria.

It should also be noted that the guidelines provided herein are not intended to take precedence over the code of record wherever differences may occur. They are, however, intended to provide a rational basis for varying from specific provisions of standards in establishing specific design requirements for items particular to petrochemical facilities. Where differences exist between the guidelines of this document and the code of record, the latter should always prevail, unless a potential deviation from the standard code of practice is authorized by the governing authority.

1.3 ORGANIZATION OF THE DOCUMENT

The remainder of the document has been organized in chapters which address specific seismic related aspects of petrochemical facility design, evaluation, or operations. A brief summary of the contents of each chapter is presented in the following paragraphs.

Chapter 2 provides a discussion of seismic design philosophy and the general intent of seismic design provisions. Performance requirements are also discussed.

Chapter 3 provides background data related to seismic hazards such as ground shaking, fault rupture, and tsunamis, and geotechnical issues such as liquefaction. Emphasis is placed on providing information which will help the engineer understand the derivation and significance of different definitions of ground motion which may be encountered on a project.

Chapter 4 addresses analysis and load definition for petrochemical facilities. Guidance is given for interpreting building code provisions for application to the types of structures commonly found in petrochemical facilities. Practical analytical tools are suggested for several necessary tasks in facility structural design and evaluations, such as calculation of structural periods for components unique to petrochemical facilities, calculation of sliding displacements, and stability checks. These can be found in the appendices to Chapter 4.

Chapter 5 provides guidance for the design of new components in petrochemical facilities. This chapter attempts to offer useful guidance from experienced engineers, emphasizing interpretation of the intent of code provisions and specific items not found in typical design codes and standards, such as special design details and configuration controls.

Chapter 6 is related specifically to the evaluation of existing facilities. Detailed guidance is provided on the performance of methodical "walkdown" screening reviews of structures and systems.

Chapter 7 covers the evaluation of flat-bottomed steel storage tanks. Different design codes are discussed and alternative methodologies, particularly useful for the evaluation of existing tanks, are presented.

Chapter 8 addresses earthquake contingency planning for a facility. It does not give specific guidance on how to author contingency plans; rather it outlines some general points that should be addressed by in-place contingency plans.

Chapter 9 provides guidance with respect to post-earthquake damage assessment of petrochemical facilities.

Chapter 10 provides guidance to the engineer faced with a task of retrofitting seismically deficient structures in a petrochemical facility.

Chapter 2
DESIGN AND EVALUATION PHILOSOPHY

2.1 INTRODUCTION

The purpose of this chapter is to articulate the broad design philosophy which is inherently incorporated into the guidance presented in this document. The design philosophy is derived from current knowledge of seismic hazards, observed and recorded behavior of structures and components during earthquakes, and consideration of consequences of failure of these structures and components. Available documents on recommended seismic design practices for conventional as well as special facilities (SEAOC, 1990; RMPP, 1992; *DOE 1020*) have been used in the overall development of design and evaluation philosophies.

The overall philosophy of this guidance document is based on the premise that proper seismic design can be achieved by:

a. determining all applicable seismic hazards for a site,

b. defining performance objectives for different usage categories of structures and components,

c. establishing design bases that meet the prescribed seismic performance objectives for these facilities, and

d. ensuring that the design and construction adhere to those bases.

2.2 CONSIDERATIONS FOR NEW DESIGN

The design philosophy for new facilities is presented assuming that the code of record is one of the major building codes currently being used in the United States (see Table 1.1). Use of these guidelines with other similar codes and standards that may be in effect in a particular community should result in comparable designs.

The seismic design forces discussed in this document are based on the assumption that ductility is provided in new design and that the occurrence of limited inelastic behavior may be acceptable in structures and components during strong ground motions. As a result, in many cases, the lateral design forces are significantly smaller than those that would be required if the structures and components were designed to remain elastic.

For structures in the inelastic regime, structural behavior is improved if the inelastic deformations are well distributed throughout the structure. The seismic force levels called for in this document are based on this consideration. Higher elastic force reduction factors are thus provided for cases where a more uniform distribution of inelastic deformation can be developed in the lateral force resisting system (e.g., a well-distributed system of moment-resisting frames). Conversely, for cases where inelastic deformation may concentrate in a few members, the reduction factors are lower (e.g., elevated tanks). In any case, it is the engineer's responsibility to develop a design that will correspond to the expected inelastic response capability of the structural system for the item under consideration.

Furthermore, the guidance provided in this document generally provides minimum design criteria. It is the engineer's obligation to interpret and adopt these guidelines to each item using experience and judgment. In selected cases, it may be advantageous to adopt more conservative criteria which may have overall long range economic benefits. Because of the great variability and options available in the design process, and because of the complexity of structures and components, it is very difficult to cover all possible variations in seismic response and to provide optional detailed criteria. Thus, the engineer has both latitude and responsibility to exercise judgment in the development of detailed design criteria and in the execution of the design.

2.3 CONSIDERATIONS FOR THE EVALUATION OF EXISTING FACILITIES

The reassessment of existing facilities may involve different techniques and acceptance criteria than used for new design, depending on the intent of the evaluation, the regulatory requirements, and the wishes of the owner. Several key considerations are as follows:

a. Evaluation acceptance criteria (stress and/or deformation limits) may be more or less conservative than those for an equivalent new facility depending on the intent of the evaluation.

b. Additional requirements related to equipment functionality as well as systems interaction may be appropriate.

c. Loads on an existing structure may have changed over time and the assessment should consider the actual loads.

d. Any changes in the operating basis (weight, operating conditions, etc.) may affect the assessment and should be incorporated.

e. Remaining design life is a factor in the evaluations and should be considered.

f. In evaluating existing facilities, actual material properties (if available) should be taken into account.

g. Information from available field observations, such as deterioration of the structural elements (e.g., corrosion), should be addressed.

In summary, the "best estimate" of the structure and material properties should be used to get the most accurate prediction of the structure's or system's performance. Anything that might affect system performance should be considered, whether structural or functional.

2.4 LIMITATIONS

Conformance to this guidance document does not guarantee that significant damage will not occur during a major earthquake. The engineer must always caution both the owners and regulators to understand that seismic risk can never be completely eliminated. Although conservatism can be added to the design and/or review criteria, and a more detailed and extensive investigation (at greater cost) may yield more accuracy and reliable information, some level of seismic risk will always exist. This is true regardless of how much time and resources are spent in the design or retrofit of a facility. Thus, the goal should always be to “minimize the risk” within the available resources.

In order to avoid conflicting expectations between engineers, owners, regulators, or other affected parties, the following points should be discussed openly, and possibly agreed to in writing, so as to avoid misunderstandings at later dates:

a. All parties must recognize the lack of complete assurance connected with seismic evaluations, particularly of existing facilities. Besides the uncertainties associated with material properties and structural behavior (uncertainties that are typically larger for existing facilities than for new designs), there are large uncertainties associated with the earthquake input motion in terms of amplitude, frequency content, and duration.

b. The engineer has an obligation to use the degree of care and skill ordinarily exercised at the time the evaluation is performed, under similar circumstances, by reputable engineering professionals in the same or similar locality.

c. All parties must recognize that geologic, seismic, environmental, structural, and geotechnical conditions can vary from those encountered when and where the engineer obtained the initial data used in the evaluation, and that the limited nature of the data necessarily causes some level of uncertainty with respect to its interpretation, notwithstanding the exercise of due professional care.

d. All parties must recognize that the extent of the engineer's evaluations are always limited by the time-frame and funds available for the investigation. A more detailed and extensive investigation, at greater cost, might yield more accurate and reliable information that might affect some of the engineer's decisions and judgments.

e. When evaluating existing facilities, all parties must agree on reasonable limits to design responsibility and liability of the engineers with regard to the adequacy of the original design and construction. Normally, responsibility for the original design and construction should not be assumed by the evaluating engineer. Owners and engineers should be made aware of extensive uncertainties that may remain in the absence of significant investigations.

Also, this document is intended to reflect current common practice and should not limit the engineer from developing designs and retrofits consistent with emerging knowledge.

2.5 PERFORMANCE OBJECTIVES AND USAGE CATEGORIES

2.5.1 Performance Objectives

The criteria in this document are based on performance objectives, defined for selected usage categories. The performance objectives are intended to provide different levels of protection from damage, consistent with the usage categories. The main elements of these performance objectives are as follows:

a. Structural Integrity. The design philosophy articulated in this document calls for maintaining structural integrity for all structures and components in a facility. This means that structures and components should not collapse or otherwise fail under the design basis ground motion specified for the site. Functionality may need to be maintained if specifically designated by the owner or jurisdictional authorities or if required to protect public health and safety. (In general, maintaining structural integrity does not imply maintaining functionality.) Maintaining structural integrity requires attention to strength, ductility and deformation limits. Subsequent chapters provide guidance for strength, ductility and deformation limits. Although the guidance presented in this document is not intended to prevent damage, much of the guidance is intended to limit damage that would adversely affect the public safety.

b. Containment: Structures, systems, and components with hazardous materials should be designed for containment of such materials during and after a major earthquake. Ensuring containment requires attention to strength, ductility, and deformation limits as well as structural details of elements with respect to potential leak paths. Prevention of release of significant quantities of hazardous materials into the environment is essential to avoid endangering facility personnel and to maintain public health and safety in the event of a major earthquake.

c. Functionality: All structures, systems, and components that are needed after an earthquake, such as fire prevention or other emergency systems, should be designed to maintain functionality (i.e., continued operability during or after the design earthquake). Maintaining functionality requires attention to strength, ductility and deformation limits as well as to stress levels, structural details, seismic interaction, and protection of essential systems and components.

2.5.2 Usage Categories

For purposes of seismic design and/or evaluation, structures and components at a petrochemical facility are divided into three usage categories: (a) general, (b) hazardous, and (c) essential.

The "general" category includes all structures and components that are not in the other two categories. This category may be further subdivided into "normal" and "special" groups. The structures and components in the "normal" category should be designed for the minimum earthquake forces as defined in the applicable codes and in this document. The structures and components in the "special" category may be designed to higher seismic requirements in order to provide more protection for an owner's investment.

The "hazardous" category includes structures and components which contain hazardous materials. Structures and components in this category should be designed to assure containment of the hazardous material and need not maintain their general functionality beyond what is required for containment. If these structures and components fail, they should fail in a manner that will preclude release of hazardous material into the environment.

The "essential" category includes structures and components that are necessary for emergency operations subsequent to strong ground motion. Consequently, structures and components in this category should be designed to maintain their functionality after the earthquake. Generally, this may be accomplished by using design criteria that will limit stress and/or deformation levels under seismic loads to values that are known to provide for continued function.

2.5.3 Relationships Between Performance Objectives and Usage Categories

Relationships between the performance objectives and usage categories are shown in Table 2.1. Design for all usage categories should provide for structural integrity. In addition, hazardous material handling facilities and components should be designed to assure confinement of such hazardous material.

Similarly, essential facilities and certain structures and components in the hazardous material handling facilities should be designed to maintain selected functionality. Finally, the qualitative seismic risk for each usage category should be consistent with the philosophy discussed in this section, as shown in the last column of Table 2.1.

TABLE 2.1: Performance Objectives for Different Usage Categories

Usage Categories		Performance Objectives			Qualitative Seismic Risk
		Maintain Structural Integrity	Maintain Containment of Hazardous Materials	Maintain Functions	
General	Normal	Yes	N/A	No	Low
	Special	Yes	N/A	Yes(1)	Very Low
Hazardous		Yes	Yes	Yes(2)	Very Low
Essential		Yes	N/A	Yes(3)	Very Low

(1) Only those items whose failure can have a significant economic impact, usually an owner's choice.
(2) Maintain only those functions which are required for containment.
(3) Maintain only those functions which are required for essential operations.

2.5.4 Basis for the Recommended Performance Objectives

The underlying basis for any seismic design criterion or procedure is the specification, either explicitly or implicitly, of an acceptable level of risk. This document was prepared with the belief that, although not quantified, the performance objectives specified for the petrochemical facilities should be consistent with public safety expectations of other civil structures. In other words, the risk of not meeting the performance objectives should not exceed commonly accepted risks associated with major commercial/industrial facilities whose failure may affect public health and safety.

Furthermore, seismic risk should be consistent with the potential consequences of failure of structures and components; those items that are likely to pose greater hazard to life safety should have a lower risk of not meeting their performance objectives. This risk is based on current knowledge of seismic behavior and is not quantified.

2.6 DESIGN APPROACH FOR NEW FACILITIES

Engineering requirements and acceptance criteria to be used to demonstrate compliance of each usage category with the applicable performance requirements should be based on approaches that are well established and consistent with current practices for seismic design. The major elements of these criteria include:

a. Strength: The structural design should be such that risk of gross failure of the structural systems and elements under the design loads is minimized. This is accomplished by demonstrating that the strength, based on the acceptance criteria, is equal to or greater than the demand resulting from the design loads. In determining the design loads, the loading combinations should account for all likely conditions, consistent with current practices.

b. Ductility: Ductility may be relied upon in determining the capability of structures and components to resist seismic loads. The ductility limits and the accompanying deformations should not exceed the limiting values found herein, consistent with the usage categories described above. Ductility limits may also be demonstrated through appropriate independent testing.

c. Seismic Analysis and Design Methods: As discussed in detail in Chapter 4, the equivalent static load method of analysis is generally appropriate for seismic analysis and design. However, specific systems may require dynamic analysis in order to provide a better understanding of seismic structural response, including a more accurate distribution of seismic forces. The engineer should use judgment in deciding whether a dynamic analysis is needed, except for the cases where the codes explicitly require such dynamic analysis (e.g., irregular structures). Consideration should be given to the fact that the formulations in the equivalent static method are generally empirical and are based primarily on building structures. At petrochemical facilities, the structures in many cases are different even if they qualify as "regular" and they may involve interaction with piping systems of significant mass. In such cases, a dynamic analysis may be a better choice.

   Both equivalent static and dynamic analyses should be performed using linear elastic methods. Seismic loads should be properly combined with the other load effects to obtain the "design forces" in accordance with the project criteria.

d. Acceptance Criteria: Either allowable stress or ultimate strength design methods may be used in establishing the acceptance criteria. In addition, where appropriate, displacement limitations should be imposed to assure acceptable behavior of structures and components.

e. Seismic Review of Systems and Components: Experience indicates that many systems and types of equipment are generally seismically rugged, i.e., they are ordinarily constructed in such a way that they have inherent seismic capacity to survive strong motions without significant loss of function. The engineer should make an assessment of the systems and components, especially those in the hazardous and essential categories, to determine their ruggedness. Those systems and components that are deemed to be susceptible to strong ground shaking should be reviewed in more detail (see SEAOC, 1990, Appendix 1G for guidance on equipment qualification). Such a review may be demonstrated by experience data, analysis, testing, or any combination thereof.

f. Redundancy: Experience indicates that redundancy is a significant factor affecting the survivability of a structure or component during strong ground motion. Many structures and components at petrochemical facilities lack redundancy. Consideration should be given to providing redundant structural systems to the maximum extent practicable. Although providing redundancy may result in a small increase in the construction costs, it will also reduce the seismic risk by providing alternate load paths and additional energy dissipation mechanisms.

g. Seismic Interaction: Seismic interaction, such as impact or differential displacement, may have adverse effects on the performance of sensitive systems and components. Therefore, separation of such items to preclude seismic interaction with other nearby structures and components is a basic design principle. If separation is not practical, then seismic interaction should be accounted for in design through analysis.

The guidance provided in this document is generally based on the above elements. Implementation of these design principles is expected to result in a design that will meet the performance objectives. In particular, both strength and ductility requirements should be specified to meet the structural integrity, confinement or functionality criteria. As expected, the permissible ductility values listed in later sections of this document are relatively high and apply to the performance criterion of maintenance of structural integrity. They would necessarily be lower if a performance criterion of functionality is specified.

2.7 CONSTRUCTION OBSERVATION AND INSPECTION

Construction of petrochemical facilities in accordance with the explicit or implicit engineering intent is essential for achieving a quality that will assure acceptable behavior of structures and components during ground shaking. Therefore, specific items for which construction observation, inspection, and/or testing is deemed necessary are listed in appropriate sections of this document. Construction observation (site visits) by the Engineer of Record is recommended to assess general compliance with the design. These site visits are not intended to constitute detailed inspections or to supplant any aspect of required testing and inspection programs.

2.8 QUALITY ASSURANCE

It is recommended that petrochemical facilities be designed using an engineering quality assurance plan. Such a plan should include the definition of the earthquake loading to be used in the design and a description of the lateral force resisting system. Any materials testing program, seismic review procedures, construction observation by the engineer of record, and other inspection programs should be clearly defined.

In evaluation and retrofit of existing facilities, the engineer who identified the need for modification may not necessarily be the engineer who provides the modification design. In such cases, it is recommended that the owner include review provisions to assure that the intent of the evaluating engineer is properly implemented. These observations are also intended to assure that the subsequent construction is carried out properly. Furthermore, deviations made in the field should be reviewed so that the intent of the retrofit is not violated.

2.9 PEER REVIEW

New design for hazardous and essential facilities should include an independent peer review. Such independent reviews may be performed by qualified engineers from the design organization who are unrelated to the project. These reviews should include the examination of design philosophy, design criteria, structural system, construction materials, and other factors pertinent to the seismic capacity of the facility. The review need not provide a detailed check, as normally performed in the design process, but as a minimum should provide an overview to help identify potential oversights, errors, conceptual deficiencies, and other potential problems that might affect a facility's seismic performance.

For new design and also for the evaluation of existing facilities, the guidance provided in this document may be different than that in the current codes. In certain instances, less stringent criteria are recommended in this document. In such cases, an independent peer review is also appropriate.

Chapter 3
SEISMIC HAZARDS

3.1 INTRODUCTION

An important step in the seismic design of new facilities and the evaluation of existing facilities is the definition of seismic hazards affecting the site. Potential earthquake related hazards include the following:

a. Inertial related loads and displacements caused by ground shaking.

b. Ground failure caused by rupture of a fault located within or immediately adjacent to a facility.

c. Ground failure or settlement caused by liquefaction and landslides.

d. Coastal inundation or loads due to large waves produced in nearby bodies of water caused by tsunamis (tidal waves) and seiches.

Engineers responsible for designing equipment and structures to resist these hazards are usually not responsible for assessing the probability of occurrence of these hazards. The definition and quantification of these hazards is generally performed by specialists in other disciplines. However, engineers are often called upon by owners and regulators to interpret those hazards and assess the validity of the hazard analysis. In addition, engineers must incorporate the hazard analysis results in a consistent and appropriate manner into the design of new facilities or the evaluation of existing facilities.

The intent of this chapter is to provide background information to familiarize civil engineers performing design or analysis tasks with the process by which these hazards are defined, and to understand the meaning and significance of various methods for performing these evaluations, especially with respect to ground shaking. Although this chapter does not intend to instruct the engineer how to perform analyses typically executed by specialists in other disciplines, it is intended to act as a resource to promote an understanding of the purposes, methodologies, terminologies, and limitations of seismic hazard evaluations. This understanding is ultimately necessary for an appropriate interface between seismologists, geotechnical engineers, civil engineers, owners, and regulators in the design and evaluation process.

This chapter is structured to present a brief overview of typical issues faced by civil engineers with regards to each of the seismic hazards listed above. More detailed discussions of several specific topics are given in appendices to this chapter.

3.2 GROUND SHAKING

The most widely used seismic input parameter for the seismic design of structures is a measure of the ground shaking, usually given in terms of ground acceleration. It is often the only parameter used for the specification of seismic design.

The evaluation of ground shaking is often misunderstood, in its terminology, interpretation, and application of its results. This section is intended to provide explanation of common ground motion descriptions and their relevance to engineering applications.

3.2.1 Earthquake Magnitude and Intensity

Earthquakes are often described in terms of their magnitudes and resulting intensities. The magnitude is a measure of the overall energy released by an earthquake. The intensity is a measure of the effects experienced at a particular location during the earthquake.

Several magnitude scales are commonly used to describe the energy released in an earthquake. These include the Richter or local magnitude (M_L), surface wave magnitude (M_S), body wave magnitude (m_b) and moment magnitude (M_W). More detailed descriptions of each of the common scales are located in Appendix 3.A. Figure 3.1 shows a comparison of several magnitude scales over a range of commonly experienced magnitudes. Although the term "Richter magnitude" is commonly used by news reports to describe earthquake magnitudes of major events, the magnitude values are typically provided by agencies such as the U.S. Geological Survey and are not necessarily the true "Richter" magnitude.

Intensity is a measure of the effects of an earthquake at a site, and is a function of the earthquake magnitude, distance from the earthquake source, local soil characteristics, and other parameters. The most common measure of intensity in the United States is the Modified Mercalli Intensity (MMI) scale, which ranges from I to XII, as described in Table 3.1. A similar scale from the Japan Meteorological Agency (JMA), ranging from 0 to 7, is used in Japan, while Eastern European countries often use the MSK scale, where intensities are similar to the MMI.

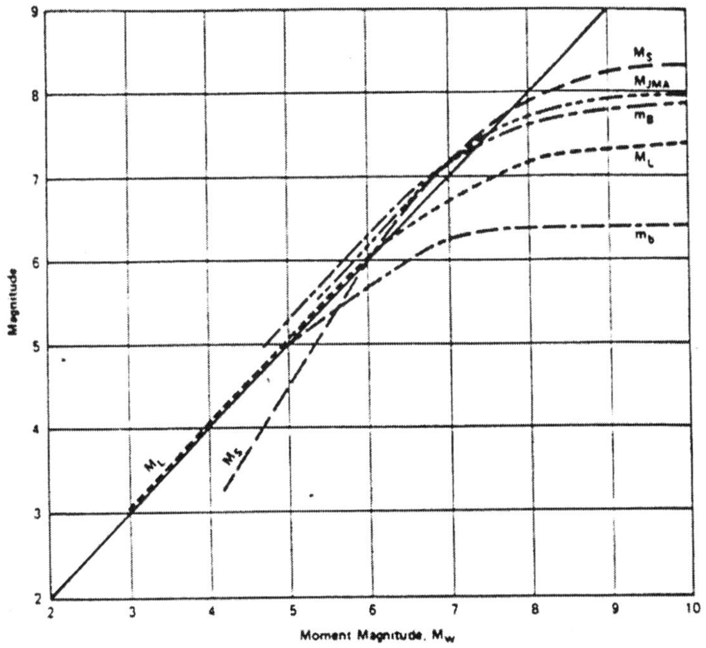

Figure 3.1: Relation between Moment Magnitude and other magnitude scales. M_L (local), M_s (surface wave), m_b (short period body wave), m_g (long period body wave), and M_{JMA} (Japan Meteorological Agency). See section 3.A.3 for definition of different magnitude scales.

3.2.2 Measures of Ground Shaking for Use in Design and Evaluation

Earthquake magnitude and intensity are of limited significance in engineering design. A much more common parameter for engineering evaluation and design is the level of ground motion expected at a given site, defined in terms of acceleration, velocity, and displacement.

Earthquake records can be presented as time histories or response spectra. Time histories are measured instrumentally and capture the duration, frequency content, and amplitude of earthquake motion. A response spectrum is the calculated response to a given earthquake time history for a series of single-degree-of-freedom oscillators of different frequencies. The response is typically presented for a given damping ratio, usually 5%. The response spectrum is useful, in that it defines the response of the structure to a given time history.

TABLE 3.1: Modified Mercalli Intensity Scale

I.	Not felt. Marginal and long-period effects of large earthquakes.
II.	Felt by persons at rest, on upper floors, or favorably placed.
III.	Felt indoors. Hanging objects swing. Vibration like passing of light trucks. Duration estimated. May not be recognized as an earthquake.
IV.	Hanging objects swing. Vibration like passing of heavy trucks; or sensation of a jolt like a ball striking the walls. Standing motor cars rock. Windows, dishes, doors rattle. Glasses clink. Crockery clashes. In the upper range of IV wooden walls and frames creak.
V.	Felt outdoors; direction estimated. Sleepers wakened. Liquids disturbed, some spilled. Small unstable objects displaced or upset. Doors swing, close, open. Shutters, pictures move. Pendulum clocks stop, start, change rate.
VI.	Felt by all. Many frightened and run outdoors. Persons walk unsteadily. Windows, dishes, glassware broken, knickknacks, books, etc., off shelves. Pictures off walls. Furniture moved or overturned. Weak plaster and masonry D cracked. Small bells ring (church, school). Trees, bushes shaken (visible, or heard to rustle).
VII.	Difficult to stand. Noticed by drivers of motor cars. Hanging objects quiver. Furniture broken. Damage to Masonry D, including cracks. Weak chimneys broken at roof line. Fall of plaster, loose bricks, stones, tiles, cornices (also unbraced parapets and architectural ornaments). Some cracks in masonry C. Waves on ponds; water turbid with mud. Small slides and caving in along sand or gravel banks. Large bells ring. Concrete irrigation ditches damaged.
VIII.	Steering of motor cars affected. Damage to Masonry C; partial collapse. Some damage to masonry B; none to Masonry A. Fall of stucco and some masonry walls. Twisting, fall of chimneys, factory stacks, monuments, towers, elevated tanks Frame houses moved on foundations if not bolted down; loose panel walls thrown out. Decayed piling broken off. Branches broken from trees. Changes in flow or temperature of springs and wells. Cracks in wet ground and on steep slopes.
IX.	General panic. Masonry D destroyed; Masonry B seriously damaged. (General damage to foundations.) Frame structures, if not bolted, shifted off foundations. Frames racked. Serious damage to reservoirs. Underground pipes broken. Conspicuous cracks in ground. In alluviated areas sand and mud ejected, earthquake fountains, sand craters.
X.	Most masonry and frame structures destroyed with their foundations. Some well-built wooden structures and bridges destroyed. Serious damage to dams, dikes, embankments. Large landslides. Water thrown on banks to canals, rivers, lakes, etc. Sand and mud shifted horizontally on beaches and flat land. Rails bent slightly.
XI.	Rails bent greatly. Underground pipelines completely out of service.
XII.	Damage nearly total. Large rock masses displaced. Lines of sight and level distorted. Objects thrown into the air.

Note: To avoid ambiguity, the quality of masonry, brick, or other material is specified by the following lettering system. (This has no connection with the conventional classes A, B, and C construction.)

Masonry A. Good workmanship, mortar, and design; reinforced, especially laterally, and bound together by using steel, concrete, etc.; designed to resist lateral forces.

Masonry B. Good workmanship and mortar; reinforced, but not designed to resist lateral forces.

Masonry C. Ordinary workmanship and mortar; no extreme weaknesses, like failing to tie in at corners, but neither reinforced nor designed to resist horizontal forces.

Masonry D. Weak materials, such as adobe; poor mortar; low standards of workmanship; weak horizontally.

Most building codes use a response spectrum as design input. For design and evaluation purposes, that response spectrum can be defined either from standard shapes or from site-specific analyses. Standard shapes are typically used for a given soil type, scaled to a value of peak ground acceleration (PGA). The PGA is the maximum response which a rigid structure would be expected to experience, moving the same as the ground itself.

Building codes generally present standard design response spectrum shapes, normalized to a PGA of 1.0. A PGA value appropriate for the seismic zone in which the site is located is used to scale such standard spectral shapes. Those standard shapes represent a smoothed average of normalized response spectra of actual ground motion records grouped by subsurface soil conditions at the location of the recording instruments.

It may be appropriate to consider a damping level of other than 5%. For example, a wood framed cooling tower would experience higher damping than liquid sloshing in an insulated tank.

The use of standard shapes may be inappropriate under certain conditions, such as very near a fault, and when soils are very soft. Under those conditions a site-specific analysis would be recommended, using one of the procedures described in the following sections.

3.2.2.1 Deterministic Seismic Hazards Analyses

In a deterministic approach, ground motions at a site are estimated by considering a single event of a specified magnitude and distance from the site. To perform a deterministic analysis, the following information is needed:

a. Definition of an earthquake source (e.g. a known fault) and its location relative to the site

b. Definition of a design earthquake magnitude that the source is capable of producing

c. A relationship which describes the attenuation, or decay with distance, of ground motion

A site may have several known active faults in its proximity. A maximum magnitude is defined for each fault, from published sources or agencies such as the U.S. Geological Survey. The maximum magnitude is a function of the fault length and historical knowledge of past earthquakes on that particular source. The attenuation relationships are developed based on statistical analyses of ground motion records from earthquakes occurring in similar geologic and tectonic conditions.

Note that deterministic ground motion estimates are not associated with a specific return period, such as 250 years or 500 years, although the particular earthquake event used may have a return period associated with it. The return period for the maximum event on a given fault may vary from several hundred to several thousand years, depending on the activity rate of the fault.

3.2.2.2 Probabilistic Seismic Hazards Analyses (PSHA)

In a probabilistic approach, ground motions at a site are estimated by considering the probability of events of different sizes on all sources that affect a given site. Combinations of individual probabilities from different sources provide total annual probabilities of exceedance for a given level of PGA or spectral response. The curve of probability of exceedance versus ground motion is often referred to as a "hazard curve." A uniform hazard spectrum provides a ground motion amplitude for different frequency values for a constant probability of exceedance. The probability of exceedance is then related to the return period for that ground motion by using the equation for a Poissonian distribution:

$$T = \frac{-t}{\ln(1-p)} \qquad (3.1)$$

where p is the probability of exceedance in t years and T is the return period.

A common value used in building codes is the 10% probability of exceedance in 50 years. Using equation 3.1, this is a 475-year return period. This is also commonly referred to as a 500-year return period for simplicity.

Since a PSHA is a probability based approach, it is important that uncertainty be accounted for in the definition of input parameters, such as the magnitude recurrence, the attenuation, or geographical boundaries or location of a source zone. These uncertainties are modeled in the PSHA. Figure 3.2 shows the different elements of a PSHA graphically. These analyses are typically done with special computer programs specifically developed for this purpose. Typical input parameters include the following:

a. Definition of earthquake sources, either as faults or as area sources of diffused seismicity not directly attributable to a known fault

b. A probability distribution of earthquake magnitudes for each source

c. A definition of earthquake ground motion attenuation, including uncertainty

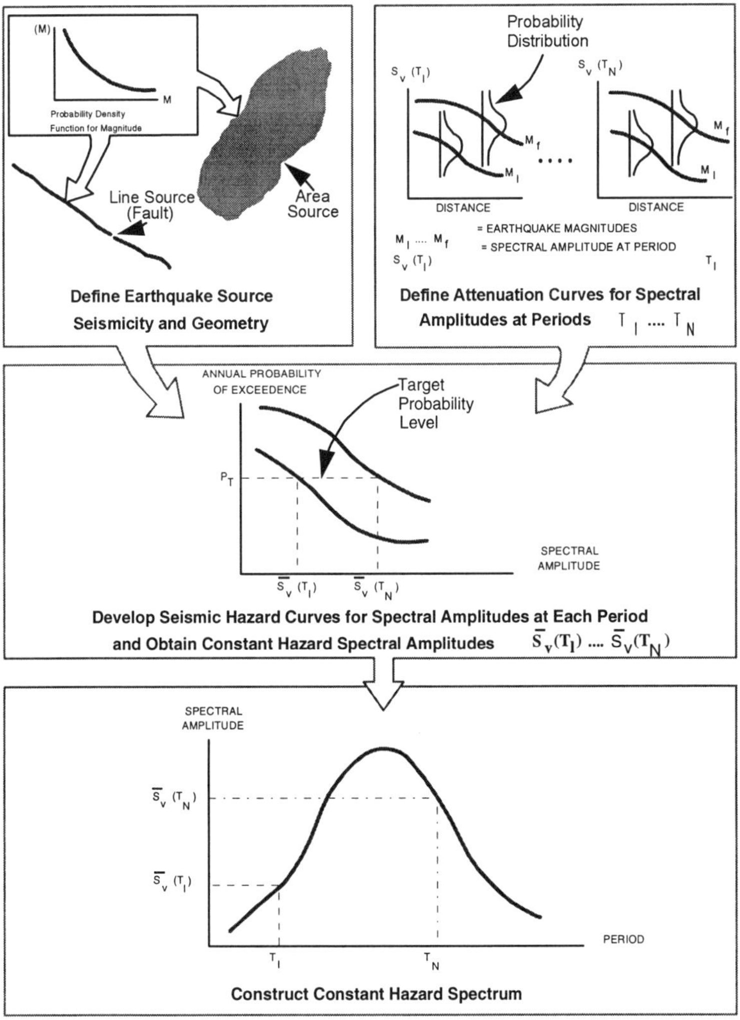

Figure 3.2: Seismic Hazard Analysis Procedure

Note also that because the ground motion values are calculated probabilistically by combining the probabilities of ground motion from many sources, the value derived is not associated with a specific fault or event. In fact, while it may sound conservative to use the ground motion from the largest possible earthquake occurringat the closest location on the nearest fault, those values may be significantly smaller than ground motion calculated probabilistically. This is particularly true if the largest earthquake on the nearest fault is associated with a shorter return period than being considered probabilistically, or if the site is affected by several faults, which each contribute to the overall probability of exceedance.

More detailed discussions of various aspects of probabilistic seismic hazards analyses are presented in Appendix 3.A.

3.2.2.3 Site Response Analysis

Other numerical methods such as site response analysis using linear or non-linear models of underlying soil are also available to estimate site-specific response spectra. Codes such as SHAKE (Schnabel et al, 1972) and 2D and 3D FLAC (Itasca, 1995) are available. Numerical site response analysis is recommended where very poor subsurface conditions (such as *NEHRP* soil type E and *UBC* soil type S4) are encountered.

3.2.2.4 Earthquake Time Histories

Sometimes it is appropriate to use a set of acceleration time histories for structural analyses, especially for nonlinear analysis or for analysis of structures of special importance. Whenever used, it is recommended that multiple time histories be used to reduce the possibility of a structural period coinciding with a frequency of low energy content for the particular time history record chosen. Additional considerations for the use of time history records, such as scaling and the use of artificial time histories, are discussed in Appendix 3.A.

3.2.2.5 Directionality Considerations

Earthquake response spectra are typically developed for application in orthogonal horizontal directions. Discussions of how to combine design input from different directions are presented in Chapter 4. While vertical response spectra can be developed in a similar manner to horizontal spectra, in practice, vertical spectra are usually obtained by scaling the horizontal spectra. Typically, a factor of 2/3 is used. This value may be inappropriate for sites near faults. See also Section 3.A.7.

3.3 GROUND FAILURE

Ground failures can be caused by liquefaction, fault ruptures within a facility, or slope failures (landslides). Earthquake induced settlement also falls into this category. Ground failures are an important concern for petrochemical facilities. When designing for ground shaking accelerations, considerations for the possibility of higher than expected accelerations are incorporated into the design process by including details to provide ductile behavior when loaded beyond the elastic range. However, unexpected ground failure often proves to be catastrophic in terms of damage and consequences, not only to the structure or equipment itself, but also to secondary systems, such as attached piping, that can not withstand the large movements associated with ground failures.

3.3.1 Liquefaction

Liquefaction is a phenomenon commonly associated with the repeated shaking or cyclic loading of saturated loose cohesionless soils and quick clays. The potential for liquefaction diminishes as soil density increases. Consolidated soils are not typically vulnerable to liquefaction, while poorly graded sands are more susceptible to liquefaction.

The process of liquefaction is associated with the tendency of loose soils to densify under shear loading. This process is replaced in saturated sands by a build-up of pore water pressures that reduces its shear strength. Eventually the strength may be reduced to the extent that soils may flow or produce water spouts and sand boils. These are the events typically associated with liquefaction. Structures may experience foundation failures at levels of loading or shaking below those that would produce liquefaction in free-field conditions because the strength of the soil may degrade to a level insufficient to support the foundation loads imposed by a structure.

EERI (1994) has noted that liquefaction has most often been observed in areas where the ground water table is within 30 feet (10 m) of the ground surface, while there are few observations of liquefaction where the ground water is deeper than 60 feet (20 m).

The evaluation of liquefaction potential most often involves an empirical or semi-empirical procedure. Seed et al (1991) summarize a few of those procedures. The evaluation of liquefaction at a particular site involves a number of physical determinations that carry with them considerable variations and uncertainties. Among the most important are:

a. physical soil characteristics (i.e., density, grain size distribution, and fabric)

b. mechanical characteristics (i.e., deformation properties and shear strength)

c. in situ stress conditions

d. site conditions (i.e., depth of soil strata, locations of water table, and ground slope)

e. characteristics of ground shaking (i.e., duration, frequency content, and magnitude of accelerations)

Ledbetter (1985) has presented a summary of methods to mitigate damage associated with liquefiable soils. Many of the methods are valid for limiting settlement-induced damage for dry soils. The methods for improving performance include:

a. increased confinement

b. densification

c. foundation drainage improvement

d. soil reinforcement

e. grouting and chemical additives

Excavation of soils with poor characteristics and replacement with select fill is a simple alternative when economically justified. Densification of shallow sands may be accomplished with vibratory compactors at the surface level. Deeper layers may be densified by explosives, driving displacement piles or dropping weights from cranes on the ground surface.

A fundamental solution to potential liquefaction or settlement hazards is to extend the foundation system to a deeper soil strata having a lesser tendency to liquefy or compact. Other elements of foundation design, such as the use of mat foundations, strap footing, and pile cap ties to reduce differential foundation movements and settlements are effective in reducing damage to structures or equipment.

As the resistance to liquefaction increases with confining stress, it may be beneficial to add a surcharge pressure to the original ground surface by depositing select material.

3.3.2 Fault Rupture

Fault rupture results in destructive shaking from a massive release of crustal energy at a fracture in the earth's crust along which separated sections have moved or displaced relative to each other. The displacement can vary from a purely horizontal to a purely vertical direction and can be as large as several meters. A ground rupture involving more than a few inches of movement can cause major damage to structures sited on or immediately adjacent to the fault. In general, the precise locations of faults are not known because they are typically covered with alluvium. Fault displacements produce forces and movements so great that the best method for limiting damage to structures is to avoid building in areas close to ground traces of active fault zones.

3.3.3 Landslides

Individual landslides induced by seismic events may encompass mass volumes and areas much larger than those due to other causes (Seed et al, 1991; Krinitzsky et al, 1993). The largest failures have involved many square miles of material. In addition, landslides may occur in an area much larger than that usually associated with structural damage for a particular event, sometimes occurring more than 100 miles from the epicenter.

Few landslides seem to be triggered by seismic events of less than magnitude 5. Landslides may be associated with liquefaction of soil layers, failure of weak or brittle soils, or sliding along seams of weak soils. Because of the spatial extent of the failures involved and the variety of failure modes that may trigger them, detailed geotechnical site investigations are necessary to evaluate these hazards.

Numerical methods of evaluating landslide potential include limit equilibrium and finite element techniques. These methods are applicable to dry, saturated, cohesive or non-cohesive soils. Finite element techniques are preferred when evaluating complex geometries of combinations of soil types, and also when calculations of displacements are required. Limit equilibrium techniques have been extended to dynamic analysis, and load duration effects can be incorporated to calculate displacements. These dynamic calculations consider rigid body motions.

3.4 TSUNAMI AND SEICHE

Tsunamis and seiches occur regularly throughout the world, but are usually only considered in the design and evaluation of facilities when making initial decisions on the location of the facility. This section briefly describes these phenomena, assessment methods, and mitigation measures. Additional discussion is provided in Appendix 3.B.

Tsunamis, or tidal waves, are typically generated by large and sometimes distant earthquakes and undersea fault movements. Traveling through the deep ocean, a tsunami is a broad and shallow, but fast moving, wave that poses little danger to most vessels. When it reaches the coastline, the wave form pushes upward from the ocean bottom to make a swell of water that sometimes (but not always) breaks and washes inland with great force.

A seiche occurs when resonant wave oscillations form in an enclosed or semi-enclosed body of water such as a lake, bay, or fjord. Seiches may be triggered by moderate or larger local submarine earthquakes, and sometimes by large, distant earthquakes.

A tsunami or seiche may result in flooding of low-lying coastal areas. The greatest hazard results from the inflow and outflow of water, where strong currents and forces can erode foundations and sweep away structures and equipment. Petrochemical facilities are especially vulnerable to the rupture of storage tanks from debris impact and foundation erosion, possibly resulting in explosion and fire. The tsunami at Seward, Alaska following the 1964 Alaska earthquake led to such destruction of the port facilities. The succession of waves spread the fire from ruptured oil tanks across and throughout the port area.

A third potential cause of coastal inundation is coastal subsidence caused by tectonic (faulting) or non-tectonic (e.g. submarine landslide) effects. Permanent coastal subsidence and submergence may occur. It is difficult, if not impossible, to predict when or if such tectonic subsidence will occur in a given area, although historical earthquake data provide evidence of such occurrences.

3.4.1 Assessment of Vulnerability

Coastal sites in active tectonic areas where dip-slip faulting is common are most susceptible to earthquake-induced inundation. Examination of the regional fault characteristics and earthquake history, with emphasis on submarine earthquakes and possible historical tsunamis, provides the best measure of site vulnerability. Estimates of maximum tsunami run-up may be based on either historical occurrences or theoretical modeling. The Federal Insurance Administration developed inundation maps to assist in setting rates for the National Flood Insurance Program (Flood Insurance Rate Maps - FIRM). Inundation levels on these maps generally consist of the higher of either riverine flood, coastal storm surge, or tsunami inundation levels.

3.4.2 Mitigation Measures

Throughout Japan, where tsunami attack is common, several mitigation measures have been implemented, such as sea walls and barriers to resist tsunami inundation. These structures are sometimes unsuccessful, as large tsunamis may overtop the barriers and flood the protected area, generating strong currents which erode the barriers and other structures. The structures could end up acting as powerful battering rams against the very structures they were designed to protect. Coastal protective structures must be carefully designed to withstand extreme events.

In practice in the United States, tsunami and seiche effects are rarely considered in facility design, unless considered in the original siting of the facility. For existing facilities, other measures are more likely to be effective in mitigating risk from coastal inundation. Some of these measures would include:

a. Tsunami warning and alert systems

b. Emergency or disaster response plans which consider the vulnerability of the facility and possible effects of tsunami attack

c. Identification of the most vulnerable components and development of possible mitigation strategies

d. Public and personnel awareness of the possible effects and impact of tsunamis.

APPENDIX 3.A

GROUND SHAKING

APPENDIX 3.A
GROUND SHAKING

3.A.1 INTRODUCTION

The most widely used seismic input parameter in the seismic design of structures is a measure of the ground shaking, usually given in terms of ground acceleration. It is often the only parameter used for specification of seismic design.

Section 3.2 provides background information on common terminology and fundamentals related to the evaluation of ground shaking hazards. This Appendix provides additional discussion on specific areas that are often misunderstood, including terminology, interpretation and the application of its results. This section is intended to provide explanation of common ground motion descriptions and their relevance to engineering applications.

3.A.2 EARTHQUAKE BASICS

Earthquakes are generally caused by the sudden release of built-up elastic strain in the earth's crust and originate as slip along geologic faults. The total energy of an earthquake is released along the entire length of the ruptured zone, propagating from the source and traveling through the earth in the form of seismic waves. The point in the earth's crust where the rupture is initiated is known as the focus or the hypocenter of the earthquake. The point on the surface of earth directly above the hypocenter is known as the epicenter of the earthquake.

The build up of elastic strain in the earth's crust can be explained by the theory of plate tectonics. According to which, the outer 70-150 km of the earth's crust is made up of approximately 12 major plates which are slowly moving relative to each other. Most of the seismically active areas are located along the plate boundaries. The relative motion between the plates results in either plates grinding past each other, or a plate subducting beneath another or several plates converging and crushing smaller plates. There are also divergent plate boundaries. Mountains and deep sea trenches are formed where plates converge and subduct beneath one another. Mid-ocean ridges are formed at divergent plate boundaries. Earthquakes are usually initiated at shallow depths at plate boundaries where plates slide past each other. Deep focus earthquakes usually occur along subduction plates. Earthquakes within a plate can also result due to other reasons such as increased compressional stress. Other causes of earthquakes can be due to nuclear explosions or due to large artificial reservoirs which change the local state of stress within the earth's crust. Also, volcanic activity can cause earthquakes at both subducting and diverging plate boundaries.

3.A.3 MAGNITUDE AND INTENSITY

The amount of energy released in an earthquake, and its size, is characterized as the magnitude of the earthquake. Some of the most commonly used magnitude scales are Richter or local magnitude (M_L), surface wave magnitude (M_S), body wave magnitude (m_b) and moment magnitude (M_W).

Gutenberg and Richter (1956) showed that the amount of energy released in an earthquake can be related to the magnitude by the following relationship:

$$\text{Log } E = 1.5M_S + 11.8 \tag{3.A.1}$$

where E is the energy in ergs. A magnitude increase by one unit releases 31.6 times more energy.

Richter (1958) defined the magnitude of a local earthquake (M_L) as the "logarithm to base ten of the maximum seismic-wave amplitude (in thousandth of a millimeter) recorded on a standard seismograph at a distance of 100 kilometers from the earthquake epicenter." (Bolt, 1988). Seismograms from deep focus earthquakes are significantly different from those for shallow focus earthquakes, even though the total amount of energy released may be the same. This results in different magnitude estimates for earthquakes which release the same amount of energy. This is a limitation of M_L.

The magnitude of an earthquake is also determined by the amplitude of the compressional or P-wave. The P-wave's amplitude is not affected by the focal depth of an earthquake. The magnitude estimated by measuring the P-wave amplitude is called the P-wave or body wave magnitude (m_b).

Magnitude calculated by measuring the amplitude of long period surface waves (periods near 20 seconds) is called the surface-wave magnitude (M_S). Surface wave magnitude is calculated only for shallow focus earthquakes which give rise to surface waves.

For small or moderate size earthquakes, the amplitude of seismic waves measured by typical or standard seismographs increases as the size of the earthquake increases. This trend, however, does not continue for large or very large earthquakes for which the amplitude of seismic waves, whose wave lengths are much smaller than the earthquake source, do not increase proportionally to the size of the earthquake. The magnitude estimated by the amplitude of seismic waves, therefore, does not continue to increase at the same rate as the size of the earthquake. Beyond a certain limit the magnitudes calculated in this way tend to remain constant for different size earthquakes. In other words, the magnitude scale saturates, resulting in no further increase in estimated magnitude with the increasing size of an earthquake.

Due to the limitations in the above defined magnitude scales, a magnitude scale based upon the amount of energy released was introduced by Hanks and Kanamori (1979) and was termed as the moment magnitude scale (M_W). Moment magnitude is defined by the following relationship:

$$M_w = \frac{2}{3}\log M_o - 10.7 \qquad (3.A.2)$$

where:

$$M_o = \mu AD \qquad (3.A.3)$$

The seismic moment M_O is defined as a product of modulus of rigidity of the rock (μ), area of rupture (A) and average fault displacement (D) in a seismic event.

M_W, therefore, is dependent upon the size of rupture unlike other magnitude scales which are dependent upon the amplitude of the seismic waves. Larger earthquakes, have larger seismic moment (product of rupture area and average fault displacement). The moment magnitude scale, therefore, does not saturate with the size of the earthquake, and also has the ability of distinguishing between a large and a great earthquake. For example, the surface wave magnitude for both 1906 San Francisco earthquake and 1960 Chile earthquakes was estimated as 8.3, although the rupture areas of the 1960 earthquake was about 35 times greater than the 1906 earthquake. The moment-magnitude for the two earthquakes has been computed to be approximately 8.0 and 9.5, respectively (Reiter, 1990).

An approximate relation between the various magnitude scales is shown in Figure 3.1 in Chapter 3. According to this figure, except for M_S, all other magnitude scales are similar to M_W up to the point they start to saturate.

Another descriptor about the size of an earthquake is the intensity at a given site. The intensity at any location is described by a qualitative scale that uses eyewitness accounts of fault motion and damage assessments to describe the amount of movement felt at that location. One commonly used scale is the Modified Mercalli Intensity (MMI). As shown in Table 3.1 in Chapter 3, the MMI scale consists of 12 different intensity levels. Whereas intensity I means the earthquake is practically not felt, intensity XII indicates almost total destruction. Intensity XII is rarely achieved except for very large earthquakes. Intensity X can be achieved in moderate to large earthquakes, especially in areas close to the rupture zone. Engineered structures can be damaged in areas experiencing intensities in about the VIII to X range.

3.A.4 MEASURES OF GROUND SHAKING FOR USE IN DESIGN AND EVALUATION

Earthquake magnitude is of limited significance in engineering design. A much more important parameter for engineering evaluation and design is the level of strong motion expected at a given site. Strong ground motion can be measured in terms of ground acceleration, velocity and displacement. Generally, ground acceleration is recorded for the duration of the earthquake by instruments known as accelerometers. Traces of acceleration versus time are known as accelerograms or acceleration time histories. Two orthogonal horizontal and one vertical component of ground acceleration are usually recorded in an earthquake. The three components of recorded motion provide a complete characterization of translational ground shaking to which any structure is subjected and provide useful information, in terms of levels of ground acceleration, frequency content and duration of strong shaking which can be utilized for engineering design purposes.

Structures respond differently to different accelerograms. This is due to differences in frequency content, amplitude and duration of each acceleration record. No two recorded accelerograms from an earthquake are exactly the same. This is because the seismic waves generated from the earthquake source are reflected, refracted and absorbed as they traverse different layers of rock and soil before they are recorded by the recording station accelerometers. Some of the important parameters defining an accelerogram are the peak value of the acceleration or peak ground acceleration (PGA), the frequency content, represented roughly by the number of zero crossings per second in the accelerogram, and the duration of strong motion, defined as the length of time between the first and the last peaks exceeding a given threshold level. Other definitions for duration of strong shaking, based on energy content of motions are also used.

A more useful measure of the intensity of a given motion can be obtained by computing its response spectrum. Response spectrum of a particular ground motion is defined as a plot of maximum response versus period of vibration of a single degree of freedom damped oscillator of a fixed damping ratio.

Peak ground acceleration, an important parameter describing the strength of shaking, may not be the most representative of engineering significance. This is because there may be isolated peaks of high frequency ground motion having little significance for most engineered structures. In ATC 3-06 (ATC, 1978), the concept of effective peak acceleration (EPA) and effective peak velocity (EPV) was introduced as a means to define a parameter with the units of acceleration that was more descriptive of the potential damaging intensity of the ground motion. As defined in ATC 3-06, *"EPA and EPV are considered as normalizing factors for construction of smoothed elastic response spectra for ground motions of normal duration. The EPA is proportional to spectral ordinates for periods in the range of 0.1 to 0.5 seconds, whereas the EPV is proportional to spectral ordinates at a period of about 1 second (McGuire, 1975). The constant of proportionality (for a 5 percent damping spectrum) is set at a standard value of 2.5 in both cases."* EPA is also used in the *UBC* as a basis for defining the "Z" factor for different seismic zones.

3.A.5 FACTORS AFFECTING GROUND MOTION

The size of the earthquake represented by the magnitude is related to the amount of energy released. Larger magnitude earthquakes usually produce higher levels of ground shaking at a given location. However this trend is not always true. Levels of ground motion at a particular site depend on several other factors such as distance from the source, type of faulting, local soil conditions and other secondary effects which are not totally understood. Typically, ground shaking intensity attenuates, or decays, with distance from the source. The source distance can generally be defined as the closest distance from the site to the seismogenic zone (or the zone of energy release). High levels of acceleration, displacement and velocity pulses are usually recorded in close proximity to active sources. Such effects are termed as near-field effects. Consideration to such effects should be given for locations close to an active seismic source.

The level of ground shaking is also significantly affected by local soil conditions at the location where the ground motions are being recorded. Soft soil sites amplify ground motion, especially in the long period range. For example, considerable amplification of ground motions due to local soil conditions occurred during the 1985 Mexico City and the 1989 Loma Prieta Earthquake.

3.A.6 DESIGN RESPONSE SPECTRA

A response spectrum used for design and analysis of structures is known as a design response spectrum, and can be classified in two main categories. The first utilizes predetermined fixed spectral shapes that can be scaled to appropriate levels based on specified design criteria. The second employs the use of site-specific information about the seismicity of the region, local and regional geology, and soil conditions.

3.A.6.1 Standard Response Spectrum Shapes

Fixed response spectrum shapes are sometimes used in lieu of site specific estimates of response spectrum. Fixed response spectrum shapes are available in various published sources. Some of these sources are the *UBC*, *ATC-14* (ATC, 1987), *NRC Regulatory Guide 1.60* (U.S. Nuclear Regulatory Commission, 1973), and the EERI monograph (Newmark and Hall, 1982).

The response spectrum shapes in the EERI monograph were developed by statistical analysis of recorded ground motions. Since there is a large variation in response spectrum shapes from recorded ground motion, both median (50th percentile) and one standard deviation (84th percentile) shapes are presented.

Normalized spectral shapes are obtained by computing effective values of maximum acceleration, velocity and displacement by scaling the corresponding peak ground acceleration, velocity and displacements by spectral amplification factors. Values of peak ground acceleration (a), velocity (v), and displacements (d) can be estimated from established ratios between a/v and ad/v^2. These ratios tend to be constant for similar soil conditions. Response spectrum for 84th percentile value can be obtained by either using median estimates of peak ground acceleration to scale the 84th percentile spectrum shape or by scaling median spectral shape with 84th percentile estimates of peak ground acceleration. Use of 84th percentile estimates of PGA to scale 84th percentile spectral shape is not recommended as it leads to excessive amount of conservatism. Median values of response spectrum from the EERI monograph form a basis for the spectrum shapes provided in *ATC-14*.

The response spectrum shape given in the *UBC* was obtained as a smoothed average of normalized 5-percent-damped response spectra of actual ground motion records grouped by subsurface soil conditions at the location of the recording instruments (SEAOC, 1990 and Seed and Idriss, 1982).

An appropriately selected response spectrum shape corresponding to the local soil conditions can be scaled on the basis of PGA or EPA obtained through procedures defined in this section. For sites in close proximity to an active fault, considerations to possible near field effects should be given.

3.A.6.2 Site-Specific Response Spectra

Two distinct approaches are generally used for site-specific estimates for developing seismic design criteria for engineered projects: the deterministic procedure and the probabilistic procedure. Descriptively, the two procedures would at first appear to be quite different with a deterministic approach offering the advantage of appearing easiest to follow. Properly applied, either procedure can lead to satisfactory seismic design.

In areas of low seismic hazard, the additional design and material costs that ensue when unsure but conservative decisions are made may not be excessive. When the seismic exposure is high, the cost associated with additional conservatism can increase significantly. This increase needs to be balanced with the likelihood that the damaging event may or may not occur during the life of the structure. Large damaging earthquakes are infrequent events that may simultaneously affect a large number of structures. The extent of damage during an earthquake can be related to the level of motions generated by the earthquake. The level of earthquake motion against which design or evaluation criteria should be developed requires subjective judgment based on experience and observation. Probabilistic methods were developed as a result of a desire to quantify some of this judgment understanding and to allow use in a repeatable way by other practitioners.

In the following sections, both the deterministic and probabilistic seismic hazard approaches are discussed.

Deterministic Seismic Hazard Analysis

In a deterministic approach, ground motions at a site are estimated by considering a single event of a specified magnitude and distance from the site. In order to perform a deterministic analysis, the following data are required:

a. Definition of an earthquake source (e.g., a known geologic fault) and its location relative to the site

b. Definition of a design earthquake that the source is capable of producing

c. A relationship which describes the attenuation of the ground motion parameter of interest, e.g., peak ground acceleration or response spectral ordinates for a specific natural period or frequency of vibration.

An earthquake source in most cases is a known active or potentially active geologic fault. A site may have several faults in close proximity to it. All of these sources must be identified. Based on the length and characteristics of the fault, a maximum magnitude potential of each source is specified. Estimation of maximum magnitude potential of geologic sources can be obtained from published sources or qualified professionals. The maximum magnitude potential of a source is determined from empirical relationships between magnitude and rupture length or through historical knowledge of past earthquakes on the particular source. Generally, the earthquake corresponding to the maximum magnitude is referred to as the Maximum Credible Earthquake (MCE), which represents the maximum earthquake potential of a source. MCE is estimated by geologists based on the characteristics of the source and factors such as historical activity and source dimensions. Several relationships exist that relate source dimensions to its maximum magnitude potential. This information is then used as input to an attenuation relationship, which relates the ground motion parameter of interest to magnitude and distance.

Attenuation of ground motion is known to vary significantly during any earthquake. While the variation is widely known, the quantification of the reasons for the variation are not fully understood. Examples of possible causes may be different rupture mechanisms in the epicentral area, directionality of the radiation pattern of the motion and regional geological variations. Research using statistical analysis of large ground motion data sets have shown that the scatter of ground motion values about a mean attenuation relationship can be represented by a log-normal distribution. Attenuation relationships are empirical relationships developed by using regression analysis techniques on ground motion data recorded during earthquakes. Several different attenuation relationships are available in published sources, and are a function of earthquake magnitude, its distance, local geology and tectonic environment (subduction zones of Pacific Northwest, Eastern U.S. and Western U.S.). Joyner and Boore (1988) summarizes some of these relationships. Some of the other well known relationships are Boore et al. (1993), Campbell and Bozorgnia (1994), and Crouse and McGuire (1994) (for Western U.S.), Atkinson and Boore (1995) and Boore and Joyner (1991) (for Eastern U.S.), and Crouse (1991) (for subduction zones).

Since attenuation relationships are empirical relationships derived using statistical analysis techniques on recorded data, they do not fit each and every data point exactly. The actual recorded data spreads around the median attenuation relationship. This spread is defined by the standard deviation. The attenuation equation with no standard deviation means that 50% of the recorded values are above and 50% are below the predicted value. An attenuation relationship with one standard deviation means that 84% of the recorded values are below the predicted values, similarly attenuation relationship with two standard deviations imply that 98% of the recorded data are below the predicted value.

The definition of earthquake magnitude and source-to-site distance sometimes vary from one attenuation relationship to another. It is important that the magnitude scale and source-to-site distance used in the analysis should be consistent with the proper definition for the particular attenuation relationship used. If the site has several sources in close proximity, an envelope of values of response spectra developed for each source can be used.

Probabilistic Seismic Hazard Analysis

Probabilistic seismic hazard analyses (PSHA) require additional seismic criteria beyond the selected magnitude, minimum distance and the attenuation equations used for the deterministic procedure defined in the previous section. The primary additional requirements are the dimensions of each source region and the means to interpret the probability of occurrence within each source.

Probabilistic seismic hazard analysis procedures were first developed and used by Cornell (1968) and Cornell and Vanmarcke (1969) and further extended by Merz and Cornell (1973) and Der Kiureghian and Ang (1977). This method involves careful consideration and incorporation of the geology, history, and tectonics of the site region into a seismotectonic source model. A probabilistic seismic hazard study requires the acceptance of several assumptions regarding earthquakes.

The first step in PSHA requires that the seismic history and geology are sufficiently well known to permit an estimate of the seismic activity of the region. This is defined as the seismicity of the region. This information is then used to develop a seismic source model. Potential sources can be defined as either point sources, line sources, or area sources (Der Kiureghian and Ang, 1977). Considerations may be needed to account for the random occurrence of small or moderate sized earthquakes (background seismicity).

The probability distribution of earthquakes to obtain the relative occurrence frequency distribution between large and small earthquakes is then obtained. Estimation of recurrence rate is a key parameter in PSHA procedures. Two approaches for estimating the recurrence rate are generally used. One is based on the historical seismicity records, and the other is a geologic slip rate model. The former is based on the recorded seismic history of the region, whereas the latter uses geologic information to define strain rate accumulation using long-term slip-rate data for a fault.

Recurrence rates can be expressed in the form of the familiar Richter's law of magnitudes (Richter, 1958), expressed as

$$\log N = a - bM \tag{3.A.4}$$

where N is the number of events of magnitude M or greater for the time period under consideration, and a and b are constants that depend on the seismicity of the region.

Other recurrence models, such as the characteristic earthquake model (Youngs and Coppersmith, 1985), may also be used.

For PSHA, the minimum value of 5.0 is usually considered for M, since earthquakes of sizes less than 5.0 are generally not damaging to engineered structures. Due to the integrative nature of PSHA, including earthquakes of magnitude less than 5.0 would tend to increase the ground motion hazard for the peak ground acceleration and short periods of the response spectrum for small return periods because of the relatively high frequency of occurrence of small earthquakes, which are not necessarily damaging to the structures.

The PSHA procedures combine the probability of occurrence of an earthquake, the probability of it being a specific size, and the attenuation of its motion to the site, to obtain the probability of exceedance of a specified ground motion level. Combination of these individual probabilities for the different source zones at each motion level of interest then provides the total annual probabilities of exceedance. Ground motions corresponding to a particular probability level can then be obtained by interpolation. Figure 3.2 shows the different elements of a PSHA graphically. There are several computer programs available for PSHA.

The choice of probability levels for ground motion usually depends upon the design criteria for each individual project, and is established based on several parameters such as level of risk and importance of the facility. Various probability levels commonly used are 50% probability of exceedance in 50 years, 10% probability in 50 years and 10% probability of exceedance in 100 years. Assuming a Poissonian distribution, these probability levels correspond to an equivalent return period of 72, 475 and 950 year return periods, respectively, or annual exceedance probabilities of 0.014, 0.002 and 0.001. The relation between return period, T and probability of exceedance for a Poissonian distribution is given as:

$$T = \frac{-t}{\ln(1-p)} \qquad (3.A.5)$$

where p is the probability of exceedance in t years. In this equation, the probability of exceedance, p, is expressed as a decimal (e.g., 0.10 stands for 10%).

A response spectrum developed from a PSHA is referred to as a uniform hazard spectrum, since each ordinate has the same associated probability of exceedance (a constant level of risk). Since the response spectrum from a PSHA analysis is calculated by a sum of individual probabilities of occurrence of several earthquakes of different magnitudes and distances within the entire area of study, it cannot be related to an earthquake of specified magnitude and distance from the source.

The level of ground motion corresponding to a 10% probability of exceedance in 50 years is the basis of design for the *UBC* and is also referred to as the maximum probable ground motion in the Title 24, Part 2, of the California Building Code (1991).

Uncertainty associated with the selection of input parameters must be included in a PSHA. Uncertainty could be in the definition of magnitude-recurrence relationship, or in the definition of slip rates, or the maximum magnitude potential, or geographical location of a source. Furthermore, there is also uncertainty in defining the ground motions. The uncertainty distribution on the attenuation model indicates that no matter how accurately we know the magnitude and distance of a postulated earthquake, there will still be some uncertainty in predicting what the ground motion will be (Reiter, 1990). The uncertainty associated with an attenuation relationship (standard deviation) is incorporated in the seismic hazard during the integration process for the calculation of the probability of occurrence of a specified ground motion level.

Sometimes there is a tendency to make conservative estimates of input parameters to be used as an input to a PSHA. This is not consistent with the philosophy of PSHA. Input parameters should be selected on "best estimate" values.

3.A.7 VERTICAL MOTIONS

Few attenuation relationships are available for vertical ground motions which can be used to developed vertical ground response spectra. In practice, vertical ground motions are usually obtained by appropriately scaling the horizontal ground response spectrum. Typically, a factor of 2/3 is used as the ratio between vertical and horizontal ground motions. Ground motions recorded during earthquakes show that for sites in the near-field, this ratio may be much higher than 2/3 in the high frequency range and lower than 2/3 in the long period (low frequency) range (Egan et. al., 1994, Nisar and Golesorkhi, 1994).

3.A.8 EARTHQUAKE TIME HISTORIES

If needed, it may sometimes by better to use a set of acceleration time histories whose average elastic response spectra is similar to the design spectrum. Time histories are usually used for non-linear analysis or for analysis of structures of special importance. Whenever used, the use of a single time history is not recommended.

Acceleration time histories to represent site-specific design ground motions are usually developed by taking recorded acceleration time histories during past earthquakes and appropriately scaling to represent the design ground motions. In the selection of time histories for use in design, consideration should be given to the duration, source-to-site distance, local soil conditions, and type of faulting.

Several methods of scaling the acceleration time histories are used, such as scaling on the basis of PGA or by obtaining a scale factor by a comparison of the response spectrum of the time history with the design response spectrum in the period range of interest. Site-specific acceleration time histories can be developed by scaling the time history in the frequency domain, whereby the Fourier amplitudes are scaled such that the response spectrum of the scaled time history matches the design response spectrum.

Artificial time histories using involved mathematical models are sometimes also developed. It is generally recommended to use recorded ground motions when available. The use of artificial time histories may sometimes become necessary when no data on recorded motions is available. If used, it is important to ensure that these time histories have realistic amplitude and phase relationships and that their response spectra is similar to the design response spectrum.

APPENDIX 3.B

EARTHQUAKE RELATED COASTAL INUNDATION

APPENDIX 3.B
EARTHQUAKE RELATED COASTAL INUNDATION

3.B.1 INTRODUCTION

Section 3.4 describes briefly the phenomena associated with tsunamis and seiches. This appendix discusses in more detail several issues associated with earthquake induced coastal inundation.

3.B.2 EARTHQUAKE INDUCED COASTAL INUNDATION HAZARDS

A given site in a coastal area may be affected by one or more of the following earthquake related inundation hazards:

a. *Coastal Subsidence* caused by tectonic (faulting) or non-tectonic (e.g., submarine landslide) effects.

b. *Tsunamis* from either large (M_W>6.5) local earthquakes or distant great (M_W>7.7) earthquakes.

c. *Seiches* in semi-enclosed bays, estuaries, lakes or reservoirs caused by moderate (M_W>5.0) local (submarine) earthquakes or regional large earthquakes.

Each of these hazards is described in detail below.

3.B.2.1 Coastal Subsidence

In areas of dip-slip faulting (normal, thrust, or oblique-slip faulting) which involve a vertical component of movement, co-seismic subsidence along coastal faults could result in permanent submergence of the coastal area. Based on worldwide experiences such as the 1964 Alaska (M_W=8.4) and the 1992 Cape Mendocino, California (M_W=7.2) earthquakes, tectonic subsidence of more than 6 feet (2 meters) could occur. Furthermore, earthquakes on blind faults, such as the 1994 Northridge California (M_W=6.7) earthquake, may create significant surface uplift or subsidence without attendant surface fault rupture.

Permanent coastal subsidence may also occur as a result of earthquake-induced seafloor slumping or landslides. During the 1964 Alaska earthquake, the Seward port area, which included petrochemical facilities, progressively slid under the bay as shaking continued. This subsidence was followed by withdrawal of the sea and subsequent inundation of the coast by a wave 30 feet high. In addition to this slide induced wave, tsunami waves some 30-40 feet high, generated by the tectonic deformation, arrived later and compounded the destruction of Seward. Similar effects on a lesser scale were experienced at Moss Landing on Monterey Bay during the 1989 Loma Prieta, California (M_W=7.1) earthquake even though the epicenter was located onshore in the Santa Cruz Mountains. At Moss Landing, subsidence and related liquefaction created large fissures, generated a small tsunami in Monterey Bay, and caused substantial damage to the Moss Landing Marine Facilities. Thus, sites located where landslides or unstable slopes are common, both on land and offshore, should assume that submarine slumping and coastal inundation could occur during large earthquakes in the region.

For disaster planning and emergency response purposes, significant coastal subsidence followed by tsunami run-up should be considered likely to exceed run-up predicted based on pre-subsidence topography alone. Combined subsidence and tsunami effects are considered the likely cause of the destruction to the city of Port Royal on the Island of Jamaica in 1692, and may occur in many seismically active areas of the world. Thus, maps of potential inundation should consider these combined effects where coastal subsidence may be expected.

3.B.2.2 Tsunami (Seismic Sea Wave)

Tsunamis are long period (T from 5 to 60 minutes) surface gravity waves, with wavelengths that may exceed 60 miles (100 km). Tsunamis are typically generated by large submarine earthquakes that displace the seafloor over large areas. The destructive effects of tsunami waves may be localized, occurring along the coasts situated close to the tsunami origin, or the waves may travel with little attenuation across entire oceans and affect coasts thousands of miles away.

Earthquake induced seafloor displacement may occur with or without seafloor fault rupture (as on a blind fault), and could generate a potentially destructive tsunami. Even strike-slip faults, although less likely to generate significant vertical seafloor displacement than dip-slip faults, may cause substantial seafloor uplift or subsidence in places where these faults bend and curve. Furthermore, large earthquakes centered on faults near the coast but on land (e.g., the 1992 Cape Mendocino, California earthquake), may also cause local tsunamis because of the broad regional tectonic uplift (or subsidence) they create.

In addition to primary tectonic deformation associated with the earthquake, large-scale slumping or landslides under the ocean or other large water bodies may generate significant local tsunamis. A large rock slide in Lituya Bay, Alaska, triggered by an earthquake in 1957 generated a tsunami that surged 1700 meters up the side of the fjord. Volcanic explosions, such as that of Krakatoa in 1883, may also generate destructive tsunamis that inundate surrounding coasts. Coastal areas in active tectonic regions are more likely to be susceptible to tsunami attack. However, large tsunamis may travel across entire ocean basins and affect areas with little or no local tectonic activity.

Around the Pacific Ocean basin, often referred to as the "Ring-of-Fire", most of the world's great earthquakes, volcanic eruptions, and destructive tsunamis occur. Earthquakes in this region have large dip-slip (vertical) movements which displace the seafloor rapidly, initiating the sea surface disturbance that becomes a tsunami. Places such as Japan, Alaska, Hawaii, and western South America are particularly vulnerable to these tsunamis, both because they have many large earthquakes (and volcanoes) locally situated, and because their geographic position and coastal configuration expose them to distantly generated tsunamis. In the contiguous U.S., recent evidence uncovered along the coasts of Washington, Oregon, and northern California show that large local tsunamis have been generated by great earthquakes in the Cascadia subduction zone. The Atlantic coast has also suffered destructive tsunamis such as the one generated by the great Lisbon earthquake in 1755, but such events are rare and generally less severe on the U.S. side of the Atlantic Ocean. Whereas the Gulf of Mexico has been relatively free of destructive tsunamis, in the Caribbean, active tectonics along the Puerto Rico trench and Antilles arc have generated notable tsunamis. Active tectonism with large earthquakes, volcanoes, and tsunamis, also occurs around the Indian Ocean.

Propagation of tsunamis often results in dispersion of the initial tsunami wave form so that several significant waves may strike the coast. The first wave to arrive may be smaller than subsequent waves, and persons in affected areas must realize that a drawdown following one wave may be soon followed by larger, more destructive, wave arrivals. The run-up speed of such waves (10-20 m/sec or 20-40 miles per hour), would outrun even the fastest human runners. In bays or other partially enclosed basins, tsunamis may also set up a seiche (see below) which can amplify wave height and prolong the tsunami duration. For example, following the 1964 Alaska (M_S=8.4) earthquake, the tsunami recorded at Santa Monica, California, measured up to 2 meters (6.5 feet) high and oscillations of half this amount were still occurring 17-19 hours after the arrival of the first wave. Consequently, destructive waves from tsunami may persist for a long time, and vulnerable areas should remain evacuated until an "All Clear" message has been broadcast by authorities.

3.B.2.3 Seiche

A seiche occurs when resonant wave oscillations form in an enclosed or semi-enclosed body of water such as a lake, bay, or fjord. Seiches may be triggered by moderate or larger local submarine earthquakes, and sometimes by large, distant, earthquakes. Tectonic deformation of Hebgen Lake during the 1959 earthquake initiated seiche oscillations of up to 8 feet over the new lake level (which changed as a result of the deformation). Such oscillations have also been triggered by meteorological disturbances. For example, the passage of a storm front across Lake Michigan tends to pile water on the eastern shore as the front advances. After the front passes, the water flows back westward, setting up the seiche. The initial storm wave setup is similar to storm surges observed along coasts affected by hurricanes and other tropical storms, but the seiche results from the resonant oscillation of the wave due to the enclosed character of the water body. Seiche oscillations may persist for several hours.

3.B.3 ASSESSING SITE VULNERABILITY

Coastal sites in active tectonic areas where dip-slip faulting is common are most susceptible to earthquake-induced inundation. Examination of the regional fault characteristics and earthquake history, with emphasis on submarine earthquakes and possible historical tsunamis, provides the best measure of site vulnerability. Estimates of maximum tsunami run-up may be based on either historical occurrences or theoretical modeling. The Federal Insurance Administration developed inundation maps to assist in setting rates for the National Flood Insurance Program (Flood Insurance Rate Maps—FIRM). Inundation levels on these maps generally consist of the higher of either riverine flood, coastal storm surge, or tsunami inundation levels. The FIRM maps show coastal run-up elevations for 100 and 500 year events based upon theoretical tsunami modeling for the Pacific Coast of the U.S. (Houston and Garcia, 1974). Some cities, particularly in Hawaii where tsunamis are relatively frequent, have prepared local tsunami inundation maps. These should be available from government agencies. Eastern U.S. cities (Atlantic and Gulf coasts) are more likely affected by hurricane storm surge inundation whereas Pacific Coast cities are affected by tsunami. Inland cities would be affected by riverine flooding, although cities adjacent to major lakes, such as Chicago, would also be susceptible to seiche. If a site lies below the inundation elevations, then it may be vulnerable to flooding and related effects. Lower elevations are also more vulnerable because deeper water levels carry greater hydrodynamic forces for impact and erosion of structures and foundations. Table 3.B.1 outlines the steps involved in assessing the potential for coastal inundation.

3.B.4 EFFECTS OF COASTAL INUNDATION

Any of the three causes of coastal inundation (coastal subsidence, tsunami, or seiche) results in essentially the same effect: low-lying coastal areas will be covered with water. The greatest hazard from coastal inundation results from the inflow and outflow of the sea during the inundation event. The strong currents from this flow may erode foundations of structures and sweep away smaller structures or equipment. Debris carried by the water will act as battering rams to pound other more solidly anchored structures. People unsafely located in the low-lying areas may be swept out-to-sea and drowned, or knocked unconscious by the debris and drowned. Normal wave action will also be superimposed on the tsunami, adding dynamic forces capable of pounding and destroying even strong structures. Petrochemical facilities would be especially vulnerable to rupture of storage tanks from debris impact and foundation erosion, possibly resulting in explosion and fire. The tsunami at Seward, Alaska following the 1964 earthquake led to such destruction of the port facilities. The succession of waves spread the fire from ruptured oil tanks across and throughout the port area.

TABLE 3.B.1: Evaluation Process for Coastal Inundation Hazards

Outline for Analysis of Coastal Inundation Potential
1) Evaluate tsunami and earthquake history
2) Inundation maps prepared by government agencies (e.g., FIRM maps, Houston and Garcia)
3) Seismotectonic study, character of faulting, location of faulting w.r.t. site
4) Site topography and adjacent coastal bathymetry, harbor or embayment configuration (resonances)
(5) Hydrodynamic analyses, long period wave response, tidal parameters
Tsunami/Seiche Inundation Evaluation Procedure
A. Is tsunami/seiche/inundation possible (history, seismotectonic study) 1) Literature Review 2) Historical Research 3) Seismotectonic Analysis 4) Geomorphic/Paleoseismic Study 5) Geotechnical Study (Landslides, Slumps, Possible Generating Mechanisms)
B. What is maximum credible run-up elevation for region 1) Tsunami inundation maps available? 2) Flood Insurance Rate Maps 3) Historical Analysis 4) Theoretical Analysis
C. Is site located within low-lying coastal area (below maximum possible run-up elevation)
D. Engineering analysis required to evaluate tsunami/seiche inundation potential
E. Engineering analysis required to identify vulnerable facility components
F. Engineering analysis required to identify/recommend specific mitigations for vulnerable facility components 1) Seawalls or Barriers 2) Facility Layout to Locate Vulnerable Components Above Inundation Zone 3) Geotechnical Studies to Identify Potential Liquefaction/Slump/Landslide Hazards that might place facility at risk (Seward, Alaska problems) 4) Facility Construction with Reinforced Foundations and Walls Below Inundation Levels to Resist Tsunami Damage 5) Response Plans — Tsunami Warning System; Evacuation to High Ground; Safe Shutdown; Automatic Fire-Fighting Equipment? Life Saving (Flotation) Devices
G. Government studies available/needed for region?

Tsunami combined with seiche could result in an oscillating water level causing several cycles of coastal inundation. Periods of inundation could last for several hours. With tectonic subsidence of the coast (or from a large submarine landslide), the inundation may be permanent. Major subsidence, ground deformation, or severe erosion could undermine bridge piers and foundations, disrupting lifelines such as highways, railroads, pipelines, and electrical power and communication lines. Such damage could isolate the area from emergency equipment, supplies, and rescue.

3.B.5 MITIGATION

3.B.5.1 Shoreline Structures

Throughout Japan, along the coast where tsunami attack is common, sea walls and other barriers have been constructed to resist tsunami inundation. These structures are sometimes unsuccessful, as large tsunamis often overtop the barriers and flood the protected area, generating strong currents which erode the barriers and other structures. In some instances, large wave dissipation structures have been carried hundreds of meters inland by major tsunamis. These structures could act as powerful battering rams against the very structures they were designed to protect. Even large storm surf sometimes throws large boulders and rip-rap inland causing damage to structures. Therefore, coastal protective structures must be carefully designed to withstand extreme events.

3.B.5.2 Tsunami Warning

Tsunamis travel across the oceans at high speeds of more than 60 miles per hour (100 km/hr), but generally require several hours before reaching distant coasts. Therefore, tsunami warnings are possible and have been established through the Pacific tsunami warning network. It is imperative that citizens take these warnings seriously—failure to heed the warnings by going to the beach to watch the incoming waves may result in needless loss-of-life. In southern California, there seems to be a serious lack of appreciation for the great hazard that tsunamis pose. This perhaps results from the absence of significant tsunamis striking the southern California coast in the recent past (one or two generations). Southern California beaches, such as Santa Monica, are most vulnerable to distant tsunamis arriving from the south or north. Such tsunamis would be generated by large or great earthquakes along the South American or Alaska and Aleutian coasts. Other coastal areas would be vulnerable to tsunamis from sources located along direct paths across the ocean. For large, approximately linear, tsunami sources such as oceanic trench areas, directional effects tend to focus the tsunami energy along an axis perpendicular to the linear source region. Sites in Hawaii are vulnerable to attack from tsunamis in many directions because of its central location in the Pacific Ocean.

A minimum of about 20-30 minutes time is required to issue a tsunami warning through the Pacific tsunami warning network. Locally generated tsunamis would arrive too quickly, in less than 10-15 minutes, for adequate warning by officials. Although the technology exists to develop more rapid, regional tsunami warning networks, the relatively rare occurrence of damaging local tsunamis and economic constraints have precluded installation of such a system in most areas (such as the southern California area). In the absence of official warning systems, persons in low-lying coastal areas vulnerable to tsunami inundation should seek shelter on higher ground immediately upon experiencing a strong earthquake in their area. Such immediate response has been conditioned into the minds of Japanese people where tsunami occurrences are relatively frequent. If no tsunami were generated in the first hour following the event, and no tsunami warning were issued based upon other earthquake data, it should be safe to return to the low-lying area. If, however, a tsunami is generated, the first wave may arrive and withdraw causing little or no damage, only to be followed by larger, possibly destructive waves. For areas that tend to have resonant oscillations, significant wave activity may persist for several hours, or even most of a day. People in these areas should wait for an all clear signal from official agencies before returning.

3.B.5.3 Land-Use Planning and Inundation Map

Theoretical and laboratory models have been used to estimate likely inundation levels for 100 and 500 year return periods along U.S. coasts affected by tsunami (FIRM Maps). The 100 and 500 year time intervals represent an estimated average recurrence interval; one must realize that so-called 100 year events may occur in shorter time spans. For example both the 1960 Chile and 1964 Alaska earthquakes generated tsunami waves equivalent to a 100 year event along the southern California coast. The runup height estimated in these maps refers to the land elevation (or contour) that the incoming tsunami will reach. This runup height includes the effects of the normal tidal range, but excludes the possible simultaneous occurrence of the tsunami with high surf and storm wave setup. Amplification of run-up by coastal topography may also occur, especially in narrow, V-shaped, canyons.

Sites located in vulnerable areas should prepare for the possibility of tsunami inundation, and important structures should be designed to resist possible inundation effects. Facilities should be evaluated to identify vulnerable components, and possible mitigation strategies identified. Emergency or disaster response plans should be prepared considering the vulnerability of the facility and the possible effects of tsunami attack. Also, an attempt should be made to anticipate otherwise unexpected consequences that may arise from the complex interaction between direct earthquake effects and subsequent tsunami inundation.

3.B.5.4 Public Awareness

McCulloch (1985) lists the following individual actions which can help to save lives in the event of a tsunami:

a. If you are on low ground near the coast and a large earthquake occurs in your area, move to high ground. There may be no time to either issue or receive an official warning.

b. If you recognize a drawdown of the sea, move to high ground.

c. The first tsunami wave may not be the highest. In major tsunamis, later waves commonly have the highest runup heights.

d. Periods between successive major waves may be similar. Thus, you may have time between waves to move to higher ground or to assist in rescue efforts.

e. Do not assume that because the incoming tsunami wave is not breaking it will not be destructive. The forces contained in this high-velocity, often debris-laden torrent are extremely destructive during runup and runoff.

f. Do not assume that areas behind beaches generally shielded from storm waves will be immune from high runup. Tsunami runup heights have historically been higher in some such areas along the California coast.

g. Do not go to the beach to watch a tsunami coming in. Not only might you hamper rescue efforts, but you may also have taken your last sightseeing trip.

Chapter 4
SEISMIC ANALYSIS

4.1 INTRODUCTION

This chapter describes the overall methodology for performing seismic analysis of petrochemical facilities in order to obtain seismically induced loads. This is applicable to structural systems or subsystems to be used either in new design or in evaluation of existing facilities. This chapter is organized in a manner such that the main contents are written primarily for design of new facilities. Considerations for the evaluation of existing facilities are summarized in Section 4.6.

The overall approach outlined in this chapter is consistent with common practice in the petrochemical industry at the time of writing of this document. The committee surveyed the design standards of seven operators and architect-engineering firms and found that all of those standards specifically reference the 1994 *UBC*. As such, many specific equations and references in this chapter are from the version of the *UBC* current at the time of writing of this document.

The intent of this chapter is not to instruct an engineer on how to use the *UBC* or any other commonly used building code. Rather, it is to give guidance as to appropriate application of typical building code provisions to the types of structures and equipment commonly found in petrochemical facilities. The reader should be aware that building code provisions are constantly being revised and that major changes are currently being incorporated into many codes, such as changing from working stress to strength-based design and changing the formulation of the basic base shear equations.

Users of codes other than the *UBC* are encouraged to still read those sections of this Chapter that primarily use *UBC* equations as a reference, such as the discussion on the base shear equation in Section 4.4.2. Much of the intent behind the guidance for application to petrochemical structures, such as interpretations of appropriate response modification factors (R_w in the *UBC*) will still be applicable to other codes.

Also, it should be noted that specific guidance given in many cases differs significantly from the current *UBC* provisions, such as in the following areas:

a. Response Modification Factors (R_w) (Sections 4.4.2 and 4.6)

b. Minimum C/R_w requirements (Section 4.4.2)

c. Use of a site specific value of the Seismic Zone Factor, Z, and response spectra (Section 4.4.2)

d. Accidental torsion for nonbuilding structures (Section 4.4.6)

e. Requirements for scaling of results when performing a dynamic analysis (Section 4.5.6)

All seismic building codes commonly used today emphasize building structures, and were developed with a primary focus on methods and earthquake experience from building performance. This chapter emphasizes application to nonbuilding-like structures, and gives guidance as to distinctions that are appropriate when using codes developed primarily for buildings. The appendices also give examples of application to typical petrochemical installations, such as vessels, elevated equipment, process columns, pipeways, etc. Much of the guidance in the appendices, such as calculation of structural periods in Appendix 4.A is directly applicable to users of any building code.

In addition, in Section 4.6 and several appendices, this chapter discusses considerations for assessing existing structures, (All building codes are primarily focused on design of new facilities). Appendices 4.D and 4.E provide alternate methods for the evaluation of the overturning potential and the potential for sliding commensurate with the overall philosophy for the evaluation of existing structures. Appendix 4.F presents a guidance document prepared by others, being used in many locations in California to assist in evaluating existing facilities for requirements of a state-mandated regulatory program. This document is presented in its entirety in Appendix 4.F because it is in use but is not published and is not readily available to interested engineers.

Some of the material presented in this chapter, including appendices, was taken from various companies (architect-engineer, consultant and owner) currently active in the petrochemical industry. Appropriate references are provided to guide the reader to the background of the presented material.

4.2 STRUCTURAL SYSTEMS IN A PETROCHEMICAL FACILITY

4.2.1 General

Structures found in petrochemical facilities fall into two main categories: building structures (Section 4.2.2) and nonbuilding structures (Section 4.2.3). Within nonbuilding structures, two sub-categories are defined depending on structural characteristics. These are building-like structures (Section 4.2.3.1) and nonbuilding-like structures (Section 4.2.3.2). Combination structures are also addressed in Section 4.2.3.2. In addition, certain equipment and anchorage design requirements in a petrochemical facility falls under the category of "subsystem" rather than structures. Subsystems are discussed in Section 4.2.4. A brief description of various structures typically found in petrochemical facilities can be found in Esfandiari and Summers (1994).

4.2.2 Building Structures

Building structures typically found in petrochemical facilities include administration buildings, control buildings, substations, warehouses, firehouses, maintenance buildings, and compressor shelters or buildings. They are typically single story buildings, but may have as many as two or three stories. Lateral force resisting systems (LFRSs) used include shear walls, braced frames, rigid frames, and combinations. The provisions of the code of record would apply in their entirety to design of these buildings. Certain buildings in petrochemical facilities may also be required to be designed for blast loading, which often controls the design.

4.2.3 Nonbuilding Structures

Other than actual buildings in a petrochemical facility, all structures are typically classified as nonbuilding structures. However, their structural systems may resemble those of buildings, for example transverse moment frames for pipeways. Therefore, these structures are classified as building-like structures. Other structures, whose structural systems do not resemble those of buildings, are classified as nonbuilding-like structures. An example is a tank or a vessel. Each of these sub-categories is defined in detail below.

4.2.3.1 Building-Like Structures

These are structures such as pipeways, equipment support frames and box-type heaters which have LFRSs similar to those of building systems, such as braced frames, moment resisting frames or shear wall systems. A flexible structure is typically defined as having a natural period of vibration (T) of 0.06 seconds or more, which is equivalent to a frequency of about 17 Hz or less. Examples of building-like structures found in petrochemical facilities include:

a. Moment resisting frames (steel or concrete) or braced frames (cross-braced or chevron-braced) supporting exchangers and horizontal vessels. Such structures can be up to four or five levels high.

b. Pipeways with LFRSs that are moment resisting frames (usually in the transverse direction to provide access beneath the pipeway) or braced frames (usually in the longitudinal direction).

c. Rectangular furnaces.

4.2.3.2 Nonbuilding-Like Structures

This category covers many structures and self supporting equipment items found in a typical petrochemical facility, such as vertical vessels, horizontal vessels and exchangers, stacks and towers. Nonbuilding-like structures typically found in a petrochemical facility typically fall into one of four categories described below:

a. Rigid structures, i.e., those whose fundamental structural period is less than 0.06 seconds, such as a horizontal vessel or exchanger, supported on short, stiff piers.

b. Flat-bottom tanks supported at or below grade. Such structures respond very differently (compared to regular structures) during an earthquake. Special issues for unanchored tanks, such as the effects of fluid sloshing and tank uplift must also be considered. Tanks are described in more detail in Chapter 7.

c. Other nonbuilding-like structures. Examples of this category of structures include skirt-supported vertical vessels, spheres on braced legs, horizontal vessels or exchangers on long piers, guyed structures, and cooling towers.

d. Combination structures. In petrochemical facilities, such structures generally support flexible nonstructural elements whose combined weight exceeds about 25% of the weight of the structure. A typical example is a tall vertical vessel, furnace or tank supported above grade on a braced or moment resisting frame. The analysis method depends on whether the nonstructural element is flexible or rigid, and whether its weight exceeds or is less than about 25% of the weight of the supporting structure. Refer to Appendix 4.B for a description of these analysis methodologies.

4.2.4 Subsystems

In addition to various structures described in the preceding sections, various equipment and components that are supported within a structure can be considered subsystems. The weight of subsystems should only be a small portion of the total weight of the supporting structure (i.e., less than about 25%). Example of subsystems typically found in a petrochemical facility include:

a. Horizontal vessels and exchangers supported on a structure, weighing less than about 25% of the weight of the supporting structure

b. Electrical and mechanical equipment supported within a structure

c. Cable tray, conduit, ductwork and/or piping supported on a pipeway or within a building

4.3 SELECTION OF ANALYSIS METHODS

4.3.1 General

When performing seismic analysis of structures in petrochemical facilities, two options are commonly used:

a. Equivalent Static Analysis
b. Dynamic Analysis

For the great majority of cases, the equivalent static analysis method is appropriate to determine lateral forces and their distribution. However, unusual structures which have significant irregularities in shape, mass or stiffness or are affected by interaction with other structures may require dynamic analysis. Further descriptions on types of irregularities are given in Section 4.3.2 below, various building codes, and SEAOC (1990). If a dynamic analysis is performed, building codes typically require that earthquake forces should also be calculated, or checked, by the equivalent static method. Section 4.5.6 provides more discussion on the background and the need to perform static analysis in addition to dynamic analysis, when one chooses the dynamic analysis option. Other options available include a nonlinear static (pushover) analysis. This method is described in *ATC-33.03*.

4.3.2 Equivalent Static Analysis

This analysis option allows the analyst to determine the seismic loads using static methods. Building codes typically contain restrictions on the use of equivalent static analyses for building-like structures, in particular when the structure has a highly irregular shape, non-uniform mass, abrupt changes in lateral stiffness, or exceeds certain heights. Dynamic analysis is usually required for determining the distribution of lateral force for these situations. Ideally, mass distribution is uniform over the entire height of a structure, and the centroids of mass and rigidity coincide at every level. This ideal condition rarely occurs in petrochemical structures, but the distributions are in general close enough so that the simplified code distribution of forces is justified. The engineer should investigate the issue carefully before concluding that the equivalent static method is appropriate.

Tables 4.1 and 4.2 define structural irregularities typical of petrochemical facilities along the structural height and in plan view, respectively.

4.3.3 Dynamic Analysis

This analysis procedure may be used for all petrochemical facility structures; however, it should be used specifically for irregular structures and for structures, regular or irregular, located on soft soil profiles, such as type S4 in the *UBC*, which have a period greater than about 0.7 seconds. Various analysis options, such as the response spectrum method, time-history method using modal superposition or direct integration techniques, either linear or nonlinear, are available to the analyst. Section 4.5 describes the dynamic analysis option in more detail.

TABLE 4.1: Vertical Structural Irregularities (from *UBC* Table 16-L)

Irregularity Type and Definition
A. Stiffness Irregularity - Soft Segment A soft segment is one in which the lateral stiffness of one segment of the structure is less than about 70 percent of that of the segment immediately above.
B. Weight (mass) Irregularity Mass irregularity should be considered to exist where the effective mass of any segment of the structure is more than about 150 percent of the effective mass of adjacent segments.
C. Vertical Geometric Irregularity Vertical geometric irregularity should be considered to exist where the horizontal dimension of the lateral force resisting system in any one segment of the structure is more than about 130 percent of that in an adjacent segment.
D. In-Plane Discontinuity in Vertical Lateral Force Resisting Element An in-plane offset of the lateral load resisting elements greater than the length of those elements.
E. Discontinuity in Capacity - Weak Segment A weak segment is one in which the strength of one segment of the structure is less than about 80 percent of that of the segment above. The segment strength is the total strength of all seismic resisting elements sharing the segment shear for the direction under consideration.

TABLE 4.2: Plan Structural Irregularities (from *UBC* Table 16-M)

Irregularity Type and Definition
A. Torsional Irregularity Torsional irregularity should be considered to exist when the maximum segment drift, at one end of the structure transverse to an axis is more than about 1.2 times the average of the segment drifts of the two ends of the structure.
B. Reentrant Corners Plan configurations of a structure and its lateral force resisting system contain reentrant corners, where both projections of the structure beyond a reentrant corner are greater than about fifteen percent of the plan dimension of the structure in the given direction.
C. Diaphragm Discontinuity Diaphragms with abrupt discontinuities or variations in stiffness, including those having cutout or open areas greater than about fifty percent of the gross enclosed area of the diaphragm, or changes in effective diaphragm stiffness of more than about fifty percent from one segment to the next.
D. Out-of-Plane Offsets Discontinuities in a lateral force path, such as out-of-plane offsets of the vertical elements.
E. Nonparallel Systems The vertical lateral load resisting elements are not parallel to nor symmetric about the major orthogonal axes of the lateral force resisting system.

4.4 EQUIVALENT STATIC ANALYSIS PROCEDURE

4.4.1 General

The concept of the equivalent static analysis procedure is to calculate the effective earthquake loads in terms of a base shear which is dependent on the mass of the structure, the imposed ground acceleration, the dynamic characteristics of the structure, the inherent ductility of the structure, and the importance of the structure. The base shear is then applied to the structure as an equivalent lateral load. This chapter also discusses how this lateral load should be distributed in plan and vertically along the height of the structure. Once this load is determined and distributed at various elevations of the structures, conventional static analysis techniques may be used to determine the seismic load in each structural member and at connections.

4.4.2 Determination of Base Shear

The total horizontal base shear (V) for a regular flexible building-like structure in any of the two orthogonal horizontal directions can be determined from a formulation similar to Equation 4.1 below, which is Equation (28-1) in the UBC.

$$V = ZICW/R_w \tag{4.1}$$

where:

V = Base shear
Z = Seismic zone factor given in *UBC* Table 16-I
I = Importance factor given in Table 4.3
R_w = Response modification factor given in *UBC* Table 16-N for buildings and Table 4.4 of this document for petrochemical facility nonbuilding structures
W = Total seismic weight
C = Numerical coefficient determined from the following formula:

$$C = 1.25S/T^{(2/3)} \tag{4.2}$$

S = Site coefficient for soil characteristics given in *UBC* Table 16-J
T = Fundamental period of vibration, in seconds, of the structure for the direction under consideration

The value of C need not exceed 2.75 and this value may be used for any structure without regard for soil type or structure period. The minimum value of the ratio C/R_w should be 0.075.

In Equation (4.1), each parameter represents a certain aspect of the earthquake loading as described below:

Z represents the level of seismic ground motion expected at the site and is therefore site dependent. For cases where site specific data exist, it is appropriate to use the site-specific Z value or site-specific spectrum in lieu of those given by the code of record, subject to the approval of the local building official.

I is a measure of the relevant importance of the structure. For more important structures, higher seismic forces are prescribed. The importance factor, I, provides a means of increasing the design force levels for facilities which may have an unusual hazard, have a potential for releasing hazardous materials, or which are important for emergency response. The I value for individual petrochemical facilities should be reviewed with the owner and/or the building official for those cases where items do not fall under the code definitions. Suggested values of I for petrochemical facilities are given in Table 4.3. Note that an entire facility need not use the same value of I. See Chapter 2 for further discussion on this topic.

TABLE 4.3: Importance Factor (I) for Different Usage Categories

Usage Categories		Seismic Importance Factor For Structures, (I Factor)	Seismic Importance Factor for Subsystems (I_p Factor)
General	Normal	1.0	1.0
	Special	≥ 1 (See Note 1)	≥ 1 (See Note 1)
Hazardous		1.25	1.50
Essential		1.25	1.50

Note 1: Quantification of Importance Factors for "Special" usage category is an owner decision, since structures in this category are likely to be designed for higher seismic forces to protect an owner's investment.

C represents potential amplification of seismic forces allowing for relative frequency content of the ground motion and considering the natural period of structure under consideration.

The product ZC represents the spectral acceleration corresponding to the period of the structure. For cases where a site-specific spectrum exists, the spectral ordinate corresponding to the period of the structure may be used in lieu of the ZC value, subject to approval of building officials. Care should be taken to allow for higher mode effects if the fundamental natural period of the structure is larger than the period corresponding to the spectral peak. One way to allow for this is to increase the ZC factor by a factor of 1.5 to allow for higher mode effects.

Appendix 4.A presents example calculations of the fundamental period of vibration, T, for several typical structures commonly found in petrochemical facilities. If using the UBC, it is recommended that the period be determined from *UBC* Equation (28-5), Section 1628.2.2, corresponding to Method "B" only. This formula is based on Rayleigh's method and uses the structural properties and deformational characteristics of the structure as determined by a static analysis. For building-like structures only, Method "A" of the *UBC* may also be used in determining structural period. Alternatively, the fundamental period of the structure may be estimated by a frequency (modal) analysis. The engineer should use judgment as to which method is most desirable for application at hand.

Seismic weight, W, includes the weight of the structure, attached equipment, equipment and vessel contents (operating loads) and code-specified portions of live and snow load.

R_w is a measure of energy absorbing capability or ductility inherent in a particular type of structural system or structure. It represents an equivalent reduction in seismic forces by allowing energy dissipation once the structure begins to respond in the inelastic range. For a more detailed definition of this term, refer to SEAOC (1990).

When earthquake forces are calculated using Equation (4.1), it is recommended that R_w factors be applied as shown in Table 4.4. That table compares suggested values with those that would likely be used if applying descriptions provided in typical building codes, which generally are intended to describe building systems. Note that the R_w values for nonbuilding structures in petrochemical facilities, as recommended in Table 4.4, are generally smaller than those for buildings. This is because buildings tend to have structural redundancy due to multiple bays and frame lines. Also, buildings contain nonstructural elements which effectively give the building greater damping and strength during strong ground motion response. The engineer should evaluate the seismic response characteristics of the specific structure to determine if a more conservative or liberal R_w value than given in Table 4.4 is appropriate for design. Note also that using higher R_w values in design tend to result in a flexible structure which will tend to increase calculated displacements.

For buildings and building-like structures, codes typically specify a minimum C/R_w value of 0.075. For nonbuilding-like structures, this minimum ratio is specified as 0.4 in the *UBC*. For petrochemical type structures which fall in the nonbuilding-like category, it is suggested by this committee that a lower minimum C/R_w value of 0.25 is appropriate.

The recommended minimum C/R_w value of 0.25 is based on a comparison by the committee of theoretical base shears calculated with no limits on C/R_w, versus the code-limited base shears calculated applying the minimum C/R_w values where appropriate. The proportional increase of code-limited base shear over theoretical base shear is larger for nonbuilding-like structures than for buildings and building-like structures, even with the minimum C/R_w value of 0.25 rather than 0.4. Furthermore, that increase in base shear also occurs over a greater period range for nonbuilding-like structures (typically 0.75 seconds or greater for nonbuilding structures versus 3.0 seconds or greater for buildings). The reason for this is because the R_w values for nonbuilding-like structures as suggested in Table 4.4 are limited to 8, and are usually less than 6, as compared to those for buildings, which can range as high as 12.

TABLE 4.4: R_w Factors for Nonbuilding Structures for Design of New Petrochemical Facilities

A. BUILDING-LIKE STRUCTURES SUPPORTING EQUIPMENT (see note (a) at end of table) This covers structures whose primary purpose is to support equipment, such as air coolers, horizontal vessels, exchangers, heaters, vertical vessels and reactors, etc.	R_W Suggested	R_W Code Value(b)
1. Steel structures		
Special moment resisting frame	8	12
Ordinary moment resisting frame	6	6
Braced frame		
a. Eccentrically braced frame	8	10
b. Concentrically braced frame	6	8
Inverted pendulum type structure (cantilever column)	3	3
2. Concrete structures		
Special moment resisting frame	8	12
Intermediate moment resisting frame	6 (c)	8 (c)
Ordinary moment frame	5 (d)	5 (d)
Shear wall	6	6
Inverted pendulum type structure (cantilever pier/column)	3	3
B. EQUIPMENT BEHAVING AS STRUCTURES WITH INTEGRAL SUPPORTS	**R_W Suggested**	**R_W Code Value(b)**
1. Vertical vessels/heaters, tanks, or spheres supported by:		
Steel skirts	4 (e)	4 (e)
Steel braced legs	4 (f)	3
Steel or concrete unbraced legs	3	3
2. Boilers		
Light steel framed wall with shear panels	6	6
Steel braced frame where bracing carries gravity load	6	6
Steel ordinary moment frame	6	6
3. Chimneys or stacks		
Steel guyed	4	4
Steel cantilever	4	4
Concrete	4	4

TABLE 4.4: R_w Factors for Nonbuilding Structures for Design of New Petrochemical Facilities (Cont.)

C. PIPEWAYS	R_W	
	Suggested	Code Value(b)
1. Steel		
Special moment resisting frame	8	(g)
Ordinary moment resisting frame	6	(g)
Braced frame	6	(g)
Cantilever column	4	(g)
2. Concrete		
Special moment resisting frame	8	(g)
Intermediate moment resisting frame	6 (c)	(g)
Ordinary moment resisting frame	5 (d)	(g)
Cantilever column	4	(g)
D. COOLING TOWERS	R_W	
	Suggested	Code Value(b)
1. Wood frame	8	(h)
2. Concrete	5	5
E. ANCHOR BOLTS	R_W	
	Suggested	Code Value(b)
1. Anchor bolt yield or other ductile failure mechanisms control	As for structure	As for structure
2. Concrete failure or anchor bolt slippage controls, or there is a non-ductile force transfer mechanism between structure and foundation	(i)	N/A

FOOTNOTES:

(a) For structures supporting equipment whose weight exceeds about 25% of the supporting structures, the lower R_w corresponding to the equipment or structure should be used for design of the entire structure, unless justified on a case-by-case basis.

FOOTNOTES (Cont.):

(b) These values are interpretations of *UBC* Table 16-N as applied to petrochemical facilities.
(c) Use R_w = 4 for moderate and high seismic zones for structures less than 50 ft (15 m) in height. If structure is taller than 50 ft (15 m) in height, concrete IMRF is typically not permitted by codes.
(d) Typically not permitted by codes except in low seismic zones.
(e) Use R_w = 3 when D/t of the skirt is greater than 0.441 *E/Fy, where E and Fy are the Young's modulus and yield stress of the skirt, respectively
(f) The suggested R_w is higher than the value found in building codes. Although codes typically do not recognize the difference between braced and unbraced support structures, this committee believes there is greater energy absorbing capability for braced structures.
(g) Codes typically do not specifically mention R_w for pipeways.
(h) The typical code-specified R_w factor for timber ordinary braced framed structures is 8. However, cooling towers are also referred to in Table 16-P of the *UBC* for nonbuilding structures with an R_w = 5.
(i) Should only occur with special justification provided by engineer on a case-by-case basis

Codes typically provide straightforward equations to calculate lateral forces for nonbuilding structures which are rigid (T < 0.06 sec.), such as a short, stiff support pier for a horizontal vessel. For example, see *UBC* Section 1632.3, Equation (32-1).

Appendices 4.B and 4.C provide examples of determination of base shear for typical petrochemical structures.

4.4.3 Combination Structures

Combinations of structural systems are often incorporated into the same structure. Structures which include more than one structural system require special attention.

Nonbuilding-like structures which support flexible nonstructural elements whose combined weight exceeds about 25% of the weight of the structure, should be designed considering the dynamic interaction effects between the structure and the supported elements. If the weight of the nonstructural element is less than about 25% of the weight of the structure, or if the nonstructural element is rigid, interaction effects need not be considered. For structures supporting equipment whose weight exceeds 25% of the supporting structures, the smaller R_w value, corresponding to the either equipment or structure, should be used for design of the entire structure.

Appendix 4.B contains guidelines for determining base shear for nonbuilding structures which are a combination of more than one structural system (e.g., finfans supported on pipeways). Specific guidance is provided for combinations of rigid and non-rigid structures, and supported equipment weighing greater than and less than 25% of the weight of the structure. Appendix 4.C also contains examples showing calculations of base shear for combination structures (e.g. examples 1.2 and 3.2b).

4.4.4 Vertical Distribution of Forces

Lateral force distribution in the vertical direction is a method for resolving the base shear into static force equivalents applied laterally to the structure. When the mass of the structure is uniformly distributed over the height of the structure (such as buildings), this force distribution is assumed to be linear (inverted triangular). For multilevel buildings and structures, the base shear, V, is distributed to different levels assuming a triangular distribution of forces. This is a close representation of the first mode shape of the structures. It also is representative of the average of the shear deflection and moment deflection curve for the fundamental modes. An example of a methodology to distribute lateral forces in such a way is found in the *UBC*, Section 1628.4.

When the structure under consideration is highly irregular in shape and/or has non-uniform mass distribution vertically, the concept of lateral load distribution as defined above is no longer valid. In such cases a proper dynamic analysis should be conducted to determine lateral load distribution.

4.4.5 Horizontal Distribution of Forces

Once horizontal forces for each elevation are determined, these forces are distributed to each of the horizontal load carrying elements in the ratio of their horizontal stiffnesses. Such an approach assumes that diaphragms are rigid. For structures with flexible diaphragms, the horizontal stiffness of the diaphragm should be incorporated when distributing horizontal forces into various load carrying elements. Alternatively, the lateral forces should be assigned based on tributary spans. In petrochemical facilities large and rigid horizontal vessels supported on a structure may be considered to act as a diaphragm. An example methodology for horizontal distribution of forces can be found in *UBC* Section 1628.5.

4.4.6 Torsional Effects

Horizontal torsional moments occur in structures with rigid diaphragms as a result of eccentricities between the center of mass and center of rigidity at each elevation. Other factors also contribute to horizontal torsion. These are:

a. spatial variation of horizontal input motions applied to long structures
b. the effects of non-structural elements
c. uncertainties in defining the structure's stiffness characteristics

Where torsional irregularities exist, the effect of horizontal torsion can be computed at each floor level and included in the analysis in accordance with requirements of building codes, such as Sections 1628.5 and 1628.6 of the *UBC*.

Where the mass location for most petrochemical facility structures can be determined with reasonable accuracy, no consideration of accidental torsion is necessary. Additionally, to a large extent structures in petrochemical facilities typically do not have rigid diaphragms. Therefore, for these types of structures, the torsional effects are minimal. However, if the mass distribution in a horizontal plane cannot be determined with accuracy and the structure has a rigid diaphragm, an allowance should be made for accidental torsion.

Accidental torsion is typically accounted for by assuming the center of mass is shifted in each horizontal direction from its calculated value by a distance equal to 5% of the structure dimension perpendicular to the direction being considered. An example of such methodology is provided in Sections 1628.5 and 1628.6 of the *UBC*.

4.4.7 Overturning Potential

Every structure should be designed and evaluated against potential overturning effects caused by earthquake forces. The overturning moment to be resisted at each level should be determined using the seismic forces which act on levels above the level under consideration. Overturning effects on every element should be carried down to the foundations.

Chapter 5 discusses safety factors to be used to check for potential against foundation overturning for new facilities. In addition, Section 4.6 presents special provisions that may be used to evaluate for foundation stability against overturning for existing facilities.

4.4.8 Sliding Potential

Building codes typically do not require any checks for stability against sliding, because building-like structures are required to be properly secured at the foundation. Likewise for the design of new petrochemical facilities, almost all structures (with the possible exception of large diameter flat bottom storage tanks) should be anchored to their foundations.

Chapter 5 discusses safety factors to be used to check for potential against sliding, if needed, for new facilities. Section 4.6 outlines requirements for checking stability against sliding for structures in existing facilities which are not anchored to their foundations.

4.4.9 Directions of Earthquake Forces

For building-like structures, various building codes generally imply that independent design for each of the principal horizontal axes will provide adequate resistance for forces applied in any direction, and therefore, the design seismic forces may be assumed to act nonconcurrently with certain exceptions; such as columns that are part of the lateral force resisting systems in both horizontal directions.

For nonbuilding structures in petrochemical facilities, the requirement that earthquake forces are to be considered to come from any direction should be carefully evaluated. The requirement that orthogonal effects be considered may be satisfied by designing such elements using one of the following methods:

a. Consider 100% of the member forces due to loads applied in one horizontal direction and 30% of the member forces due to loads applied in the orthogonal horizontal direction. This is mostly done in hand calculations, and it has the advantage of retaining signs when performing various combinations of earthquake loads.

b. Alternatively, the effects of the two orthogonal directions may be combined on a square root of the sum of the squares (SRSS) basis. This is usually implemented in computer analyses. Because the SRSS method loses the signs of the terms, use of the results require great care since knowledge about member equilibrium has been suppressed.

4.4.10 Vertical Motions

Response effects due to vertical components of ground motion are not usually calculated. They are considered to be allowed for by the following special provisions:

a. Combined vertical gravity loads and horizontal seismic forces must be considered in designing building components. Uplift effects due to seismic forces must also be considered. For materials designed using working stress procedures, dead loads are multiplied by 0.85 when used to check against uplift.

b. The following apply in high seismic zones:

- Horizontal cantilever components should be designed for a net upward force of $0.5ZW_p$, where W_p is the weight of the component.

- Horizontal prestressed components should be designed using not more than 50% of the dead load for the gravity load, alone or in combination with the lateral force effects.

It should be noted that for facilities which are located in areas of known high seismicity and close to active faults, close attention must be given to near field effects. Near field terminology is used when the epicenter of the earthquake is close to a site of interest (see Chapter 3). Since compression waves attenuate much faster than horizontal shear waves, the vertical component of the earthquake tends to be dominant only in the near field. For these special cases, the designer/analyst should give appropriate consideration to the effects of vertical accelerations on design.

c. If vertical earthquake forces are to be considered explicitly in design or analysis, they can be obtained by scaling corresponding ground horizontal accelerations by a factor of 2/3 (higher factors may be required in the near-field; see Section 3.A.7). Alternate factors may be used if substantiated by site specific data. Once the vertical ground motion is defined, appropriate consideration should be given to the dynamic response of the structure in the vertical direction. Member forces and moments due to the vertical component of the earthquake should be obtained and combined with the forces and moments resulting from the horizontal component of the earthquake in accordance with the procedure of Section 4.4.9. Refer to Chapter 3 for more guidance on the definition of vertical earthquake motion.

4.4.11 Subsystems

Subsystems refer to any non-structural elements, equipment and components which are supported by the structure under consideration. Examples are horizontal vessels supported on a structure. It should be noted that the procedures described here for subsystems are sometimes confused and misused with those for actual structures. As a general guide, a subsystem is one which is attached to a primary structure and weighing less than about 25% of the total weight of the supporting structure. Any component or structure founded directly on soil/ground is not considered a subsystem.

An equation similar to *UBC* equation (30-1) can be used to determine the lateral load for subsystems. In that equation, a term C_p is introduced as a measure of amplification of ground response through the structure into the subsystem, based on the assumption that the subsystem is categorized as rigid. Any subsystem whose period is less than 0.06 seconds is considered rigid. Subsystem periods greater than 0.06 seconds are considered flexible. Refer to Table 4.5 for recommended C_p coefficients.

TABLE 4.5: Horizontal Force Factor, C_p

Elements of Structures and Nonstructural Components and Equipment	Value of C_p
I. Equipment	
1. Tanks and vessels (include contents), including support systems and anchorage	0.75
2. Electrical, mechanical and plumbing, distributed systems including conduit, ductwork and piping	0.75
3. Machinery and equipment such as boilers, chillers, heat exchangers, pumps, air-handling units, control panels, motors, switch gear, transformers and life-safety equipment	0.75
II. Nonstructural Components	
1. Chimneys, stacks, trussed towers, relatively light elevated air coolers and tanks on legs:	
a. Supported on or projecting as an unbraced cantilever above the roof more than one half their total height	2.00
b. All others, including those supported below the roof with unbraced projection above the roof less than one half its height, or braced or to the structural frame at or above their centers of mass	2.00
2. Exterior and interior ornamentations and appendages	0.75
3. Signs and billboards	2.00
4. Storage racks (include contents)	0.75
5. Anchorage for permanent floor-supported cabinets and book stacks more than 5 feet in height (include contents)	0.75
6. Anchorage for suspended ceilings and light fixtures	0.75
7. Access floor systems	0.75

As an alternative to the method provided in the *UBC*, other organizations are working on rules and provisions for design and evaluation of subsystems. Once such alternative can be found in *NEHRP* (1994). The *NEHRP* provisions offer improvements over the *UBC* procedures in the sense that they allow for the following:

a. Subsystem mass distribution, including dynamic properties.
b. Seismic response which includes site effects.
c. Location of the subsystem within the structure.
d. Subsystem anchorage ductility and energy absorption capability.

For flexible subsystems, the lateral force on the subsystem must be determined giving consideration to the dynamic characteristics of both the primary structure and the subsystem. These calculations are performed using period calculations for both the primary structure and the subsystem to determine the extent of structural amplification. The resulting C_p factor should not be less than those specified in Table 4.5. In the absence of such calculations, the value of C_p should be taken as twice that given in Table 4.5, but need not exceed 2.0.

If a subsystem is located at or below ground elevation, C_p may be taken as 2/3 of that in Table 4.5.

The total base shear determined using the above procedure should be distributed in proportion to the mass distribution of the subsystem.

4.5 DYNAMIC ANALYSIS METHODS

4.5.1 General

Dynamic analyses of structures are typically conducted using structural computer programs. Dynamic analysis can be performed for any type of structures at the engineer's discretion. However, it must be performed for cases where structural irregularities exist.

In recent years with the advances of the computer industry resulting in availability of high performance computers at low prices, as well as availability of various structural analysis software packages, the option of dynamic analysis seems more and more attractive to engineers and is thus encouraged. In general, dynamic analyses are believed to result in more accurate determination of the dynamic properties of a structure and hence its response to a seismic event. They better capture local effects in addition to global response, often leading to a more economical design of a new facility, and avoiding unnecessary conservatism in the evaluation of an existing facility.

In choosing the dynamic analysis option, the analyst should have a good understanding of the expected global behavior and should review the dynamic analysis results carefully, to ensure response is as expected. This is often achieved by comparing the base shear with that obtained using the equivalent static approach.

4.5.2 Ground Motion

The ground motion to be used in a dynamic analysis is defined in terms of either a ground response spectrum (most common) or a time history. Generally, the ground response spectrum is first defined. Chapter 3 describes the logic of the choice of the ground motion and its development. The response spectrum shape is either a standard shape scaled to an appropriate peak ground acceleration, or is a site-specific shape. The spectral shape for new design typically corresponds to a 10% probability of exceedance in 50 years and is generally defined for a number of damping ratios. For petrochemical type structures, analysis is usually performed using the 5% damped spectral shape; therefore as a minimum, the ground response spectra should be defined for 5% damping.

If a time history analysis methodology is chosen, the ground motion must be defined in terms of time history of response (usually acceleration, sometimes velocity or displacement). Either actual earthquake time histories or time histories generated artificially to represent a spectral shape are suitable for use. However, in both cases, the response spectrum associated with the chosen time history should match the site specific response spectrum at the frequencies of interest. Chapter 3 discusses the development of the ground (free-field) time-history for use in dynamic analysis.

4.5.3 Mathematical Model

A finite element or lumped mass model of the structure is a mathematical representation of the structure which properly allows for the distribution of mass and stiffness of the structure to an extent which is adequate for the calculation of the significant features of its dynamic response.

A three dimensional structural model should be used for the dynamic analysis of structures with highly irregular plan configuration such as those having a plan irregularity defined in Table 4.2 and having a rigid diaphragm. For regular structures, use of a two dimensional model is usually adequate. Generally, two 2-D models, each representing an orthogonal principal axis of the structure, are developed and used in the analysis.

Structures whose dynamic response can be characterized by either a shear type response or bending type response, can be reasonably modeled using beam elements. Three dimensional finite element models utilizing plate/shell or 3-D solid elements may be used for more complex structures.

4.5.4 Response Spectrum Analysis

A response spectrum analysis is an elastic dynamic analysis of a structure utilizing the peak dynamic response of significant modes which contribute to total structural response. Peak modal responses are calculated using the ordinates of the input spectrum which correspond to modal periods. Maximum modal responses are then combined to obtain the peak structural response.

The following considerations should be given when performing a response spectrum analysis:

a. Number of Modes. All significant modes which capture at least 90% of the participating mass of the structure in each direction should be included in the analysis.

b. Combining Modes. In a response spectrum analysis option, the maximum response of the structure during each mode is first computed. These modal responses must be combined in order to obtain the peak response of the structure. Modal responses are generally combined by the SRSS method. However, the SRSS method may be unconservative for structures with closely spaced modes. Other more accurate methods of modal combination are also available in certain structural programs. An example is the complete quadratic combination (CQC) method.

c. Directional Effects. The response of the structure subject to two or three (if required) directional components of the input motion should also be combined in order to account for directional effects when designing corner elements. Directional effects are usually accounted for by either an SRSS or a 100%-30%-30% method of combination.

4.5.5 Time History Analysis

A time history analysis is generally a more complex and expensive method of performing a dynamic analysis, but is considered to give a more realistic estimate of structural response to a given earthquake than a response spectrum analysis. In a time history approach, the input is defined in terms of a time history of ground motion. Modal and directional combinations are performed in the time or frequency domains, accounting for duration, frequency content and phasing for a particular earthquake time history.

Generally, two options are available for performing time history analyses: the modal superposition and the direct integration schemes. A modal superposition approach is similar in concept to the response spectrum approach, with the exception that individual modal responses are obtained as a time history, and, as such, can be combined with other modal responses in an algebraic sense in the time domain. Hence, the phasing between modes is retained. The direct integration scheme determines the total response of the structure at each time step by solving the equations of motion using direct integration.

The above discussion concerns linear dynamic time history analysis. In rare occasions, one might need to perform nonlinear dynamic analysis. Although, this option is rarely used in practice for petrochemical facilities, special circumstances might warrant a nonlinear analysis. Only the direct integration scheme can be used in nonlinear dynamic analysis. In performing nonlinear analysis, special consideration should be given to actual structural nonlinearity in contrast to the ductility values (R_w factors) which are used as means of energy dissipation capability of a structure or structural system.

Similar to the response spectrum analysis, in a time history modal superposition analysis, enough modes must be considered to capture at least 90% of the total mass participating. In a direct integration scheme, by definition, 100% of the mass is considered in the solution at each time step.

4.5.6 Scaling of Results

When a dynamic analysis is performed, various building codes generally require that the base shear (after dividing by R_w) be compared to that of an equivalent static analysis. If the dynamic base shear is less than the equivalent static base shear, the resulting response parameters are scaled such that the dynamic base shear equals the following values:

a. 90% of the static base shear for irregular building-like structures

b. 80% of the static base shear for regular building-like structures or nonbuilding-like structures

The rationale for this scaling of the results lies with the fact that the earthquake force levels determined using the equivalent static method reflect the influence of structural period, ductility and damping for various structural systems. Because it is difficult to reflect these influences on a consistent basis for dynamic analysis design, the code requires the above mentioned scaling. This is also tied to the fact that the great majority of building structures designed using modern equivalent static methods and ductile detailing requirements have, in general, performed well during past earthquakes. In addition, scaling is introduced as a safeguard against unrealistically low forces obtained through inappropriate modeling assumptions.

Because structures in petrochemical facilities typically have simple and straightforward structural configurations with well defined mass and stiffness characteristics, it is felt that this code requirement is not appropriate for typical petrochemical facility structures. However, because it is specifically required in building codes, it is recommended that an independent peer review be used to ensure that the seismic input and results predicted by the dynamic analysis are adequate and reasonable to be used directly in design. Special care should be taken when the static analysis base shears are much higher than those predicted by dynamic analyses.

If dynamic analysis results indicate a base shear greater than the equivalent static base shear, the dynamic analysis results can be scaled down to 100% of the static value. However, care must be exercised in doing so; there may be special circumstances which result in increased dynamic response, such as torsional eccentricity.

4.5.7 Soil-Structure Interaction

Soil-Structure Interaction (SSI) refers to dynamic interaction effects between a structure and the underlying soil during a seismic event. SSI effects are pronounced for heavy embedded structures founded on soft or medium soil, and in general can be ignored for light and surface founded structures or structures founded on competent material (stiff or rock).

For structures founded on rock or very stiff soils, the foundation motion is essentially that which would exist in the soil at the level of the foundation in the absence of the structure and any excavation; this motion is denoted the free-field ground motion. For soft soils, the foundation motion differs from that in the free field due to the coupling of the soil and structure during the earthquake. This interaction results from the scattering of waves from the foundation and the radiation of energy from the structure due to structural vibrations. Because of these effects, the state of deformation (particle displacements, velocities, and accelerations) in the supporting soil is different than that in the free field. In turn, the dynamic response of a structure supported on soft soil may differ substantially in amplitude and frequency content from the response of an identical structure supported on a very stiff soil or rock.

SSI effects usually result in potential amplification or de-amplification of the structural response depending on the site specific conditions and the combined soil and structure dynamic characteristics. Generally, there tends to be a shift in the combined soil-structure natural period when compared to the period of the structure only. Where profound, this shift tends to increase the system period.

Methodologies for considering SSI effects are available in the literature (Wolf, 1985 and *NEHRP*, 1994). These effects can be simply allowed for, if the underlying soil happens to be a uniform medium, and as such, can be represented by an equivalent spring and a damper. If the underlying soil is layered, to properly allow for the effects of SSI, one must resort to more complicated techniques such as finite element analysis, or other alternate methods.

As a rule of thumb, when SSI effects are profound, the following tends to happen:

a. The system period increases

b. There is an overall reduction in structural response unless the structure and the underlying soil happen to be in resonance (e.g., Mexico City, mid-rise buildings)

c. Subsystems which are more flexible may have increased response and should be given more attention in the seismic design

d. The rocking effects are more profound resulting in higher structural displacements

4.6 CONSIDERATIONS FOR EXISTING FACILITIES

4.6.1 General

The procedures outlined above apply primarily to the design of new facilities. This section summarizes specific guidance for the evaluation of existing facilities. Different philosophies and methodologies are appropriate for existing facilities for several reasons, including the following:

a. Older facilities were probably designed to earlier codes and standards that were not as restrictive or appropriate as current standards with respect to seismic design.

b. While the objective is to enhance the seismic safety of the existing facility under consideration, it would be very difficult to upgrade it to meet all the requirements of current standards.

c. At the time of new design, the designer can afford to be more conservative compared to the time of retrofit, where options are more limited in meeting a given set of seismic upgrade criteria.

Furthermore, it is also recognized that structures found in existing facilities tend to be older, and therefore, were designed to lower levels of seismic demand with far fewer of the ductile detailing provisions found in today's codes, thus increasing the need for accurate assessment of these structures with appropriate levels of ductility.

4.6.2 Methods for Evaluation

There are no widely accepted and used methods for evaluating existing petrochemical facilities. It is recommended that an appropriate evaluation methodology incorporate on-site visual reviews of the existing structures and systems, as described in detail in Chapter 6, in conjunction with appropriate analytical reviews.

One method, which is currently being used in several municipalities in California, was developed to satisfy the requirements of the state-mandated Risk Management and Prevention Program (RMPP), for facilities with threshold quantities of certain Acutely Hazardous Materials (AHMs). Because the RMPP criteria are not readily obtainable by practicing engineers, they have been included in their entirety as Appendix 4.F. Those criteria differ from a typical building code approach in the following areas:

a. The method is based on ultimate strength rather than working stress, with the R_w factors for existing facilities adjusted to reflect the difference.

These new factors are referred to as Q factors and are generally lower than R_w factors.

b. The input motion used for new facilities, by definition, corresponds to a ground motion with a "mean plus one standard deviation" response spectrum, i.e., there is 84% chance that this motion will not be exceeded at the site, given the seismicity of the region. In contrast, for existing facilities, the ground motion is defined as a median response spectrum. This corresponds to a ground motion that has 50% chance of exceedance. Therefore, the ground motion definition for evaluation of existing facilities is less conservative than a corresponding motion to be used for design of a new facility.

c. The importance (I) factor to be used in Equation 4.1 is always set to unity (1.0) for evaluation of existing facilities unless it exceeds 1.0 for "special" structures at the owner's request. In contrast, for design of new facilities, appropriate "I" factor, depending on importance of the structure and functional requirements, may be higher than 1.0 (as much as 1.5) as specified in Table 4.3.

d. For evaluation of existing facilities, site-specific Z values and site specific response spectra may be used without the consent of the building official. For new facilities, if a site-specific Z value or response spectrum is specified which differs from code specified values, the consent of a building official must be obtained.

For existing building-like structures, some guidance is also offered in *ATC-33.03*.

4.6.3 Overturning Potential

In evaluation of existing structures, it is recommended that the safety factor against overturning be limited to 1.0; however, the dead load reduction of 0.90 should be allowed for. Alternatively, more refined overturning checks, such as the "Energy Balance" approach, may be used. The energy balance approach checks that the potential energy to overturn the structure is not exceeded by the imposed kinetic energy caused by the earthquake. Strain energy effects in the structure and, more importantly, in the soil can be included.

Appendix 4.D provides further description of the energy balance approach for checking against overturning.

4.6.4 Sliding Potential

For structures in existing petrochemical facilities, a factor of safety of 1.5 against sliding is recommended for free-standing structures that are not bolted or otherwise anchored to their foundations and that cannot otherwise tolerate movement.

For free-standing structures resting directly on soil, a factor of safety against sliding of 1.0 at the foundation/soil interface is considered appropriate, as it is observed that movement of foundations resting on soil does not usually occur.

In the event sliding displacements are required (for example for evaluation of tolerance requirements, pipe displacements, etc.), the methodology prescribed in Appendix 4.E can be used. The methodology considers the vertical upward accelerations present during earthquakes that can reduce the effective friction force between structure and support surface. The maximum sliding displacement can be related to the velocity imparted into the structure during the earthquake.

Time history studies of dynamic stability show that the calculated maximum inertia forces act for only short periods of time, reversing in direction many times during an earthquake. Considering these maximum forces as static forces for purposes of stability and sliding analysis is very conservative. In fact, the factor of safety against sliding and overturning has been shown to drop below unity for short periods of time during the seismic event without failure. This is because any rigid body movement is arrested when dynamic forces decrease or reverse directions.

APPENDIX 4.A

TYPICAL PERIOD (T) COMPUTATIONS FOR NONBUILDING STRUCTURES

NOTE: Equations in this Appendix are presented in English Units only, as coefficients are developed for English units only.

A. METHODOLOGY

A. Natural Period of Vibration - One Mass, Bending Type Structure

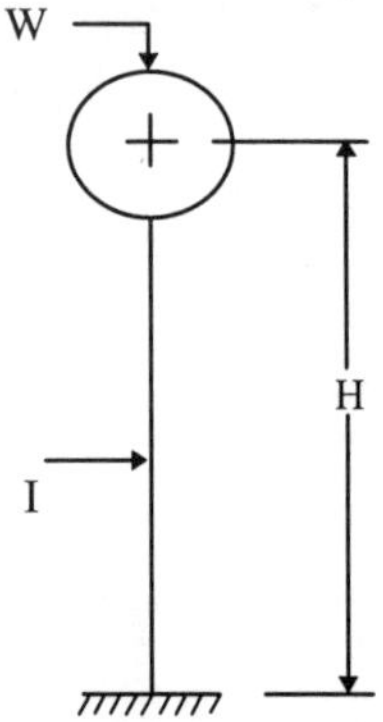

$$T = 3.63\sqrt{\frac{WH^3}{EIg}}$$

Where:
W = Weight of Mass
H = Height of Cantilever
E = Modulus of Elasticity
I = Moment of Inertia

B. Natural Period of Vibration - One Mass, Rigid Frame Type Structure

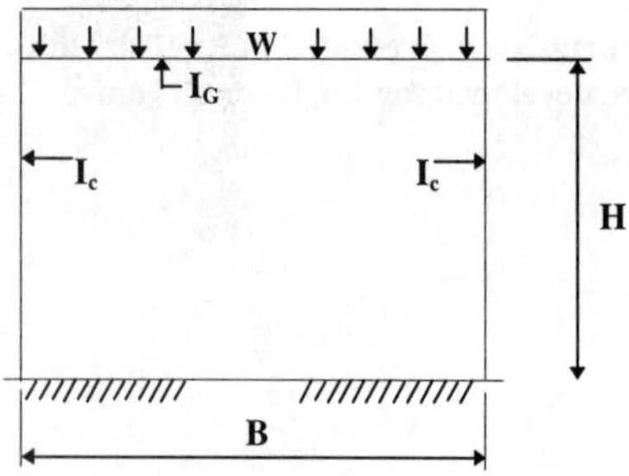

$$T = 1.814\sqrt{\frac{\alpha WH^3}{EI_c g}}$$

For Columns Hinged at Base

$$\alpha = \frac{2K+1}{K}$$

For Columns Fixed at Base

$$\alpha = \frac{3K+2}{6K+1}$$

$$K = \left(\frac{I_G}{I_C}\right)\left(\frac{H}{B}\right)$$

C. Natural Period of Vibration - Two Mass Structure

$$T = 2\pi\sqrt{\frac{W_A C_{aa} + W_B C_{bb} + \sqrt{(W_A C_{aa} - W_B C_{bb})^2 + 4W_A W_B C_{ab}^{\ 2}}}{2g}}$$

where: C_{aa} = Deflection at A Due to Unit Lateral Load at A

C_{bb} = Deflection at B Due to Unit Lateral Load at B

C_{ab} = Deflection at B Due to Unit Lateral Load at A

$W_A \cdot W_B$ = Summation of Vertical Loads at Level A or B

See Example 1 for Application

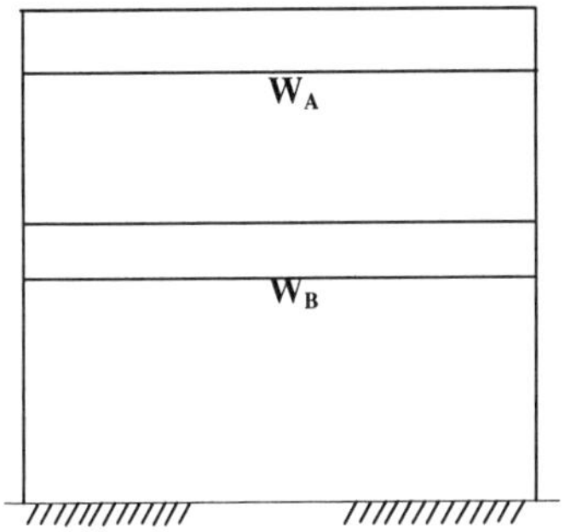

D. Natural Period of Vibration - Bending Type Structure, Uniform Weight Distribution and Constant Cross Section

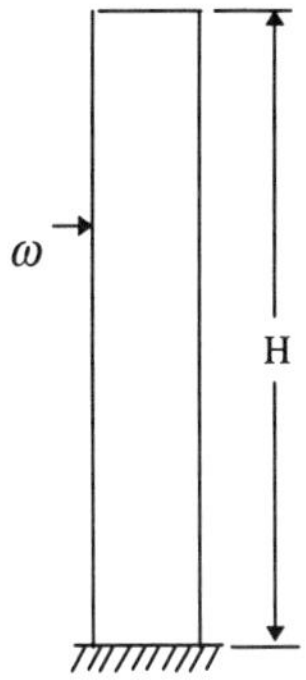

$$T = 1.79\sqrt{\frac{\omega H^4}{EIg}}$$

where: ω = Weight Per Unit Height

E. Natural Period of Vibration - Uniform Vertical Cylindrical Steel Vessel

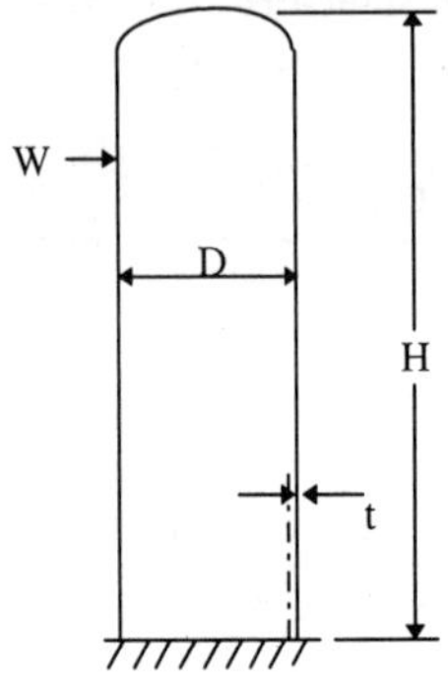

$$T = \frac{7.78}{10^6}\left(\frac{H}{D}\right)^2 \sqrt{\frac{12WD}{t}}$$

where:
T = Period (sec)
W = Weight (lb/ft)
H = Height (ft)
D = Diameter (ft)
t = Shell Thickness (inch)

F. Natural Period of Vibration - Non-uniform Vertical Cylindrical Vessel

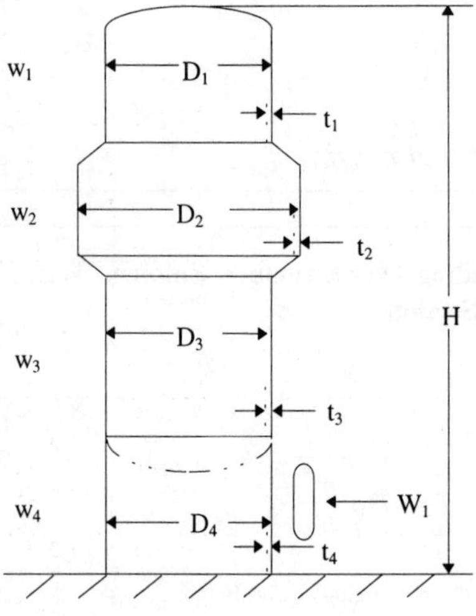

$$T = \left(\frac{H}{100}\right)^2 \cdot \sqrt{\frac{\Sigma w.\Delta\alpha + \frac{1}{H}.\Sigma W.\beta}{\Sigma E.D^3.t.\Delta\gamma}}$$

Where:

T = period (sec)
H = overall height (ft)
w = distributed weight (lbs/ft) of each section
W = Weight (lb) of each Concentrated Mass
D = diameter (ft) of each section
t = shell thickness (inch) of each section
E = modulus of elasticity (millions of psi)

α, β, and γ are coefficients for a given level depending on h_x/H ratio of the height of the level above grade to the overall height. $\Delta\alpha$ and $\Delta\gamma$ are the difference in the values of α and γ, from the top to the bottom of each section of uniform weight, diameter and thickness. β is determined and for each concentrated mass. Values of α, β, and γ are tabulated on the following table.

Coefficients for Determining Period of Vibration of Free-Standing Cylindrical Shells with Non-Uniform Cross Section and Mass Distribution

h_x/H	α	β	γ	h_x/H	α	β	γ
1.00	2.103	8.347	1.000000	0.50	0.1094	0.9863	0.95573
0.99	2.021	8.121	1.000000	0.49	0.0998	0.9210	0.95143
0.98	1.941	7.898	1.000000	0.48	0.0909	0.8584	0.94683
0.97	1.863	7.678	1.000000	0.47	0.0826	0.7987	0.94189
0.96	1.787	7.461	1.000000	0.46	0.0749	0.7418	0.93661
0.95	1.714	7.248	0.999999	0.45	0.0578	0.6876	0.93097
0.94	1.642	7.037	0.999998	0.44	0.0612	0.6361	0.92495
0.93	1.573	6.830	0.999997	0.43	0.0551	0.5372	0.91854
0.92	1.506	6.626	0.999994	0.42	0.0494	0.5409	0.91173
0.91	1.440	6.425	0.999989	0.41	0.0442	0.4971	0.90443
0.90	1.377	6.227	0.999982	0.40	0.0395	0.4557	0.89679
0.89	1.316	6.032	0.999971	0.39	0.0351	0.4167	0.88864
0.88	1.256	5.840	0.999956	0.38	0.0311	0.3801	0.88001
0.87	1.199	5.652	0.999934	0.37	0.0275	0.3456	0.87033
0.86	1.143	5.467	0.999905	0.36	0.0242	0.3134	0.86123
0.85	1.090	5.285	0.999867	0.35	0.0212	0.2833	0.85105
0.84	1.038	5.106	0.999317	0.34	0.0185	0.2552	0.34032
0.83	0.938	4.930	0.999754	0.33	0.0161	0.2291	0.82901
0.82	0.939	4.758	0.999674	0.32	0.0140	0.2050	0.81710
0.81	0.892	4.589	0.999576	0.31	0.0120	0.1826	0.80459
0.80	0.847	4.424	0.999455	0.30	0.010293	0.16200	0.7914
0.79	0.804	4.261	0.999309	0.29	0.008769	0.14308	0.7776
0.78	0.762	4.102	0.999133	0.28	0.007426	0.12576	0.7632
0.77	0.722	3.946	0.998923	0.27	0.006249	0.10997	0.7480
0.76	0.683	3.794	0.998676	0.26	0.005222	0.09564	0.7321
0.75	0.646	3.645	0.998385	0.25	0.004332	0.08267	0.7155
0.74	0.610	3.499	0.998047	0.24	0.003564	0.07101	0.6981
0.73	0.576	3.356	0.997656	0.23	0.002907	0.06056	0.6800
0.72	0.543	3.217	0.997205	0.22	0.002349	0.05126	0.6610
0.71	0.512	3.081	0.996689	0.21	0.001878	0.04303	0.6413
0.70	0.481	2.949	0.996101	0.20	0.001485	0.03579	0.6207
0.69	0.453	2.820	0.995434	0.19	0.001159	0.02948	0.5902
0.68	0.425	2.694	0.904681	0.18	0.000893	0.02400	0.5769
0.67	0.399	2.571	0.993834	0.17	0.000677	0.01931	0.5536
0.66	0.374	2.452	0.992885	0.16	0.000504	0.01531	0.5295
0.65	0.3497	2.3365	0.99183	0.15	0.000368	0.01196	0.5044
0.64	0.3269	2.2240	0.99065	0.14	0.000263	0.00917	0.4783
0.63	0.3052	2.1148	0.98934	0.13	0.000183	0.00689	0.4512
0.62	0.2846	2.0089	0.98739	0.12	0.000124	0.00506	0.4231
0.61	0.2650	1.9062	0.98630	0.11	0.000081	0.00361	0.3940
0.60	0.2464	1.8068	0.98455	0.10	0.000051	0.00249	0.3639
0.59	0.2288	1.7107	0.98262	0.09	0.000030	0.00165	0.3327
0.58	0.2122	1.6177	0.98052	0.08	0.000017	0.00104	0.3003
0.57	0.1965	1.5279	0.97823	0.07	0.000009	0.00062	0.2669
0.56	0.1816	1.4413	0.97573	0.06	0.000004	0.00034	0.2323
0.55	0.1676	1.3579	0.97301	0.05	0.000002	0.00016	0.1965
0.54	1.1545	1.2775	0.97007	0.04	0.000001	0.00007	0.1597
0.53	0.1421	1.2002	0.96683	0.03	0.000000	0.00002	0.1216
0.52	0.1305	1.1259	0.96344	0.02	0.000000	0.00000	0.0823
0.51	0.1196	1.0547	0.95973	0.01	0.000000	0.00000	0.0418

G. Period of Vibration - Generalized One-Mass Structure

$$T = 2\pi \left(\frac{y}{g} \right)^{0.5}$$

where:

y = static deflection of mass resulting from a lateral load applied at the mass equal to its own weight.

g = acceleration due to gravity.

See Example 4 for application.

B. EXAMPLES

Example 1 -- Two-Story Concrete Vessel Support Structure

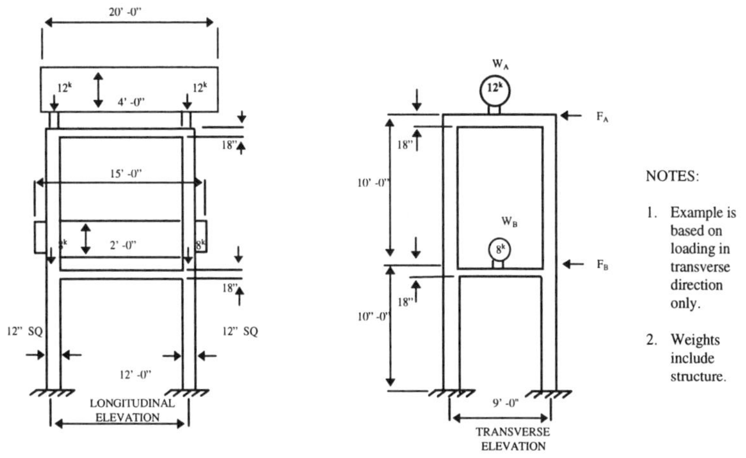

Two-Story Concrete Vessel Support Structure

Period of Vibration:

Earthquake Forces (Transverse direction — Loads on one bent)

W = 20 kips (includes structure weight)

Deflections from 1 kip at A and B (calculations not shown):

C_{aa} = 0.0384 in., C_{ab} = 0.0180 in., C_{bb} = 0.0157 in.

$$T = 2(3.14)\left\{\frac{12(0.0384) + 8(0.0157) + \left[\left[12(0.0384) - 8(0.0157)\right]^2 + 4(12)(8)(0.0180)^2\right]^{0.5}}{2(386)}\right\}^{0.5}$$

$$= 0.234 \text{ sec}$$

Example 2 -- Uniform Cylindrical Column

In most columns of constant diameter, the entire mass can be assumed uniformly distributed over the height. Where there are large concentrations of mass or variations in cross-section, the analysis should be made as shown in Example 3.

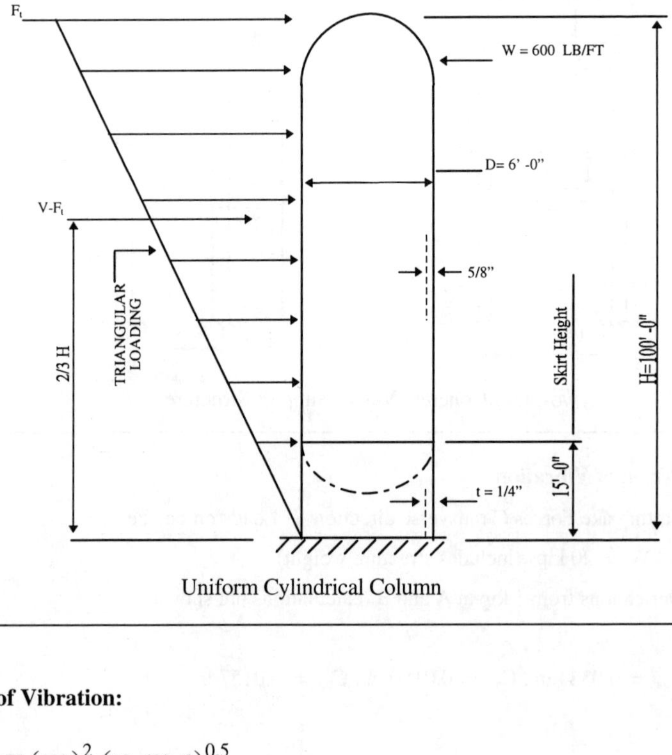

Uniform Cylindrical Column

Period of Vibration:

$$T = \frac{7.78}{10^6}\left(\frac{100}{6}\right)^2\left(\frac{12x600x6}{0.25}\right)^{0.5} = 0.898\,\text{sec}$$

Example 3 -- Column with Variable Cross Section and Mass Distribution

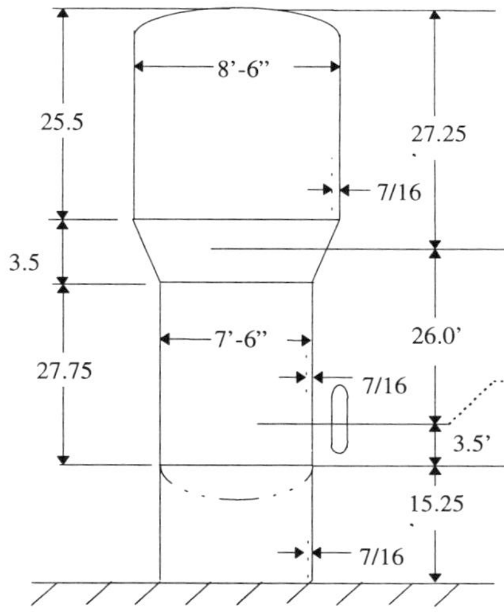

w (lb-ft) or W (lbs)	$\frac{h_x}{H}$	α	$\Delta\alpha$ or β	$w\,\Delta\alpha$ or $W\,\beta/H$	γ	$\Delta\gamma$	$ExD^3xt\,x\Delta\gamma$
	1.00	2.103			1.000		
1,580			1.8143	2,867		0.0122	95
	0.622	0.2887			0.9878		
1,530			0.2835	434		0.2557	1,369
60,800	0.260	0.005222	0.09564	81	0.7321		
2,570			0.00325	8.4		0.0869	465
	0.212	0.001972			0.6452		
1,250			0.001972	2.5		0.6452	3,494
				Σ=3,393			Σ=5,423

Period of Vibration: $T = (72/100)^2\,(3{,}393/5{,}423)^{0.5} = 0.41$ sec

Example 4 -- Sphere on Braced Columns

The common bracing system for spheres consists of x-bracing connecting adjacent pairs of columns as illustrated below. The bracing for large spheres subject to earthquake loads should be effective both in tension and compression to better resist the lateral forces.

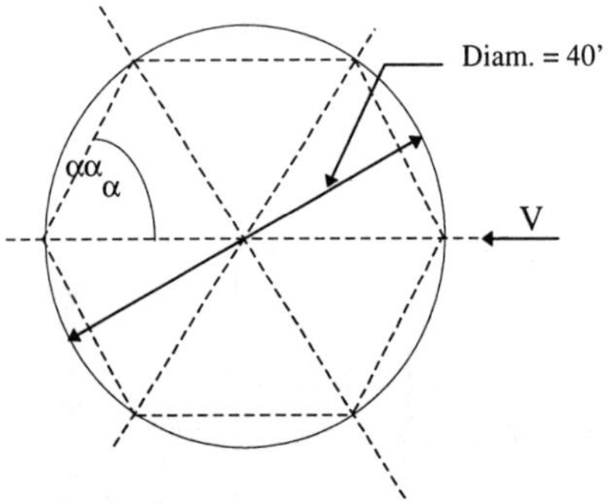

PLAN

The shear in each panel and the max maximum panel shear could be found by the following formula:

$$V_p = (2V/n) \cos \alpha$$

$$V_{pmax} = 2V/n$$

where:

V_p = panel shear
V_{pmax} = maximum panel shear
V = lateral force
n = number of panels
α = angle between plane of panel and direction of lateral force.

Period of Vibration:

The period of vibration is found using the general formula for one-mass structure previously. The static deflection, y, is found by determining the change in length of the bracing resulting from a total lateral load equal to the weight of the sphere. Deformation of the columns and balcony girder are usually neglected for one-story.

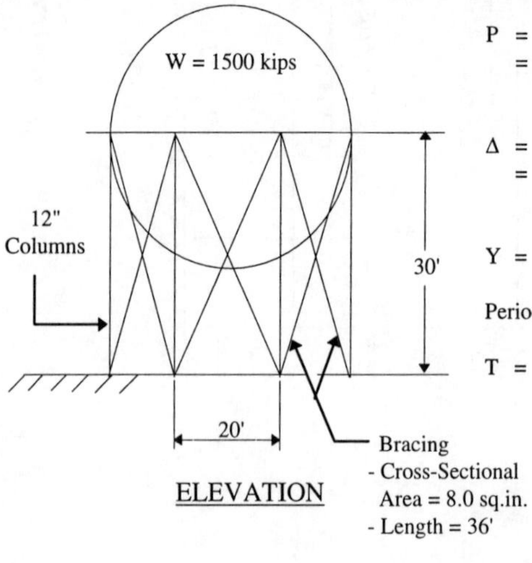

ELEVATION

P = Maximum force in brace
= $(1/2)\ (2 \times 1500/6)\ (36.0/20.0)$ = 450 kips

Δ = Change in length of brace
= $PL/EA = [(450)\ (36.0)\ (12)] / [(29{,}000\ (8.0)] = 0.838$ in.

$Y = \Delta/\sin\theta = (0.838)\ (36.0/20) = 1.51$ in.

Period of Vibration, $T = 2\pi\ [y/g]^{0.5}$

$T = 2\pi\ [1.51/(32.2)(12)]^{0.5} = 0.393$

APPENDIX 4.B

GUIDELINES FOR DETERMINATION OF BASE SHEAR FOR COMBINATION STRUCTURES

A. METHODOLOGY

NON-BUILDING STRUCTURES SUPPORTED ABOVE GRADE
($W_E \leq 0.25\ W_S$)

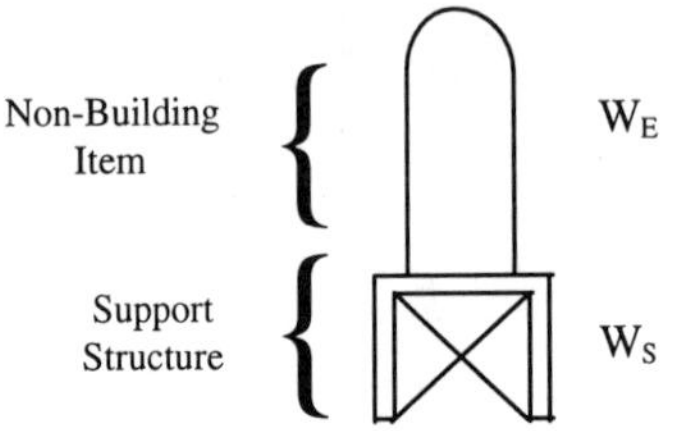

W_E less than $0.25\ W_S$
T_E less than 0.06 sec.

(Rigid)

Support Structure

$$V = \frac{ZICW}{R_W} \text{ with } R_W \text{ for structure from Table 4.4}$$

(Lump mass of item with mass of structure)

Non Building Item and Anchorage

Use larger of $V = 0.5ZI_pW_E$

or $V = ZC_p I_p W_E$ with C_p from Table 4.5
(Note: use 2.0 x C_p if support structure is flexible and 2.0 x C_p need not exceed two)

CASE 1

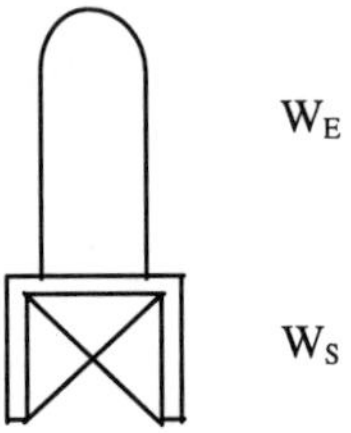

W_E less than $0.25\ W_S$
T_E greater than 0.06 sec.

(Flexible)

Support Structure

$$V = \frac{ZICW}{R_W} \text{ with } R_W \text{ for structure from Table 4.4}$$

(Lump mass of item with mass of structure)

Non Building Item and Anchorage

Use larger of $V = \frac{ZICW_E}{R_w}$
with R_w (for equipment) from Table 4.4

or $V = Z(2.0 \text{ x } C_p) I_p W_E$ with C_p from Table 4.5
(Note: 2.0 x C_p need not exceed two)

CASE 2

NON-BUILDING STRUCTURES SUPPORTED ABOVE GRADE
($W_E > 0.25\ W_S$)

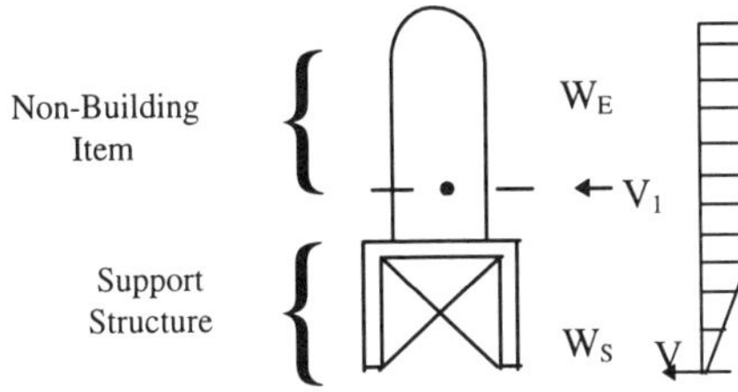

W_E greater than $0.25\ W_S$
T_E less than 0.06 sec.

Note: Case 4 may always be used

(Rigid)

Support Structure

$$V = \frac{ZICW}{R_w}$$

with R_w equal to the smaller of the values for the equipment or structure from Table 4.4

with $\frac{C}{R_w} \geq 0.25$

$C_{max} = 2.75$
C based on combined system T

(Lump mass of item with mass of structure)

Non-Building Item and Anchorage

Use larger of $V_1 = 0.5\ ZI_pW_E$

or $V_1 = ZC_pI_pW_E$ with C_p from Table 4.5

(Note: use 2.0 x C_p if support structure is flexible and 2.0 x C_p need not exceed two)

CASE 3

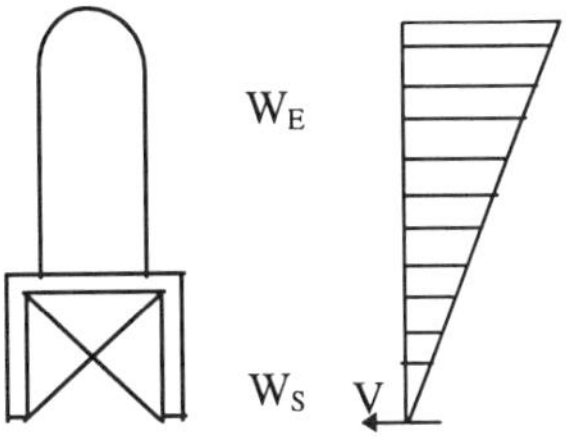

W_E greater than $0.25\ W_S$
T_E greater than 0.06 sec.

(Flexible)

Support Structure & Non-Building Item

$$V = \frac{ZICW}{R_w}$$

with R_w equal to the smaller of the values for the equipment or structure from Table 4.4

with $\frac{C}{R_w} \geq 0.25$

$C_{max} = 2.75$
C based on combined system T

CASE 4

B. EXAMPLES

Example: Table Top Reinforced Concrete Structure Supporting Reactor Vessels

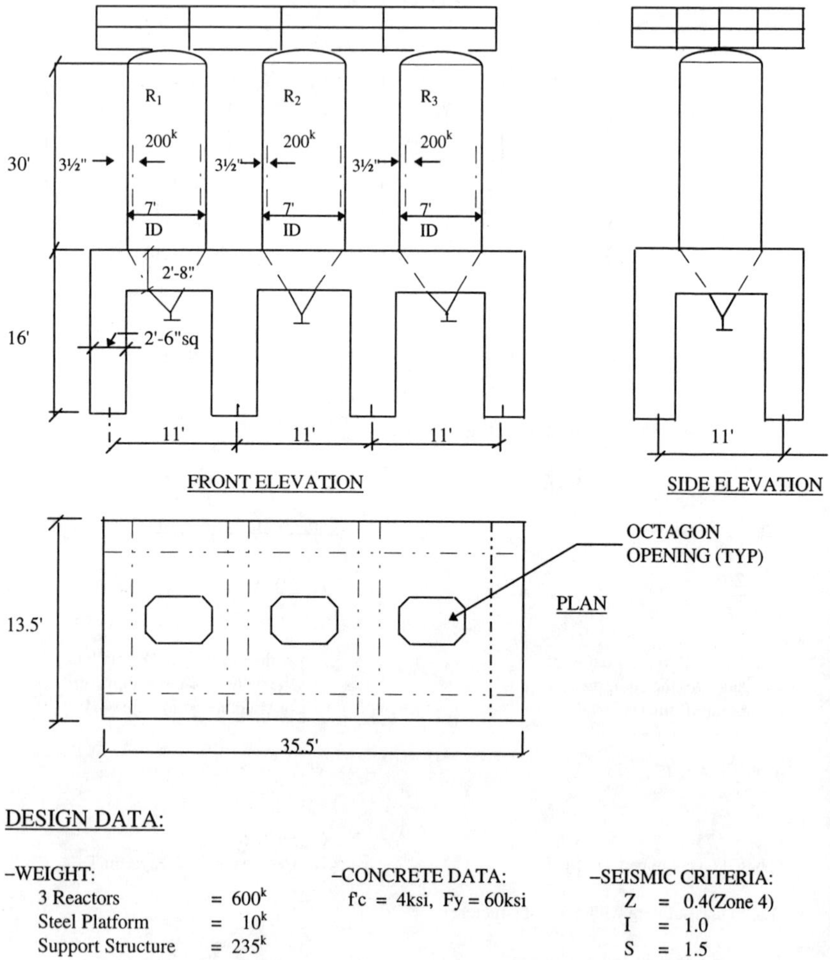

DESIGN DATA:

–WEIGHT:

3 Reactors	=	600^k
Steel Platform	=	10^k
Support Structure	=	235^k
TOTAL W	=	845^k

–CONCRETE DATA:

f'c = 4ksi, Fy = 60ksi

–SEISMIC CRITERIA:

Z = 0.4(Zone 4)
I = 1.0
S = 1.5
R_w = 4.0 (See Note 1)

DETERMINE STRUCTURAL PERIOD, T :

By inspection, each of the reactors is rigid and thus the fundamental period of the combined structure will be determined based on the stiffness of the supporting structure. If the reactor vessels are not rigid (i.e. T > .06 seconds), then the structure may be considered as a two lumped mass system whose period may be determined using other methods.

1) TRANSVERSE DIRECTION

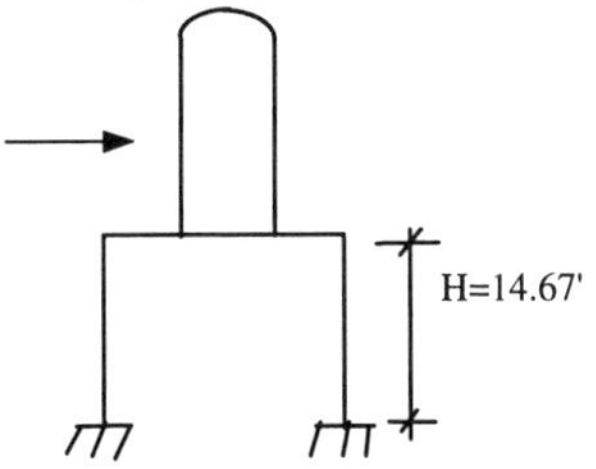

Assume the table top slab is a Rigid diaphragm. (See Note 2)

Support stiffness per Bent :

For simplicity, assume as a moment with infinitely rigid girder.

$$K = \frac{12EI}{H^3} X\ 2$$

$$= \frac{12x3605x33750x2}{(14.67x12)^3}$$

$$= 535 \text{ kips / in. (per bent)}$$

$$\Sigma K = 4x535 = 2140\ k\ /\ in.$$

Member properties :

$$\left(I_C\right)_{gross} = \frac{bh^3}{12} = \frac{(30)(30)^3}{12} = 67{,}500\ in.^4$$

Assume $\left(I_C\right)eff = 50\%$ x $I_{gross} = 33{,}750$ in.^{4}

$E_C = 57\sqrt{4000} = 3605$ ksi

Fundamental Period :

$$T = 2\pi\sqrt{\frac{M}{\Sigma K}}$$

where: M = total mass of vessel + support

K = support stiffness

$$T = 2\pi\sqrt{\frac{845}{2140x386.4}} = 0.20 \text{ Sec.}$$

NOTE 1: The supporting structure is a concrete special moment-resisting frame, therefore, under ordinary circumstances its R_w equals 8.0. However, because the weight of the vessel dominates that of the structure, we choose not to use Case 3 (as presented in the methodology section). Instead we consider the combined structure to be representative of Case 4, with the system R_w taken to be that of the vessel supported by a steel skirt, i.e., R_w = 4.0.

NOTE 2 : If diaphragm is not rigid, then the period calculation should be performed based on the tributary mass per bent.

2) LONGITUDINAL DIRECTION

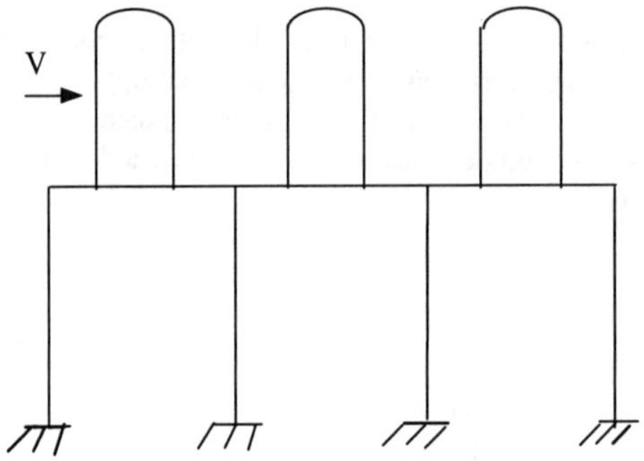

Similarly like in the transverse direction, the structural period of the Support can be determined as follows :

$$K = \frac{12EI}{H^3} X4$$
$$= \frac{12x3605x33750x4}{(14.67X12)^3}$$
$$= 1070k / in\ (per\ bent)$$
$$\Sigma K = 2X1070 = 2140\ k / in.$$

Fundamental Period:

$$T = 2\pi\sqrt{\frac{M}{\sum K}}$$
$$= 2\pi\sqrt{\frac{845}{2141x386.4}} = 0.2 \text{ Sec}$$

DETERMINE BASE SHEAR:

Since the period and R_w are both the same in both directions, so too will be the base shear:

$$V = \frac{ZIC}{R_w} W$$

$$R_w = 4.0$$
$$C = \frac{1.25S}{T^{2/3}} = \frac{1.25x1.5}{(0.20)^{2/3}} = 5.51 > 2.75 \rightarrow Use\ \text{C} = 2.75$$
$$\frac{C}{R_w} = \frac{2.75}{4.0} = 0.69 > 0.25$$
$$V = 0.4x1.0x0.69xW$$
$$= 0.276x845$$
$$= 233\ kips$$

LATERAL FORCE DISTRIBUTION :

Since the subject table top structure has a rigid diaphragm, the lateral force is distributed to each bent per its relative stiffness. Since the stiffness of each bent is the same, the lateral force to each bent is essentially identical.

TRANSVERSE DIRECTION :

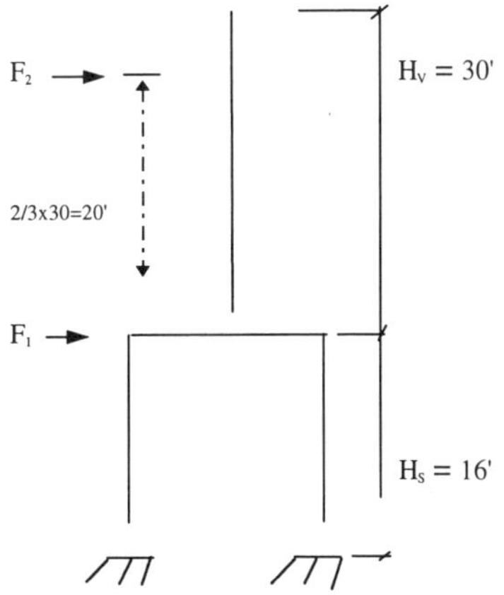

Wt. of reactor + platform, $W_2 = 610^k$

Wt. of support, $W_1 = 235^k$

$$F_x = \frac{(V - Ft) w_x h_x}{\sum w_i h_i}$$

Where F_x = Force at level x

F_t = Force at top level

Since T < 0.7 , Ft = 0

$$F_2 = \frac{(610)(36)}{(610)(36) + (235)(16)} \text{ x } 233 = 199 \text{ kips}$$

$$F_1 = \frac{(235)(16)}{(610)(36) + (235)(16)} \text{ x } 233 = 34 \text{ kips}$$

LONGITUDINAL DIRECTION: Same as for transverse direction calculated above.

APPENDIX 4.C

DETERMINATION OF BASE SHEAR FOR SELECTED STRUCTURES

NOTE: 1. Maximum value of C = 2.75 is used for all examples in this table

Equipment/Structure Types	Components	R_w	Base Shear Equation			Remarks
1.0 Vertical vessels and stacks (w/ or w/o guyed)			$V=\frac{ZICW}{R_w}$	$F_p=ZI_pC_pW_p$	$V=0.5ZI_pW$	
1.1 Supported on thick skirt 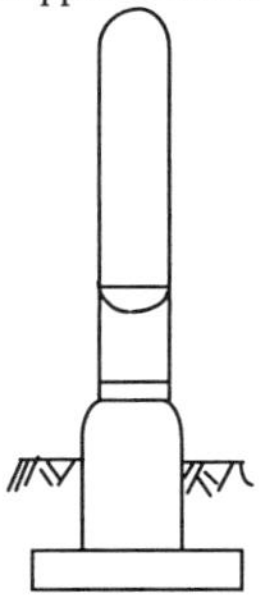	Anchorage	4.0	0.69ZIW			
1.2 Supported on structure 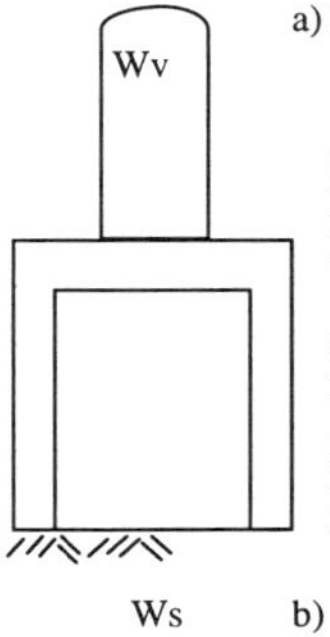						
a) For Wv ≤ 25% Ws	Vessel & anchorage			$ZI_px2x.75W_p$		Rigid or flexible equipment supported on flexible structure
steel/concrete, Special Moment Resisting Frame (SMRF)	Support structure	8.0	0.34ZIW			
steel Ordinary Moment-Resisting Frame (OMRF) & conc. Intermediate Moment-Resisting Frame (IMRF)		6.0	0.46ZIW			Non building structure with structure system similar to building
b) For Wv > 25% Ws steel & conc. SMRF, steel OMRF, and conc. IMRF	Vessel & anchorage and support structure	4.0	0.69ZIW			

Equipment/Structure Types	Components	R_w	Base Shear Equation			Remarks
2.0 Horizontal vessels/Exchangers			$V=\frac{ZICW}{R_w}$	$F_p=ZI_pC_pW_p$	$V=0.5ZI_pW$	
2.1 On short/rigid piers 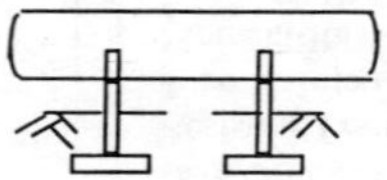 For both longitudinal and transverse directions (T < 0.06 sec)	Vessel and anchorage			ZIpx 2/3 x .75W_p		
	Support structure				$0.5ZI_pW$	Non building structures
2.2 On flexible piers/tees 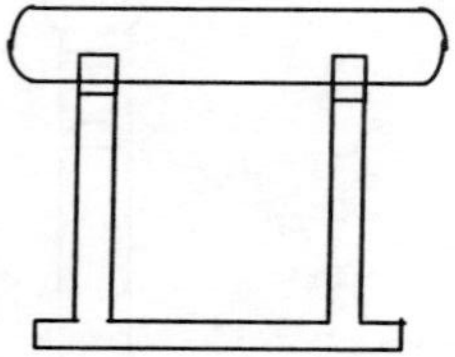 For both longitudinal and transverse directions T > 0.06 sec	Vessel and anchorage			ZI_px2x.75W_p	$0.5ZI_pW$	Use larger of two
	Support structure	3.0	0.92ZIW			Considered as inverted pendulum structure

Equipment/Structure Types	Components	R_w	Base Shear Equation			Remarks
3.0 Aircooled exchangers (fin fans)			$V=\frac{ZICW}{R_w}$	$F_p=ZI_pC_pW_p$	$V=0.5ZI_pW$	
3.1 Mounted at grade a) Longitudinal bent concentric steel brace frame	Braced frame	6.0	0.46ZIW			Non building structure with a structural system similar to buildings
b) Transverse bent steel OMRF	Moment frame	6.0	0.46ZIW			Same as above
3.2 Mounted on top of pipeway (less than 25% of structure weight) a) Transverse bent 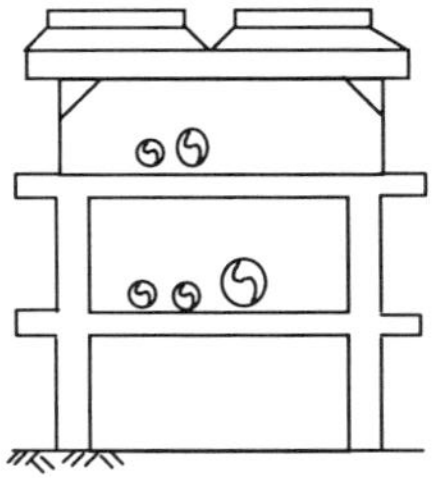 Steel OMRF	Finfan design	6.0	0.46ZIW	ZI_px2xW_p		Use larger of two
Steel & conc. SMRF or OMRF	Pipeway design	SEE	ITEM NO. 4.0			Include reaction from fin fan
b) Longitudinal Bent 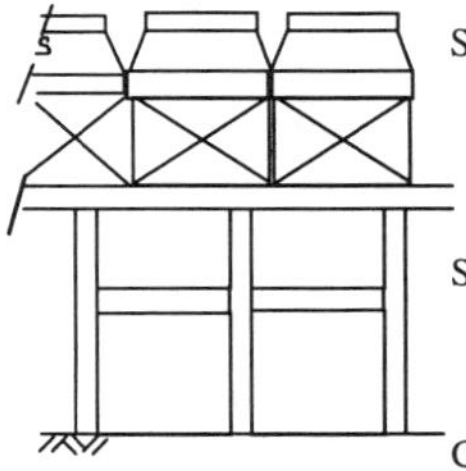 Steel concentric braced frame (CBF)	Fin fan design	6.0	0.46ZIW	ZI_px2xW_p		Use larger of two
Steel concentric braced frame (CBF)	Pipeway design	SEE	ITEM NO. 4.0			Include reaction from fin fan
Concrete SMRF or OMRF	Pipeway design	SEE	ITEM NO. 4.0			Same as above

Equipment/Structure Types	Components	R_w	Base Shear Equation			Remarks
4.0 Pipeway			$V = \frac{ZICW}{R_w}$	$F_p = ZI_pC_pW_p$	$V = 0.5ZI_pW$	
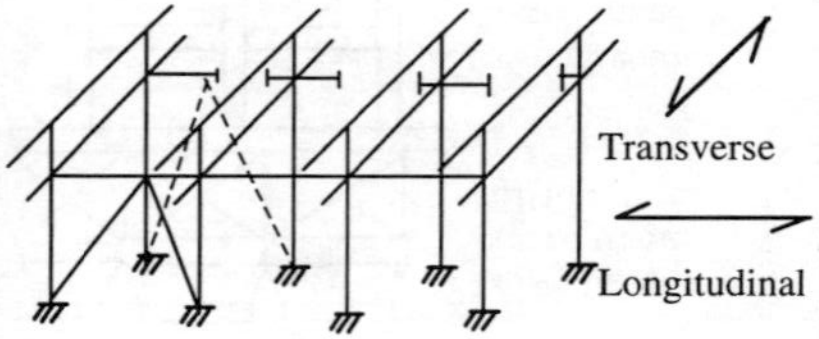 						
4.1 Steel frame main pipeway a) Transverse bent	SMRF OMRF	8.0 6.0	0.34ZIW 0.46ZIW			Non building structure with structural system similar to building
b) Longitudinal bent	EBF CBF	8.0 6.0	0.34ZIW 0.46ZIW			
4.2 Concrete frame main pipeway a) Transverse bent	SMRF IMRF OMRF	8.0 6.0 5.0	0.34ZIW 0.46ZIW 0.55ZIW			Non building structure with structural system similar to building
b) Longitudinal bent	SMRF IMRF OMRF Steel Bracing	8.0 6.0 5.0 6.0	0.34ZIW 0.46ZIW 0.55ZIW 0.46ZIW			
4.3 Steel/concrete cantilever stanchion 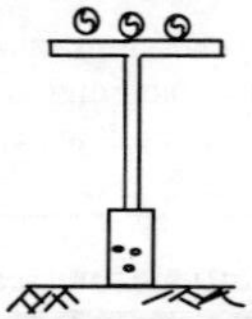	Cantilever Column	4.0	0.69ZIW			Note difference between pipeway and inverted pendulum

Equipment/Structure Types	Components	R_w	Base Shear Equation			Remarks
5.0 Horizontal box heater/furnace			$V = \frac{ZICW}{R_w}$	$F_p = ZI_pC_pW_p$	$V = 0.5ZI_pW$	
5.1 Longitudinal braced frame and/or shear panel 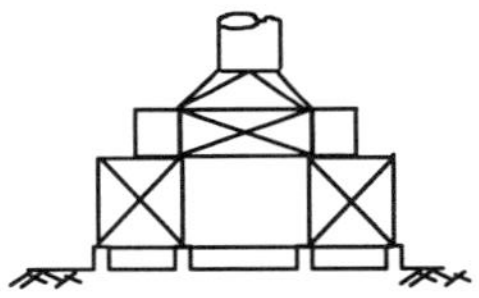	CBF or shear panel design (usually redundant system)	6.0	0.46ZIW			Non building structure with structural system similar to building
5.2 Transverse moment frame 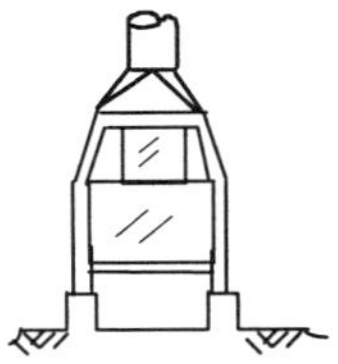	OMRF	6.0	0.46ZIW			Non building structure with structural system similar to building
5.3 Tall concrete pier/pedestal	pier/pedestal	3.0	0.92ZIW			Inverted pendulum type system

Equipment/Structure Types	Components	R_w	Base Shear Equation			Remarks
6.0 Vessel on braced/unbraced legs			$V = \frac{ZICW}{R_w}$	$F_p = ZI_pC_pW_p$	$V = 0.5ZI_pW$	
6.1 Sphere (without top girder or stiffening ring) 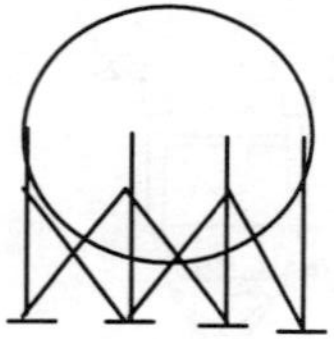	Sphere and braced frame design	4.0	0.69ZIW			Non building structure Use same base shear for design of anchorage and support structure
6.2 Stack/cylindrical furnace, vertical vessel, or hopper on cantilever or braced legs (without top girder or stiffening ring) 	Steel braced legs Steel cantilever legs Concrete cantilever	4.0 3.0 3.0	0.69ZIW 0.92ZIW 0.92ZIW			

Equipment/Structure Types	Components	R_w	Base Shear Equation			Remarks
7.0 Boilers			$V = \frac{ZICW}{R_w}$	$F_p = ZI_pC_pW_p$	$V = 0.5ZI_pW$	
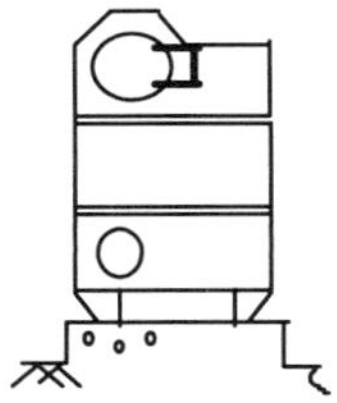 Transverse 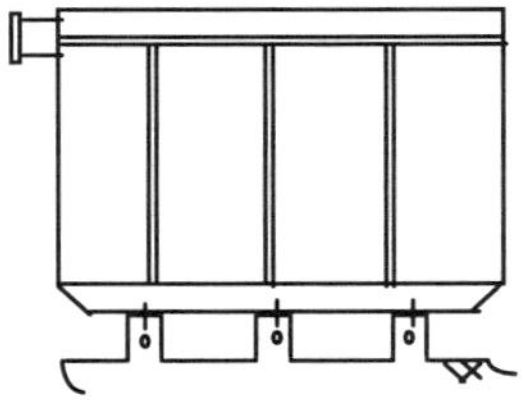 Longitudinal	Light steel framed wall or Steel braced frame where bracing carries gravity or Steel OMRF	6.0	0.46ZIW			Non building structure with structural system similar to building

Equipment/Structure Types	Components	R_w	Base Shear Equation			Remarks
8.0 Cooling Tower			$V=\frac{ZICW}{R_w}$	$F_p=ZI_pC_pW_p$	$V=0.5ZI_pW$	
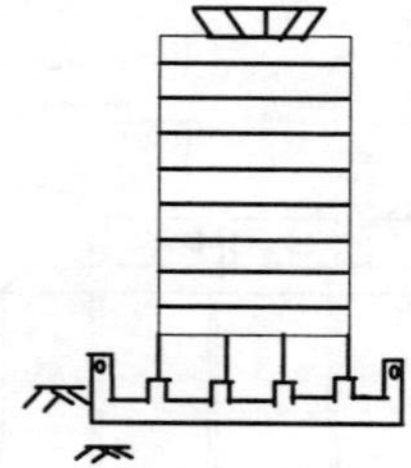 Transverse 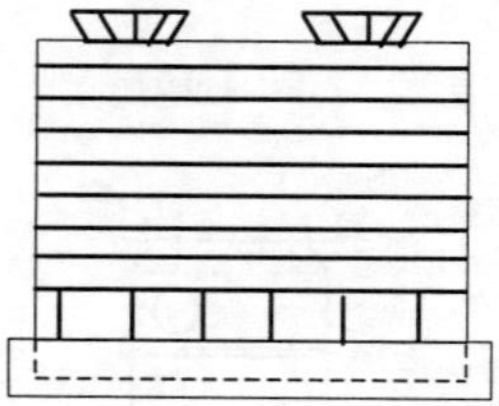 Longitudinal	Wooden braced frame	8.0	0.34ZIW			Non building structure with structural system similar to building

APPENDIX 4.D

STABILITY CHECK USING ENERGY BALANCE APPROACH (Existing Facilities Only)

4.D.1 INTRODUCTION

The factor of safety against overturning under static loading is defined as the ratio of the resisting forces to the overturning forces. However, this classical approach may be overly conservative when used for earthquake loadings since it does not recognize the dynamic character of the loading. The methodology described in this Appendix is adapted from material presented by Bechtel (1980) and presents an approach based on energy balance. In this method, the factor of safety against overturning during earthquake loading is defined as the ratio of potential energy (Pe_o) required to cause overturning about one edge of the structure to the maximum kinetic energy (Ke_s) in the structure due to the earthquake. This factor of safety should be at least 1.5. Presented below is an overview of the methodology.

4.D.2 CALCULATION OF FACTOR OF SAFETY AGAINST OVERTURNING

The structure is considered unstable in the overturning mode when the amplitude of rocking motion causes the center of structural mass to reach a position over any edge of the base (Fig. 4.D.1). The mechanism of rocking motion is that of an inverted pendulum with a very long natural period compared with that of the linear, elastic structural response. Hence, so far as overturning evaluation is concerned, the structure can be treated as a rigid body.

The factor of safety against overturning (FS) is given by:

$$FS = \frac{PE}{KE}$$

where:

$PE =$ Potential energy to overturn the structure
$= mg\ \Delta h$
$KE =$ Kinetic energy of earthquake input to the structure
$= \frac{1}{2} mV^2$
$m =$ total mass of the structure
$g =$ acceleration due to gravity
$V =$ resultant total velocity of the structure
$\Delta h =$ height to which the center of mass of the structure must be lifted to reach overturning position for a block as shown in Fig.4D.1, Δh is given by:

$$\Delta h = \left(\bar{h}^2 + \frac{L}{2}^2 \right)^{1/2} - \bar{h}$$

$\bar{h} =$ height of center of mass
$L/2 =$ half width of shorter side of structure

The factor of safety, FS, is then given by:

$$FS = \frac{mg\ \Delta h}{1/2mV^2} = \frac{2g\ \Delta h}{V^2}$$

The velocity, V, is calculated as follows:

Total vertical velocity, $Vv = \left(Vvg^2 + Vvs^2\right)^{1/2}$

Total x - direction velocity, $Vx = \left(Vxg^2 + Vxs^2\right)^{1/2}$

Total y - direction velocity, $Vy = \left(Vyg^2 + Vys^2\right)^{1/2}$

where:

Vvg, Vxg, Vyg are the peak ground velocities in the vertical, x and y directions

Vvs, Vxs, Vys are the structure velocities in the vertical, x and y directions

Using the component factor method to obtain total structure response from separate lateral and vertical analyses, there are three different load combinations to consider:

Combination 1: 100% Vertical + 30% Horizontal x + 30% Horizontal y

$$V = \left[Vv^2 + (0.3Vx)^2 + (0.3Vy)^2\right]^{1/2}$$
$$= \left[Vvg^2 + Vvs^2 + 0.09\,(Vxg^2 + Vxs^2 + Vyg^2 + Vys^2)\right]^{1/2}$$

Combination 2: 30% Vertical + 100% Horizontal x + 30% Horizontal y

$$V = \left[0.09(Vvg^2 + Vvs^2) + Vxg^2 + Vxs^2 + 0.09(Vyg^2 + Vys^2)\right]^{1/2}$$

Combination 3: 30% Vertical + 30% Horizontal x + 100% Horizontal y

$$V = \left[0.09(Vvg^2 + Vvs^2 + Vxg^2 + Vxs^2) + Vyg^2 + Vys^2\right]^{1/2}$$

For cases where the specified x and y horizontal ground motions and structural responses are the same (i.e., conservative use of the peak of the velocity response spectra), Combinations 2 and 3 are identical and hence only two load combinations need to be considered.

Note that in the above computation of total vertical and horizontal velocities, the true relative velocity is more appropriate to use than the peak ground velocity. However, for long period oscillators, this value approaches the ground velocity, whereas the commonly used pseudo-spectral velocity tends to zero. Therefore, to guard against the use of velocities that are below the ground velocity, the peak ground velocity has been added to the estimates of the peak structural velocity. No penalty is associated with this conservative approach since the factor of safety is ordinarily a very large number, despite the use of conservative peak velocities. The peak horizontal ground velocity can be obtained from any appropriate source. It is recommended that, lacking other information, a value of 4 ft./sec. for lg maximum ground acceleration can be used for competent soils (Newmark and Hall, 1982). For the vertical ground motion, the peak ground velocity shall be 2/3 of this value. Structure velocities can be obtained knowing the structural periods and the appropriate acceleration response spectra in all three directions.

4.D.3 OTHER EFFECTS

The above analysis assumes rigid body rotation about one edge of the structure that is not free to work. Other effects such as soil flexibility, embedment and buoyancy can significantly influence the computed factor of safety depending upon local conditions.

4.D.4 EFFECT OF SOIL FLEXIBILITY

Considering soil flexibility has two significant effects. First it changes the axis about which "effective" rotation occurs. The axis of rotation moves inboard from the edge of the structure, as shown in Fig. 4.D.2, towards the center, thereby making it easier to rotate the structure towards instability. Second, the soil can now absorb energy (since it has flexibility). The amount of energy absorbed can be significant and this effect adds to the "resistance" to overturning. The instability equation now becomes

$$KE = PE + SE$$

where:

SE = strain energy of the soil block

A factor of safety of 1.5 is now required on the angle causing overturning versus the angle at which the above equation holds true (i.e., $\theta ov/\theta \geq 1.5$). A check of the computed maximum soil pressure against the allowable bearing capacity should also be performed.

4.D.5 EFFECT OF EMBEDMENT

Embedment gives rise to additional resistance against overturning due to the side passive soil pressure considered as follows.

Let "d" be the depth of embedment and "d'" be the submerged depth where the ground water table is above the elevation of the base. The structure is assumed to rotate about the toe edge for the overturning evaluation. To simplify the analysis for practical purposes, only the passive soil pressure developed on the toe-side is considered, and the wall friction and action of the soil on the opposite side of the structure are neglected. The passive pressure diagram is modified to be consistent with the assumption that the structure rotates about one edge. Free-draining soil conditions are also assumed. Figures 4.D.3(a) through (c) show the resultant idealized passive pressure diagram (P_z) for different elevations of the ground water table when it is above the base (i.e., $d' \geq 0$).

As was the case when considering soil flexibility at the base of the structure, the effect of embedment is to include some strain energy absorbed by the soil in the instability equation KE = PE + SE. Calculation of the strain energy can be performed through integration of the pressure and strain distribution over the volume of soil affected.

4.D.6 EFFECT OF BUOYANCY

When the ground water table is above the base (d' > 0), the buoyant force has the effect of increasing the overturning potential of the structure. The buoyant force B acts at the centroid of the volume of water displaced by the submerged portion of the structure, and its magnitude varies during the overturning process. At any position before overturning takes place, the centroid of the displaced volume of water is located at height z above the elevation of the edge R and the corresponding buoyant force is B_z (Fig. 4.D.4). The work done by the buoyant force is:

$$W_B = \int_{z_a}^{z_b} B_z dz$$

where z_a and z_b are the heights of the centroid of buoyant force above the edge for the equilibrium and tipping positions, respectively.

In the instability equation, the work done by the buoyant force is additive to the kinetic energy imposed by the earthquake, i.e.,

$$KE + W_B = PE + SE$$

In addition to buoyancy effects, if the block is sitting on saturated ground, suction is created when the block tries to lift off. It should be noted that the positive effect of this suction in resisting overturning is difficult to quantify, but may be much larger than any effects of buoyancy, especially when the water is very shallow.

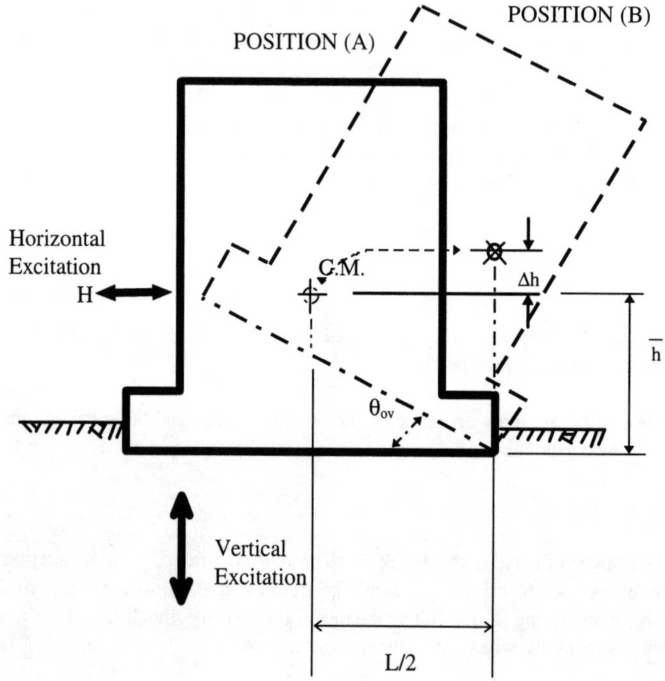

Figure 4.D.1: Position of the Structure when Overturning About One Edge

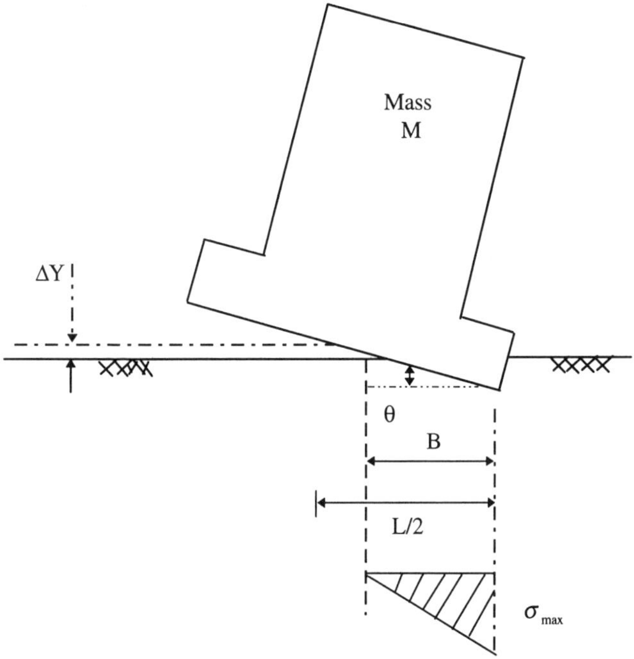

$$KE = \frac{1}{2} mV^2$$

$$PE = mg(L/2 - B)\theta$$

SE = Strain Energy of Soil Block

$= 1/2\sigma_{AV}(E_{AV})$(Volume of Soil Block)

σ_{AV} = Average stress in soil block

E_{AV} = Average strain in soil block

$$KE = PE + SE$$

$\frac{\theta ov}{\theta} > 1.5$ (factor of safety of 1.5 against overturning)

$\sigma_{MAX} < Q_{ALL}$ (check maximum soil pressure less than allowable bearing capacity)

Figure 4.D.2: Effect of Soil Flexibility

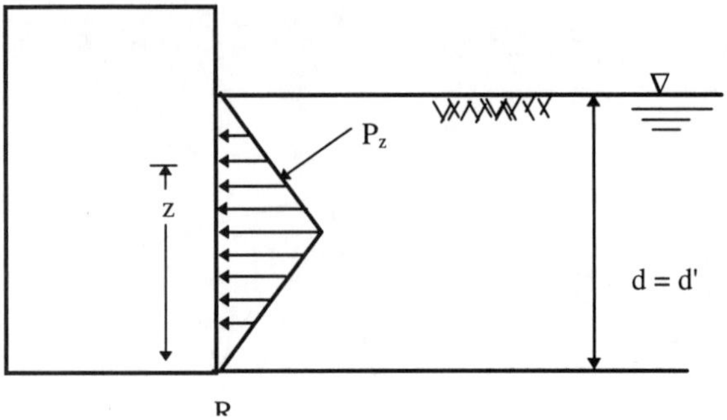

(A) d' = d

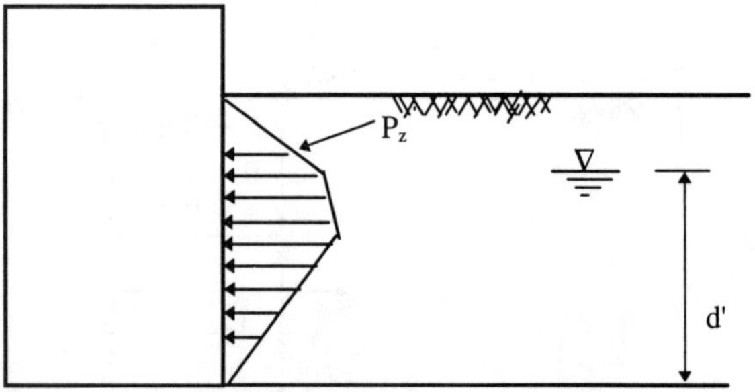

(B) d/2 <d' <d

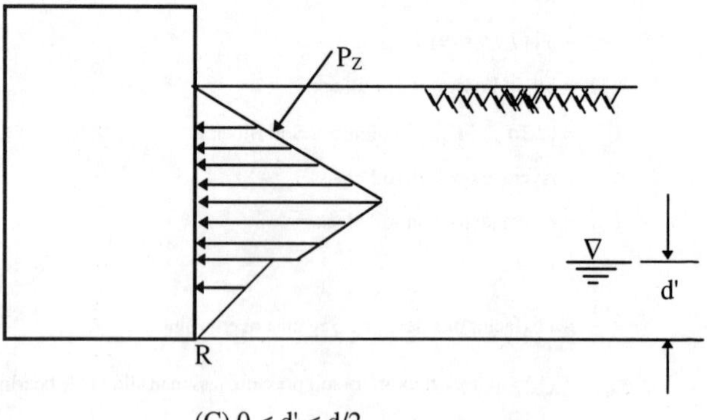

(C) 0 < d' < d/2

Figure 4.D.3: Idealized Passive Soil Pressure for Overturning About Edge R

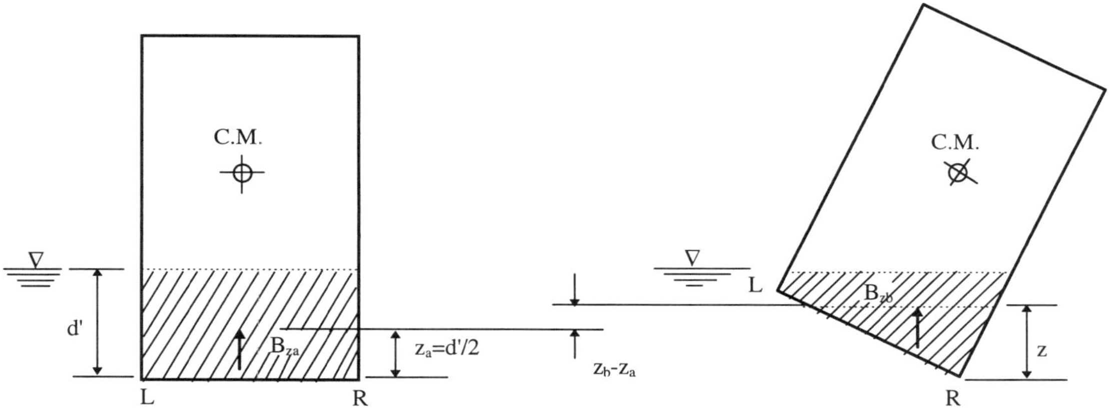

(A) EQUILIBRIUM POSITION

(B) TIPPING-OVER POSITION

Figure 4.D.4: Buoyancy Effects for Overturning Evaluation

APPENDIX 4.E

METHODOLOGY FOR DETERMINATION OF SLIDING DISPLACEMENTS
(Existing Facilities Only)

E.1 INTRODUCTION

The occurrence of sliding of the structure as a rigid body due to earthquake loads does not necessarily lead to a failure mode as long as sliding is within tolerable limits. A measure of the factor of safety then is the ratio of the calculated to allowable displacements. The methodology described in this appendix is adapted from material presented by Bechtel (1980) that follows and procedure originally developed by Newmark in which an acceleration, ng, is defined that would just cause a rigid block to slide.

E.2 METHODOLOGY

Assuming a single acceleration pulse, of magnitude $a_h g$ and of duration t_1, is applied to the rigid block (Figure 4.E.1-b), a velocity plot, as shown in Figure 4.E. 1-c, can be constructed. Given the maximum horizontal ground velocity, $V_{H\max}$, time t_1 is then estimated from:

$$t_1 = \frac{V_{H\max}}{a_h g}$$

The velocity due to the resisting acceleration is given by ngt. At time t_2, the two velocities are equal and the rigid block comes to rest relative to the ground. From Figure 4.E.1-c, time t_2 is given by:

$$t_2 = \frac{V_{H\max}}{ng}$$

The maximum displacement of the rigid block relative to the ground is obtained by integrating the velocity curves up to time t_2 and subtracting the results. This is equivalent to computing the area of the shaded triangle. The maximum is then given by:

$$\Delta_s = \frac{V_{H\max}^2}{2ng}\left(1 - \frac{n}{a_h}\right)$$

where:

Δ_s = Maximum sliding displacement

$V_{H\max}$ = Maximum total velocity of the structure in the horizontal direction

g = Acceleration due to gravity

a_h = Maximum total horizontal acceleration in g' s

n = Fraction of gravitational acceleration that would cause the structure to slide $= \mu(1 - a_v)$

μ = Coefficient of friction between structure and ground

a_v = Maximum vertical acceleration

Using the component factor method, $V_{H\max}$, a_h and n are calculated as follows:

Combination 1: 100% Vertical + 30% Horizontal x + 30% Horizontal y

$$V_{H\max} = \left[0.09\left(Vxg^2 + Vxs^2 + Vyg^2 + Vys^2\right)\right]^{1/2}$$
$$a_h = \left[0.09\left(ax^2 + ay^2\right)\right]^{1/2}$$
$$n = \mu\,(1 - a_v)$$

Combination 2: 30% Vertical + 100% Horizontal x + 30% Horizontal y

$$V_{H\max} = \left[\left(Vxg^2 + Vxs^2 + 0.09(Vyg^2 + Vys^2\right)\right]^{1/2}$$
$$a_h = \left[a_x^2 + 0.09\,a_y^2\right]^{1/2}$$
$$n = \mu\,(1 - 0.3av)$$

Combination 3: 30% Vertical + 30% Horizontal x + 100% Horizontal y

$$V_{H\max} = \left[Vyg^2 + Vys^2 + 0.09\,(Vxg^2 + Vxs^2)\right]^{1/2}$$
$$a_h = \left[a_y^2 + 0.09\,a_x^2\right]^{1/2}$$
$$n = \mu\,(1 - 0.3a_v)$$

In the above equations; Vxg, Vyg, Vvg are the peak ground velocities in the x, y and vertical directions; Vxs, Vys, Vvs are the structure velocities in the x, y and vertical directions; a_x, a_y, a_v are the peak amplified structural accelerations in the x, y and vertical directions. Vertical ground response parameters can be taken as 2/3 of horizontal values and values of peak ground velocity can be estimated from empirical equations.

It is to be noted from the equation for Δ_s that when the applied acceleration coefficient a_h is less than or equal to the resisting acceleration coefficient n, Δ_s is equal to zero. This result is compatible with the definition of the coefficient n. Relative displacement would occur only when a_h is greater than n. Setting n/a_h in the equation equal to zero will provide an upper bound estimate of Δ_s; however, it must be recognized that this simplification leads to finite displacements for all cases.

Note that in order to calculate total displacement, the sliding displacement needs to be added to the in-structure deformation, assuming the structure does not move at its base.

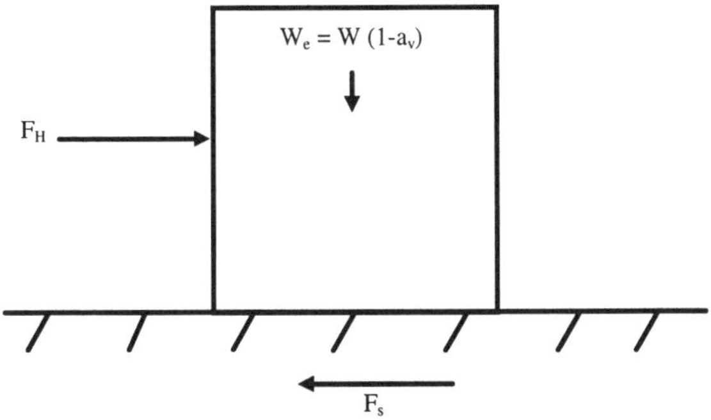

(A) SLIDING MODEL

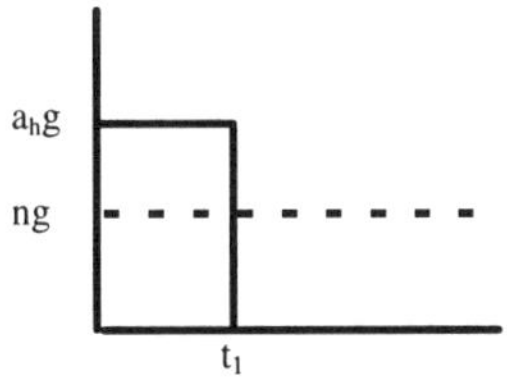

(B) RECTANGULAR ACCELERATOR PULSE

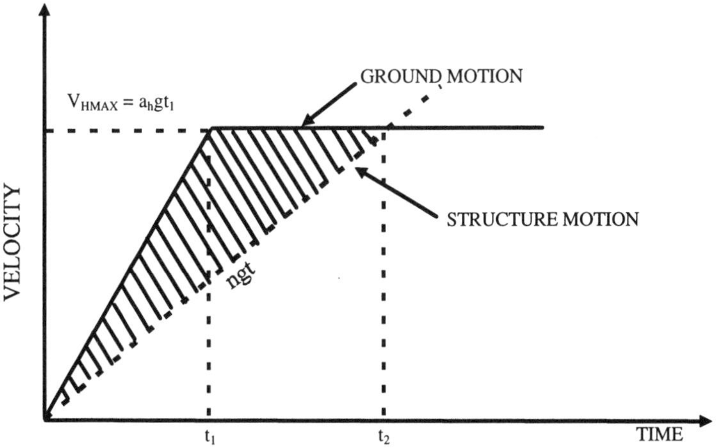

(C) MAXIMUM VELOCITY VS. TIME

Figure 4.E.1: Sliding due to Earthquake

APPENDIX 4.F

RISK MANAGEMENT AND PREVENTION PROGRAM (RMPP) GUIDELINES FOR SEISMIC ASSESSMENT OF FACILITIES CONTAINING ACUTELY HAZARDOUS MATERIALS

Committee Note: This appendix contains a document prepared by others for use in evaluating existing facilities. It is reprinted in its entirety because it is currently being used by regulators throughout California for facilities containing Acutely Hazardous Materials, but it is not published and is not easily obtainable by practicing engineers.

PROPOSED GUIDANCE

FOR

RMPP SEISMIC ASSESSMENTS

Prepared for the

RMPP SUB-COMMITTEE of the

SOUTHERN CALIFORNIA FIRE CHIEFS ASSOCIATION

Prepared by the

RMPP SEISMIC GUIDANCE COMMITTEE

June 1992

RMPP SEISMIC GUIDANCE COMMITTEE

<u>Technical Authors</u>

Robert Bachman, Chair	Fluor Daniel, Inc.
Lee Benuska	Lindvall Richter Benuska Associates
Sohrab Esfandiari	ABB Impell Corporation
Orhan Gurbuz	Bechtel Corporation
Gordon Hau	ABB Impell Corporation
Lucien Hersh	Bechtel Corporation
Mike Knarr	Southern California Edison Company
Alfredo Lopez	Bechtel Corporation
John Masek	Dames & Moore
Allan Porush	Dames & Moore
Mayasandra Ravindra	EQE International
Philip Richter	Fluor Daniel, Inc.
Kenneth Saunders	Hopper & Associates
Ian Stubbs	E&L Engineering, Inc.
Paul Summers	WGP Engineering, Inc.
Wen Tong	EQE International
Larry Wesselink	Chevron Research & Technology Company
Joe Young	East Bay Municipal Utility District

<u>Other Contributors</u>

Catherine Caraway	California Office of Emergency Services
Jim Goodfellow	California Seismic Safety Commission
Fred Lercari	California Office of Emergency Services
Tony Markham	Los Angeles City Fire Department
Edward Muehlbacher	South Coast Air Quality Management District
David Myers	Los Angeles City Fire Department
Jeanne Perkins	Association of Bay Area Governments
Barbara Yu	Los Angeles County Fire Department

CONTENTS

PROPOSED GUIDANCE FOR RMPP SEISMIC ASSESSMENTS

1.0 INTRODUCTION

The objective of Risk Management and Prevention Program (RMPP) seismic assessments is to provide reasonable assurance that a release of Acutely Hazardous Materials (AHM) having offsite consequences would not occur as the result of a major earthquake. The purpose of this document is to provide guidance regarding acceptable criteria to be used in such assessments. The guidance provided is applicable to structural systems and components whose failure would result in the release of sufficient quantities of AHM to be of concern.

The guidance given in this document provides for a deterministic evaluation of structural systems and components. This evaluation is generally performed considering an earthquake level which has a low probability of occurrence. The seismic capacity of structures and components to withstand this level of earthquake is calculated using realistic criteria and assumptions. An alternate approach is to perform a probabilistic risk assessment which provides estimates and insights on the relative risks and vulnerabilities of different systems and components.

Conformance to this document does not guarantee or assure that an AHM release will not occur in the event of strong earthquake ground motions. Rather, the guidance provided is intended to minimize the risk of release of AHM by reducing uncertainties and increasing resistance to earthquake ground motions.

It is assumed that the owner, administering agency, and consultant performing the hazard and operability study will identify the systems and components of concern to the RMPP seismic consultant. It is expected that three classes of items will be evaluated. These are:

1) Systems which contain sufficient quantities of AHM to be of concern.

2) Adjacent facilities whose structural failure or displacement could result in the failure of systems which contain AHM.

3) Utility systems which would be required to operate following an earthquake for emergency reaction or to maintain the facility in a safe condition, e.g., firewater or emergency power systems.

At this time, California state law requires that all new facilities built after January 1, 1990, be designed in accordance with the 1988 edition of the Uniform Building Code (*UBC*). It is the consensus of the Seismic Guidance Committee that AHM systems and components designed in accordance with the 1988 *UBC* (or later) provisions provide reasonable assurance of withstanding earthquake effects without either structural failure or a release of AHM having offsite consequences. Two situations exist for which the Committee feels it is appropriate to exceed the minimum requirements of the *UBC*. The first case is when the facility is situated near an active fault. The earthquake ground motions in the near field zone of a major earthquake may be greater than those specified in the *UBC*. The second case is when the facility is situated on a soft soil site identified as *UBC* Soil Profile S4. Here, the site response amplification effect may need to be increased beyond the amplification factors currently provided by the *UBC*. It is the judgment of the Committee that guidance provided in the Recommended Lateral Force Requirements and Commentary of the Structural Engineers Association of California may be utilized to assess the extent of possible higher ground motions in these two cases.

2.0 SEISMIC HAZARD EVALUATION CRITERIA FOR EXISTING FACILITIES

A site specific seismic hazard assessment should address and, where appropriate, quantify the following earthquake effects:

1) Ground shaking, including local site amplification effects
2) Liquefaction
3) Fault rupture
4) Seismic settlement
5) Landslide
6) Tsunami/seiche

It is the consensus of the Seismic Guidance Committee that the earthquake hazard which should be used as the basis for evaluation is that which has only a 10% probability of being exceeded in 50 years, i.e., one with a mean return period of 475 years. This probability of seismic hazard is the same as that used for establishing the design earthquake ground motion for new facilities as specified in the 1991 *UBC*.

Three procedures are available to characterize ground motions associated with the above return period.

1) Utilize the *UBC* static base shear equation or *UBC* standard spectral shapes anchored to the effective peak ground acceleration (PGA).

2) Utilize ATC-14 spectral shapes anchored to the effective PGA.

3) Develop site specific criteria for ground shaking in terms of elastic response spectra at 5% of critical damping.

The philosophy of the Committee is to use mean estimates of ground shaking for assessment of existing facilities. Therefore, response spectra, liquefaction potential, and seismic settlement hazard estimate values should be based on mean estimates of occurrence. The Committee recognizes that combining the *UBC* base shear equation or spectral shapes with a site specific mean effective PGA represents a mean plus one standard deviation ground motion estimate, which is conservative.

Any procedure used to characterize ground motions should be adjusted for soil conditions and near field fault zone effects. Effective ground motion parameters may also be utilized.

3.0 WALKTHROUGH CONSIDERATIONS

The evaluation program should be geared to finding, evaluating and, if necessary, strengthening governing elements in the system. Thus, a systematic walkthrough should be an integral part of the seismic evaluation program. Walkthroughs should concentrate on governing elements and potential areas of weaknesses due to design or construction deficiencies, modifications, or deterioration. These areas of weakness may not be apparent in design drawings or calculations. The walkthroughs should be conducted by experienced engineers familiar with seismic design and the effects of earthquakes so that they can readily identify the areas of weakness and prioritize the detailed evaluations that may be needed.

4.0 ANALYTICAL EVALUATION METHODOLOGY FOR EXISTING STRUCTURES AND SYSTEMS

4.1 Define ground motion for evaluation in terms of elastic response spectra with 5% critical damping adjusted if necessary for near field and soft soil effects. These spectra may be based on mean estimates of occurrence.

4.2 Acceptance for existing structures, systems, and their foundations may be accomplished by one of the following procedures:

4.2.1 Perform elastic modal analysis or equivalent static analysis.

The evaluation consists of demonstrating that capacity exceeds demand for identified systems. Acceptance is presumed if the following equation is satisfied:

DEMAND	CAPACITY BASED ON
$D + L + \frac{E}{Q} \leq$	1.6 x Working Stress Allowable (without 1/3rd increase) or $\varnothing U$ or $\varnothing R_n$ with Load Factors of Unity

where D = Dead load

L = Live/operating load
E = Elastic 10% probability in 50 year earthquake load at 5% damping
ø = Capacity reduction factor (per ACI) or resistance factor (per AISC)
Q = Ductility based reduction factor per the attached Table 1
R_n = Nominal capacity per AISC Load & Resistance Factor Design (LRFD)
U = Nominal capacity per ACI

1) For systems whose fundamental period (T) is less than the period at which the peak spectral acceleration occurs (Tpeak), one of the following approaches should be used to determine the appropriate level of seismic acceleration for the fundamental and higher modes.

a. The peak spectral acceleration should be used for the fundamental mode of the structure. When considering higher modes, either the peak or actual spectral accelerations values may be used.

b. For structures whose fundamental period are less than 0.67xTpeak, the maximum spectral acceleration in the range of 0.5xT to 1.5xT may be used in lieu of the peak spectral acceleration. When considering higher modes, either the peak or actual spectral accelerations values may be used.

2) For redundant structural systems, e.g., multiple bents, in which seismic loads in individual members may be redistributed without failure, the demand (from the previous equation) on individual members may exceed capacity by up to 50 percent.

3) Relative displacements shall be considered and shall include torsional and translational deformations. Structural displacements that are determined from an elastic analysis that was based on seismic loading reduced by Q shall be multiplied by 0.5Q [but not less than 1.0 (one)], to determine displacements to be used in an evaluation.

Generally, the drift (relative horizontal displacement) shall be less than 0.01H, where H is the height between levels of consideration. This drift limit may be exceeded if it can be demonstrated that greater drift can be tolerated by structural and nonstructural elements or the equipment itself.

To obtain relative displacements between different support points, absolute summation of the individual displacements can conservatively be used. Alternatively, the square root of the sum of squares (SRSS) method for combining displacements may be used where appropriate.

4) When evaluating overturning, a 15 percent reduction in dead load should be assumed to account for vertical acceleration effects.

5) The capacity of anchor bolts embedded in concrete may be evaluated in accordance with the strength design provisions of Section 2624 of the 1991 *UBC*.

6) Structures that do not pass these evaluation criteria can be re-assessed using a more rigorous approach to determine if structural retrofit is actually required.

4.2.2 Structures that are judged to meet the intent of the 1988 (or later) *UBC*, and for which a visual field inspection reveals well-proportioned and complete lateral force resisting systems, may be deemed to meet the intent of these requirements without further evaluation.

4.2.3 Alternative procedures using rational analyses based on well established principles of mechanics may be used in lieu of those prescribed in these recommendations. Methods such as non-linear time history analyses would be acceptable. The resulting inelastic deformations must be within appropriate levels to provide reasonable assurance of structural integrity.

5.0 ASSESSMENT OF EQUIPMENT AND NON-STRUCTURAL ELEMENTS

The anchorage of equipment and non-structural elements supported within or by structures may be evaluated in accordance with Section 2336 of the 1991 *UBC*.

6.0 ACCEPTANCE PROCEDURE FOR ABOVE GROUND PIPING SYSTEMS

6.1 Evaluation of piping systems are primarily accomplished by field walkthroughs. Such qualitative evaluations of piping systems are best done by an engineer experienced in this area, visually inspecting the piping system under concern. This is preferred because some piping is field routed and, in some instances, piping and supports have been modified from that shown on design drawings.

This guidance is primarily intended for ductile steel pipe constructed to a national standard such as ASME B31.3. Evaluation of other piping material is discussed in Section 6.6.

6.2 The procedure for evaluating above ground piping systems will generally be as follows:

1) Identify piping systems to be evaluated.

2) Determine original design code basis and materials of construction.

3) Assess extent of corrosion/erosion.

4) Assess extent of significant cyclic operational loading conditions which may substantially reduce system fatigue life.

5) Perform a walkthrough of the piping systems for seismic capability. Document the walkthrough and identify areas for detailed evaluation.

6) Complete the detailed evaluation of any identified areas and recommend remedial actions.

6.3 Compliance with these procedures does not assure compliance with current construction codes and standards. It must be emphasized that damage to or failure of pipe supports should not be construed as a piping failure unless it directly contributes to a pressure boundary failure. The intention here is to preserve the essential pressure containing integrity of the piping system but not necessarily leak tightness. Therefore, this procedure does not preclude the possibility of small leaks at bolted flanged joints.

6.4 Ductile piping systems have, in general, performed adequately in past earthquakes. Where damage has occurred, it has been related to the following aspects of piping systems:

1) Excessive seismic anchor movement.
2) Interaction with other elements.
3) Extensive corrosion effects.

Seismic anchor movements could result in relative displacements between points of support/attachment of the piping systems. Such movements include relative displacements between vessels, pipe supports, or main headers for branch lines. Interaction is the seismically induced impact of piping systems with adjacent structures, systems, or components, including the effects of the falling hazards. Corrosion could result in a weakened pipe cross section that could fail during an earthquake.

Additional aspects of piping systems which should also be reviewed during the walkthrough for seismic capability are:

1) Large pipe displacements from inertial effects.

2) Brittle elements.

3) Threaded connections, flange joints, and special fittings.

4) Inadequate supports.

Special features or conditions to illustrate the above concerns include:

1) Inadequate anchorage of attached equipment.

2) Short/rigid spans that cannot accommodate the relative displacement of the supports, e.g., piping spanning between two structural systems.

3) Damaged supports including corrosion.

4) Long vertical runs subject to inter level drift.

5) Large unsupported masses (e.g., valves) attached to the pipe.

6) Flanged and threaded connections in high stress locations.

7) Existing leakage locations (flanges, threads, valves, welds).

8) External corrosion.

9) Inadequate vertical supports and/or insufficient lateral restraints.

10) Welded attachments to thin wall pipe (i.e., pipe less than Schedule 40).

11) Excessive seismic displacements of expansion joints.

12) Brittle elements, such as cast iron pipes.

13) Sensitive equipment impact (e.g., control valves).

14) Fatigue of short to medium length rod hangers.

6.5 After the walkthrough is performed and an analysis is deemed necessary, the following general rules should be followed:

1) Friction resistance should not be considered for seismic restraint, except for the following condition: for long straight piping runs with numerous supports, friction in the axial direction may be considered.

2) Spring supports (constant or variable) should not be considered as seismic supports.

3) Short rod hangers can be considered as effective lateral supports if justified.

4) Appropriate stress intensification factor ("i" factors) should be used.

5) Allowable piping stresses should be reduced to account for fatigue effects due to significant cyclic operational loading conditions. In this case the allowables presented in Section 6.5.1 may need to be reduced.

6.5.1 Procedures for seismic anchor movement evaluation of piping are as follows:

1) Use the relative seismic anchor displacements as determined in the Section 4.2.1.

2) Piping stress due to seismic anchor displacement should meet the following criteria:

$$\frac{iM_{sam}}{Z} \leq 3.0S_h$$

where,

i = stress intensification factor from ASME B31.3 or other appropriate reference

M_{sam} = moment amplitude due to seismic anchor movement using nominal pipe wall thickness

Z = elastic section modulus of pipe = $\pi r^2 t$

S_h = basic material allowable stress at pipe operating temperature from ASME B31.3 or other appropriate reference

r = mean cross-sectional radius

t = design nominal wall thickness minus design corrosion/erosion allowances or actual wall thickness minus future anticipated corrosion/erosion

3) Flange connections should be checked to ensure that moments due to seismic anchor movement do not result in significant leakage. Factors to be considered are flange type and material; gasket design; bolt material, number, and preload; rated pressure and operating pressure. If the rated pressure is greater than the operating pressure, the moment capacity of the flange body may be significant, and an equivalent pressure approach may be used. Bolt loads should also be assessed. Bolt stresses above preload may result in intermittent leakage. Bolt stresses above yield are potential concerns.

6.5.2 Procedures for interaction evaluation of piping are as follows:

1) AHM piping shall be visually inspected to identify potential interactions with adjacent structures, systems, or components. Those interactions which could cause unacceptable damage to piping, piping components (e.g., control valves), or adjacent critical items should be mitigated.

Note that restricting piping seismic movement to preclude interaction may lead to excessive restraint of thermal expansion or inhibit other necessary operational flexibility.

2) The walkthrough should also identify the potential for interaction between adjacent structures, systems or components, and the AHM piping being investigated. Those interactions which could cause unacceptable damage to AHM piping should be mitigated. Note that falling hazards should be considered in this evaluation.

6.5.3 Procedures for corrosion evaluation of piping are as follows:

1) During walkthrough identify conditions conducive to external corrosion.

2) Wall thickness should be evaluated for potential reduction due to erosion or corrosion.

3) Extent of internal corrosion/erosion can be evaluated by any of the following methods:

   a. Review of existing corrosion inspection program for AHM piping systems.

   b. Review of successful operating experience.

   c. Wall thickness measurements.

4) Compare existing corrosion experience and future anticipated corrosion to original design corrosion allowance.

5) This seismic evaluation guidance is not applicable if excessive corrosion is evident.

6.5.4 Procedures for seismic inertia evaluation of piping are as follows:

1) Large unsupported spans of piping should be checked for inertia loads. The inertial moments should not exceed those allowed in Section 6.5.1. It is not necessary to combine moments from seismic anchor movement and inertial loading. Inertial loading shall be based on the appropriate pipe support motions and the characteristics of the piping configuration. Seismic inertial loading usually can be evaluated by simplified calculations.

2) If the intent of ASME B31.3 or other appropriate reference can be demonstrated to have been met for seismic effects, then the piping system is deemed acceptable.

3) Flange connections shall be checked to ensure that moments due to seismic inertia loading do not result in significant flange leakage. Refer to Section 6.5.1(3).

6.6 Procedures for determination of allowable stress levels for piping materials other than ductile steel accepted by ASME B31.3 are as follows:

Piping made from materials other than ductile steel accepted by ASME B31.3 may be required to withstand seismic loading. The criteria outlines above for ductile steel piping should be followed for piping made from other materials with the following allowable stress values:

1) When ductile material piping is designed and constructed to a national standard with basic allowable stresses given, then those values should be used.

2) When piping materials meet a national standard with a minimum specified tensile strength, σ_t, then the basic allowable stress at operating temperature should be:

Ductile Materials: $S_h = \frac{1}{3} \sigma_t$ at temperature

Brittle Materials: $S_h = \frac{1}{40} \sigma_t$ at temperature

3) When piping materials cannot be identified with a national standard with a minimum specified tensile strength, then one should be estimated from published literature or a testing program. The basic allowable stress at temperature should be determined using the appropriate equation in (2) above, unless a higher allowable can be justified by seismic testing.

4) If a strength cannot be determined with a reasonable level of confidence, then the piping material should be replaced with one having known properties.

7.0 <u>NEW FACILITIES</u> (designed after adoption of these rules)

Design of new facilities containing AHM must satisfy the seismic provisions of the 1991 *UBC*. An I-factor of 1.25 and I_p-factor of 1.5 (for parts and elements of structures) should be utilized. These factors are defined in the *UBC*.

The following two *UBC* criteria modifications should be included in new designs:

7.1 Modify site peak ground acceleration for fault near field effects. Use the larger of the seismic zone factor (Z) per the 1991 *UBC* or the site specific effective peak ground acceleration corresponding to a 10% probability of being exceeded in 50 years.

7.2 Make a rational determination of the effects of soft soil amplification of bedrock motion if the site is determined to have a *UBC* Soil Profile S4.

8.0 STRENGTHENING CRITERIA

In the event a structure, system, or component is deemed unacceptable based on the guidance provided in this document, a strengthening program should be initiated. Appropriate strengthening criteria must be developed to provide reasonable assurance that retrofitted items will perform adequately when subjected to strong ground shaking.

It should always be kept in mind that the intent of retrofitting these structures, systems, or components is not "to bring them up to current code." In many instances this may not be practical. The retrofit design criteria should be consistent with this proposed guidance. It is always advisable to meet code requirements to the extent practical.

An important point to consider when retrofitting is that over strengthening areas of the structure that are currently deficient in strength can force the weak link(s) to occur in other elements that are perhaps more brittle. This can have a negative impact on overall structural performance during a major earthquake. In other words, a structure that is presently weak, but ductile, should not be strengthened to the point that its failure mode becomes brittle with a lower energy absorbing capacity.

9.0 REFERENCES

ACI 318-89 Building Code and Commentary - *Building Code Requirements for Reinforced Concrete*, American Concrete Institute, November 1989.

AISI, *"Steel Tanks for Liquid Storage,"* in Steel Plate Engineering Data, Volume 1, 1976 Edition.

ANSI/AWWA D100-84, *AWWA Standard for Welded Steel Tanks for Water Storage*, American Water Works Association.

ANSI/ASME B31.3, *ASME Code for Pressure Piping Chemical Plant and Petroleum Refinery Piping*, 1986 Edition.

ANSI/ASME B31G-1984, *Manual for Determining the Remaining Strength of Corroded Pipelines, a Supplement to ANSI/ASME B31 Code for Pressure Piping.*

API Standard 650, *Welded Steel Tanks for Oil Storage*, 8th Edition, November 1988.

ASCE 7-88, *Minimum Design Loads for Buildings and Other Structures*, American Society of Civil Engineers, 1988.

ASCE 1987, *"The Effects of Earthquakes on Power and Industrial Facilities and Implications for Nuclear Power Plant Design,"* Working Group on Past Behavior, Sub-Committee on Dynamic Analysis, Committee on Nuclear Structures and Materials, Structural Division, American Society of Civil Engineers, New York, 1987.

ASME Boiler and Pressure Vessel Code Section VIII, 1989 Division 2, Appendix III, *Rules for Bolted Flange Connections.*

ATC-14, *Evaluating the Seismic Resistance of Existing Buildings,* Prepared by Applied Technology Council, 1987.

Bachman, R.E., April 1992, *"Proposed Guidance for Preparation of RMPP Seismic Assessments"* in Proceedings of HAZMACON '92, Session on *"New Developments in Earthquake Caused Hazardous Materials Releases,"* Long Beach, CA.

Baughman, Paul D., Mani L. Aggarwal, Steven P. Harris, and Robert D. Campbell, *"Seismic Evaluation of Piping Using Experience Data,"* Second Symposium on Current Issues Related to Nuclear Power Plant Structures, Equipment, and Piping with Emphasis on Resolution of Seismic Issues in Low Seismicity Regions. EPRI NP-6437-D. Prepared by Electric Power Research Institute, Palo Alto, California.

Bechtel Power Corporation, Bechtel Topical Report BC-TOP-4, Revision 4, "Seismic Analyses of Structures and Equipment for Nuclear Power Plants", 1980.

Electric Power Research Institute (EPRI) Report NP-5617, *"Recommended Piping Seismic-Adequacy Criteria Based on Performance During and After Earthquakes,"* Volumes 1 and 2, Prepared by EQE Incorporated, January 1983.

Gurbuz, O., Lopez, A., Summers, P., April 1992, *"Implementation of the Proposed RMPP Seismic Assessment Guidance to Perform a Structural Seismic Evaluation of Existing Facilities"* in Proceedings of HAZMACON '92, Session on *"New Developments in Earthquake Caused Hazardous Materials Releases,"* Long Beach, CA.

Manual of Steel Construction, Ninth Edition, American Institute of Steel Construction, 1989.

NEHRP Handbook for the Seismic Evaluation of Existing Buildings, Developed by the Building Seismic Safety Council for the Federal Emergency Management Agency Based on a Preliminary Version Prepared by the Applied Technology Council, 1992.

Newmark, N.M. "Effects of Earthquakes on Dams and Embankments", Geothechnique, Vol. 15, No. 2, January 1965, pp 139-160.

Newmark, N.M. and Hall, W.J., "Earthquake Spectra and Design, EERI Monograph", 1982.

NFPA-13, Standard for the Installation of Sprinkler Systems, 1988 Edition, National Fire Protection Association.

Perkins, J.B., Wyatt, G.E., Schmidt, J.H., and Selvaduray, G., November 1990. Hazardous Materials Problems in Earthquakes: A Guide to Their Cause and Mitigation: Association of Bay Area Governments, Oakland, CA, 72 pages.

Perkins, J.B., Wyatt, G.E., Schmidt, J.H., and Selvaduray, G., November 1990. Hazardous Materials Problems in Earthquakes: Background Materials: Association of Bay Area Governments, Oakland, CA, 281 pages.

Perkins, J.B., Wyatt, G.E., November 1991. *Toxic Gas Releases in Earthquakes: Existing Programs, Sources and Mitigation Strategies:* Association of Bay Area Governments, Oakland, CA, 306 pages.

Perkins, J.B., Wyatt, G.E., and Selvaduray, G., April 1992. *"Mitigating Toxic Gas Releases in Earthquakes"* in Proceedings of HAZMACON '92, Session on *"New Developments in Earthquake Caused Hazardous Materials Releases,"* Long Beach, CA: Association of Bay Area Governments, Oakland, CA, pp 562-573.

RMPP Publication No. 101, RMPP *"Development Guidelines,"* Published by Los Angeles City Fire Department, Hazardous Materials Section, Risk Management & Prevention Programs Unit, September 1990.

Ravindra, M.K., *"Seismic Assessment of Chemical Facilities Under California Risk Management and Prevention Program,"* International Conference on Hazard Identification and Risk Analysis, Human Factors and Human Reliability in Process Safety, January 15-17, 1992, Orlando, Florida.

SEAOC - *Recommended Lateral Force Requirements and Commentary*, Seismology Committee Structural Engineers Association of California, 1990.

Stevenson, J.D. and Lapay, W.S., *"Amplification Factors to be Used in Simplified Seismic Dynamic Analysis of Piping Systems,"* ASME Paper No. 74-NE-9.

State of California Guidance for the Preparation of a Risk Management and Prevention Program, Prepared by California Office of Emergency Services Hazardous Material Division, November 1989.

Uniform Building Code, 1988 Edition, International Conference of Building Officials.

Uniform Building Code, 1991 Edition, International Conference of Building Officials.

1992 Supplement to the Uniform Building Code, International Conference of Building Officials.

TABLE 1: Ductility-Based Reduction Factors (Q) for Existing Structures and Systems

A. STRUCTURES SUPPORTING EQUIPMENT This covers structures whose primary purpose is to support equipment, such as air coolers, spheres, horizontal vessels, exchangers, heaters, vertical vessels and reactors, etc.	Q
1. Steel structures	
Ductile moment frame Use Q=6 if there is a significant departure from the intent of the 1988 (or later) *UBC* for special moment-resisting frames.	6 or 8
Ordinary moment frame The following structural characteristics are usually indicative of a Q=2 value (also see Note 6): a. There is a significant strength discontinuity in any of the vertical lateral force resisting elements, i.e., a weak story. b. There are partial penetration welded splices in the columns of the moment resisting frames. c. The structure exhibits "strong girder-weak column" behavior, i.e., under combined lateral and vertical loading, hinges occur in a significant number of columns before occurring in the beams. The following structural characteristics are usually indicative of a Q=4 value (also see Note 6): d. Any of the moment frame elements is not compact. e. Any of the beam-column connections in the lateral force resisting moment frames does not have both: (1) full penetration flange welds; and (2) a bolted or welded web connection. f. There are bolted splices in the columns of the moment resisting frames that do not connect both flanges and the web.	2, 4, or 5
Braced frame The following structural characteristics are usually indicative of a Q=2 value (also see Note 6): a. There is a significant strength discontinuity in any of the vertical lateral force resisting elements, i.e., a weak story b. The bracing system includes "K" braced bays. Note: "K" bracing is permitted for frames of two stories or less by using Q=2. For frames of more than two stories, "K" bracing must be justified on a case-by-case basis. c. Brace connections are not able to develop the capacity of the diagonals. d. Column splice details cannot develop the column capacity.	2, 4, or 5

** The notes following the table should be read in conjunction with the tabulated Q-factors.

TABLE 1: Ductility-Based Reduction Factors (Q) for Existing Structures and Systems (Continued)

A. STRUCTURES SUPPORTING EQUIPMENT (Continued)	Q
Braced frame (Cont.) The following structural characteristics are usually indicative of a Q=4 value (also see Note 6): e. Diagonal elements designed to carry compression have (kl/r) greater than 120. f. The bracing system includes chevron ("V" or inverted "V") bracing that was designed to carry gravity load.	
Cantilever column The following structural characteristics are usually indicative of a Q=1.5 value (also see Note 6): a. Column splice details cannot develop the column capacity. b. Axial load demand represents more than 20% of the axial load capacity.	1.5 or 2.5
2. Concrete structures **Ductile moment frame** Use Q=6 if there is a significant departure from the intent of the 1988 (or later) *UBC* for special moment-resisting frames.	6 or 8
Intermediate moment frame	4
Ordinary moment frame The following structural characteristics are usually indicative of a Q=1.5 value (also see Note 6): a. There is a significant strength discontinuity in any of the vertical lateral force resisting elements, i.e., a weak story. b. The structure exhibits "strong girder-weak column" behavior, i.e., under combined lateral and vertical loading, hinges occur in a significant number of columns before occurring in the beams. c. There is visible deterioration of concrete or reinforcing steel in any of the frame elements, and this damage may lead to a brittle failure mode. d. Shear failure occurs before flexural failure in a significant number of the columns. The following structural characteristics are usually indicative of a Q=2.5 value (also see Note 6): e. The lateral resisting frames include prestressed (pretensioned or post-tensioned elements)	1.5, 2.5 or 3.5

TABLE 1: Ductility-Based Reduction Factors (Q) for Existing Structures and Systems (Continued)

A. STRUCTURES SUPPORTING EQUIPMENT (Continued)	Q
Ordinary moment frame (Cont.) f. The beam stirrups and column ties are not anchored into the member cores with hooks of 135° or more. g. Columns have ties spaced at greater than d/4 throughout their length. Beam stirrups are spaced at greater than d/2. h. Any column bar lap splice is less than $35d_b$ long. Any column bar lap splice is not enclosed by ties spaced $8d_b$ or less. i. Development length for longitudinal bars is less than $24d_b$. j. Shear failure occurs before flexural failure in a significant number of the beams.	
Shear wall The following structural characteristics are usually indicative of a Q=1.5 value (also see Note 6): a. There is visible deterioration of concrete or reinforcing steel in any of the frame elements, and this damage may lead to a brittle failure more. b. There is a significant strength discontinuity in any of the vertical lateral force resisting elements, i.e., a weak story. c. Any wall is not continuous to the foundation. The following structural characteristics are usually indicative of a Q=3 value (also see Note 6): d. The reinforcing steel for concrete walls is not greater than 0.0025 times the gross area of the wall along both the longitudinal and transverse axes. The spacing of reinforcing steel along either axis exceeds 18 inches. e. For shear walls with H/D greater than 2.0, the boundary elements are not confined with either: (1) spirals; or (2) ties at spacing of less than $8d_b$. f. For coupled shear wall buildings, stirrups in any coupling beam are spaced at greater than $8d_b$ or are not anchored into the core with hooks of 135° or more.	1.5, 3 or 5

TABLE 1: Ductility-Based Reduction Factors (Q) for Existing Structures and Systems (Continued)

A. STRUCTURES SUPPORTING EQUIPMENT (Continued)	Q
Cantilever pier/column The following structural characteristics are indicative of a Q=1.5 value (also see Note 6). a. There is visible deterioration of concrete or reinforcing steel in any of the elements, and this damage may lead to a brittle failure mode. b. Axial load demand represents more than 20% of the load capacity. The following structural characteristics are usually indicative of a Q=2.5 value (also see Note 6). c. The ties are not anchored into the member cores with hooks of 135° or more. d. Columns have ties spaced at greater than d/4 throughout their length. Piers have ties spaced at greater than d/2 throughout their length. e. Any pier/column bar lap splice is less than $35d_b$ long. Any pier/column bar lap splice is not enclosed by ties spaced $8d_b$ or less. f. Development length for longitudinal bars is less than $24d_b$.	1.5, 2.5 or 3.5
B. EQUIPMENT BEHAVING AS STRUCTURES WITH INTEGRAL SUPPORTS	Q
1. Vertical vessels/heaters or spheres supported by: **Steel skirts** The following structural characteristics are usually indicative of a Q=2 value (also see Note 6): a. The diameter (D) divided by the thickness (t) of the skirt is greater than $0.441{*}E/F_y$, where E and F_y are the Young's modulus and yield stress of the skirt, respectively.	2 or 4
Steel braced legs without top girder or stiffener ring The following structural characteristics are usually indicative of a Q=1.5 value (also see Note 6): a. The bracing system includes "K" braced bays.	1.5, 3 or 4

TABLE 1: Ductility-Based Reduction Factors (Q) for Existing Structures and Systems (Continued)

B. EQUIPMENT BEHAVING AS STRUCTURES WITH INTEGRAL SUPPORTS (Continued)	Q
Steel braced legs without top girder or stiffener ring (Cont.) b. Brace connections are not able to develop the capacity of the diagonals. c. Column splice details cannot develop the column capacity. The following structural characteristics are usually indicative of a Q=3 value (also see Note 6): d. Diagonal elements designed to carry compression have (kl/r) greater than 120. e. The bracing system includes chevron ("V" or inverted "V") bracing that was designed to carry gravity load.	
Steel unbraced legs without top girder or stiffener ring The following structural characteristics are usually indicative of a Q=1.5 value (also see Note 6): a. Column splice details cannot develop the column capacity. b. Axial load demand represents more than 20% of the axial load capacity.	1.5 or 2.5
2. Chimneys or stacks	
Steel guyed	4
Steel cantilever	4
Concrete	4

C. PIPEWAYS	Q
Note: This includes pipeways supporting equipment that does not weight more than 25% of the other dead loads. For pipeways supporting equipment that weighs more than 25% of the other dead loads, see Section A, STRUCTURES SUPPORTING EQUIPMENT	
1. Steel	
Ductile moment frame	8
Ordinary moment frame	6
Braced frame	6
Cantilever column	5

TABLE 1: Ductility-Based Reduction Factors (Q)
for Existing Structures and Systems (Continued)

C. PIPEWAYS (continued)	Q
2. Concrete **Ductile moment frame** **Ordinary moment frame** **Cantilever column**	 8 5 4
D. FLAT-BOTTOMED TANKS (See Note 4)	Q
1. Anchored **2. Unanchored**	4 3
E. FOUNDATIONS (See Note 5)	Q
1. Piled **2. Spread footings**	6 6
F. ANCHOR BOLTS (See Note 6)	Q
1. Anchor bolt yield controls **2. Concrete failure or anchor bolt slippage controls, or there is a non-ductile force transfer mechanism between structure and foundation (also see Note 7)**	As for structure 1.5

NOTES:

1. The use of the highest Q-factors in each category requires that the elements of the primary load path of the lateral force resisting system have been proportioned to assure ductile rather than brittle system behavior. This can be demonstrated by showing that each connection in the primary load path has an ultimate strength of at least equal to 150% of the load capacity (governed by either yielding or stability) of the element to which the load is transferred. Alternatively, Q-factors should be reduced consistent with the limited ductility of the governing connection and/or the governing connection should be modified as required.

NOTES (Cont.):

2. A Q-factor different from the tabulated values (higher or lower) may be justified on a case-by-case basis.

3. If more than one of the conditions specified in the table applies, the lowest Q-factor associated with those conditions should be used.

4. Other approved national standards for the seismic assessment of tanks may be used in lieu of these guidelines.

5. These values of Q apply to overturning checks, soil bearing, and pile capacities.

6. If bolt yielding controls the evaluation of the anchor bolts (as opposed to concrete failure or anchor bolt slippage), and there is a ductile force transfer mechanism between the structure and foundation (such as the use of properly proportioned anchor bolt chairs between skirts or tank shells and the foundation), then the Q-factor to be used for both the evaluation of the anchor bolts and the rest of the structural system corresponds to that for the structural system itself.

   If concrete failure or anchor bolt slippage controls the evaluation of anchor bolts (as opposed to bolt yielding), or there is a non-ductile force transfer mechanism between the structure and foundation, then a Q-factor of 1.5 should be used for the evaluation of the anchor bolts and the rest of the structural system. Also see Note 7.

7. Alternatively, for structures that may contain localized/single features with limited ductility, such as limiting connections or splices, noncompact steel members, high (kl/r) members and nonductile anchor bolts, that do not occur at a significant number of locations, the load capacity of the specific limiting feature(s) may be evaluated and/or improved in lieu of using system-wide lower Q-factors that tend to generically penalize all elements of the structural system. The evaluation for these localized features may be performed using a Q-factor equal to 0.4 times the Q-factor normally recommended (i.e., unreduced) for the system. The evaluation for the remainder of the system may then be performed using the Q-factor normally recommended without consideration of the localized feature with limited ductility.

Chapter 5
PRIMARY STRUCTURAL DESIGN

5.1 INTRODUCTION

This chapter provides guidance for the seismic structural design of petrochemical facilities. Once the design forces are established using analysis techniques as discussed in Chapter 4, the design may proceed as outlined in this chapter. The methods described are applicable to structures and components, including supports and anchorages of electrical and mechanical systems. Seismic design of electrical and mechanical components (e.g. transformers, pumps, compressors, vessels, etc.) is outside the scope of these guidelines. Both new design, retrofit and modification of existing facilities are addressed.

The guidelines provided herein are based mainly on current practice. For this purpose, criteria and specifications from several petrochemical companies and architectural and engineering firms were collected and reviewed. The criteria and practices most commonly used were generally preferred and were therefore adopted. Criteria related to special cases may not be universally applicable and therefore were not included. As a result, this chapter includes design recommendations for which a general consensus exists.

Where specific building code requirements are referenced, this chapter primarily uses the 1994 *UBC*, as that is the most commonly used code for seismic design in petrochemical facilities (see discussion in Chapter 4). Some material is based on *ASCE 7*, when the material is not addressed in the *UBC*. Use of these guidelines with other codes and standards (e.g., *SBC* and *BOCA*, which are based on the *NEHRP* (1994) provisions) is expected to result in comparable designs.

5.2 DESIGN CRITERIA

5.2.1 Introduction

Section 5.2 addresses the loading combinations to be used in design and the acceptance criteria to be met. The loading combinations are derived mainly from the

UBC and *ASCE 7* and are delineated to provide specific guidance for common structures and components at petrochemical facilities. The loading combinations currently in use by the major petroleum firms have also been considered. The acceptance criteria are defined by reference to accepted industry codes and standards.

5.2.2 Loads and Load Combinations

5.2.2.1 Loads

At petrochemical facilities, more types of loads affect the design of members than those generally included in codes. Thus the engineer should carefully review all applicable loads and design the structures and components for their effects, including:

D = Dead Load is the total weight of materials forming the permanent part of a structure, including structural framing, platforms, walls, fixed equipment, vessels, piping, insulation and fireproofing.

DV = Vessel Operating Load includes the weight of any liquids or solids within the vessel, attached equipment, and piping during normal operation.

DP = Piping Operating Load includes weight of any liquids or solids within piping and on line equipment during normal operation.

L = Live Load is the weight of all movable loads such as personnel, tools, stored material, movable partitions, cranes and hoists, maintenance loads, snow and ice loads, impact, surge forces, vibration, and longitudinal and transverse horizontal forces from moving equipment. The design live loads should be the maximum loads likely to result from the intended use and should not be less than those given in applicable building codes.

E = Earthquake Loads include the inertia effects due to a design earthquake. For determination of earthquake loads, refer to Chapter 4.

W = Wind Loads are those stipulated in applicable codes.

S = Snow Loads are those stipulated in applicable codes. Roof live load should be replaced by the snow load when the snow load is greater.

TL = Longitudinal Pipe Thermal Loads, include pipe anchor forces, if any. In lieu of detailed calculations, the thermal sliding force can be approximated as, 10% of the vertical operating pipe load plus pipe weight being supported. When there are three or fewer pipes use 30% of the vertical operating pipe load plus pipe weight of the heaviest pipe.

T = Thermal Loads are the loads caused by a change in temperature and may result from both operating and environmental conditions. Such forces should include those caused by vessel, piping, and structure expansion and contraction.

TE = Test Loads, include the weight of equipment and of test fluid related to the test condition.

H = Soil Loads include the effects due to weight and lateral pressure of soil and water in soil.

5.2.2.2 Combinations of Loads - General

Structures and foundations should be designed for the most critical effects resulting from the combination of all applicable loads which may reasonably occur simultaneously.

The load combinations for allowable stress and strength design methods are given below. It should be noted that codes differ in the treatment of load combinations. These differences often exist between allowable stress design and strength design. The local building jurisdiction for a particular project is the final authority. The combinations shown in subsections 5.2.2.3 and 5.2.2.4 should be considered as representative of common practice and are recommended for use in the industry.

In the application of the load combinations, the following caveats should be adhered to:

a. Loads other than those specifically identified in the loading combinations, such as lateral soil pressures (H), settlement effects, vibration loads, impact effects, relative anchor movements, bundle loads, occasional extreme operating loads, fluid pressures, rain loads, test loads, blast effects, and vehicle loads that could occur simultaneously, should also be considered, as appropriate.

   Any of the above concurrent loads present in allowable stress design should be included in the loading combination with a factor of unity.

   Any of the above concurrent loads present in factored load design should be added to the loading combination with a factor greater than unity. The load factor should be determined considering the accuracy of estimate and probability of occurrence and should range between 1.2 (low probability of occurrence of full value) to 1.6 (high probability of occurrence with high uncertainty of magnitude).

b. When the effects of design loads counteract one another, special care should be exercised to ensure adequate safety against maximum load effects, e.g., temperature effects should not be permitted to reduce the strength requirements.

When the effect of the dead load is to reduce the design requirements, a load factor of 0.9 is used for the dead load. This factor is somewhat greater than the *UBC* value of 0.85. This is justified since the dead loads at petrochemical facilities are more precisely defined (i.e., absence of nonstructural elements common in buildings). However, in the case of vessels, the engineer is cautioned to consider the situations when part of the dead load is removed, e.g., dead load inside a vessel. For example, in the loading combinations that include wind or seismic loads, a reduction in full design live load is in order since it is unlikely that full live load will exist at the time of maximum design wind load or design earthquake. A value of 0.5 for allowable stress design and 1.7 x 0.5 for strength design is recommended in this document.

5.2.2.3 Loading Combinations and Load Factors - Allowable Stress Design

In the allowable stress design method, the combined loading effects, with load factors of unity, are compared with the allowable values (stress, strain, or displacements) in the applicable code. For some combinations of loads, the allowable values may be increased by the allowable stress multiplier as shown.

The following combinations of loads are recommended for use in conjunction with the allowable stress method of design.

General

Load Combination	Allowable Stress Multiplier
1. D	1.00
2. D + L	1.00
3. D + L + T	1.33
4. D + 0.5L + (**E** or W) + T	1.33
5. 0.9D - (**E** or W)	1.33

Vessel Support Design

Load Combination	Allowable Stress Multiplier
1. D + DV	1.00
2. D + DV + (**E** or W) + T	1.33
3. D + TE + 0.25W	1.33
4. 0.9D - (**E** or W)	1.33

Pipeway and Pipe and Equipment Support Design

Load Combination	Allowable Stress Multiplier
1. D + DP + TL	1.00
2. D + DP + (**E** or W) + T	1.33
3. 0.9(D) - (**E** or W)	1.33

5.2.2.4 Loading Combinations and Load Factors - Strength Design

In the equations below, U designates the required design strength.

General

1. U = 1.4D
2. U = 1.4D + 1.7L
3. U = 1.4D + 1.7L + 1.4T
4. U = 0.75(1.4D + 0.85L + (1.9**E** or 1.7W) + 1.4T)
5. U = 0.9D - (1.4**E** or 1.3W)

Vessel Support Design

1. U = 1.4(D + DV)
2. U = 0.75(1.4D + 1.4DV + (1.9**E** or 1.7W) + 1.4T)
3. U = 0.75(1.4D + 1.4TE + 0.4W)
4. U = 0.9D - (1.4**E** or 1.3W)

Pipeway and Pipe and Equipment Support Design

1. 1.4(D + DP + TL)
2. 0.75(1.4D + 1.4DP + (1.9**E** or 1.7W) + 1.4T)
3. 0.9D - (1.4**E** or 1.3W)

5.2.3 Acceptance Criteria

5.2.3.1 General Requirements

Design of petrochemical facilities should comply with the project criteria which should be developed based on the owner's specifications, design criteria and applicable standards, some of which are listed in Sections 5.2.3.2 through 5.2.3.5 below.

All projects should conform to the safety requirements of OSHA. Local building officials should be consulted to determine codes applicable to the project. The edition date, and any addenda and/or supplements should be determined. When more than one code may be applicable, the more stringent provisions should be used.

5.2.3.2 Steel Acceptance Criteria

The design, fabrication and erection of steel structures should be in accordance with the requirements of the following applicable references: AISC (1989), AISC (1993), AISI (1986), *ASCE 8*, SJI (1990) or AISI (1973).

Design and construction of steel framing systems in *UBC* Seismic Zones 1 through 4 should also conform to the requirements of applicable sections of the *UBC*. In case of conflict, the more stringent requirement should apply.

5.2.3.3 Concrete Acceptance Criteria

Design and construction of reinforced concrete structures should conform to the requirements of *ACI 318*.

In *UBC* Seismic Zones 2 through 4, design and construction of reinforced concrete structures should conform to the requirements of applicable sections of the *UBC*. In case of conflict, the more stringent requirement should apply.

5.2.3.4 Masonry

The design, construction, and quality assurance of masonry components that resist seismic forces should conform to the requirements of *ACI 530* and *ACI 530.1* except as modified by the provisions of the *UBC*.

5.2.3.5 Wood

The design, construction, and quality assurance of members and their fastenings in wood systems that resist seismic forces should conform to the requirements of the *UBC*.

5.3 DESIGN CONSIDERATIONS

5.3.1 Introduction

This section describes typical structures and components found in petrochemical facilities and provides special design recommendations for them.

5.3.2 Buildings

The buildings typically found in petrochemical facilities are administration buildings, control buildings, substations, warehouses, fire houses, maintenance buildings, and compressor shelters or buildings. They are most often single story buildings, but can be multi-story. Typical construction materials are masonry, concrete and structural steel. Lateral load resisting systems used are shear walls, braced frames, rigid frames or combinations. Unlike nonbuilding structures, these buildings can be designed with direct application of the *UBC* or other model building codes. For the purpose of differentiating these building types from nonbuilding structures, it is noted that they are building shells which generally do not support operating petrochemical equipment and piping systems. In some petrochemical facilities, control buildings or substations are designed additionally to resist blast effects from a postulated explosion within the facility.

5.3.3 Nonbuilding Structures

5.3.3.1 General

As noted in Chapter 4, nonbuilding structures represent the bulk of items in a petrochemical plant. They can be classified as nonbuilding structures with structural systems similar to buildings, or other nonbuilding structures.

5.3.3.2 Drift and P-Delta Effects

It is important to note that for nonbuilding structures it is not necessary to meet drift criteria specified for other structures in the *UBC*. However, P-Delta effects should be considered when drift limits, which would otherwise apply, are exceeded. An acceptable P-Delta analysis procedure is presented in the Commentary to Sect. 1E.9 of SEAOC (1990). For this analysis, drift determined using code design forces should be multiplied by $3(R_W/8)$. Code design forces have been reduced by $1/R_W$. Multiplying the resulting deflections by $3(R_W/8)$ gives a better approximation of real seismic deflections. This requirement is not clearly stated in SEAOC (1990). The SEAOC (1990) Commentary equation (C1-1), should be modified to multiply $P \times \Delta$ by $3(R_W/8)$. Section 5.5 herein should be referred to for other precautions relative to structure drift. Note that SEAOC (1990) also uses the quantity $3(R_W/8)$ as a force amplification factor for the design of critical elements.

The SEAOC (1990) Commentary contains several cautions relative to use of the $3(R_W/8)$ factor to estimate inelastic deflections. The factor is a direct carryover of the 3.0/K factor from previous editions and is therefore based more on tradition than on hard facts. The Commentary states that the force amplification of $3(R_W/8)$ is generally on the high side while the deformation factor of $3(R_W/8)$ is on the low side, and could be as high as R_W. When R_W is less than 6, the $3(R_W/8)$ factor may become smaller than the Engineer wants to use in design. The value should never be less than

1. Where there is reason for concern, the value should probably not be less than 2. An example of such a situation would be when inelastic deformation would cause damage to a component containing hazardous or flammable material. The Commentary also states that P-Delta effects are potentially much more significant in lower seismic zones than in higher seismic zones, because the relative stiffness of lateral load resisting systems in higher seismic zones is required to be greater than those in lower seismic zones.

5.3.3.3 Building-Like Structures

Pipeways and equipment support structures are the two main categories of building-like structures found in petrochemical facilities. Materials are concrete or structural steel. Lateral load resisting systems used are braced frames and moment-resisting frames.

Pipeways and equipment support structures, are building-like because of the lateral load resisting systems commonly used. However, they differ from buildings in that they are most often open structures. They lack the non-structural components found in buildings, such as wall panels, which increase damping and energy absorption during a seismic event. Also, they generally have less redundancy than buildings. They include complex piping systems which may or may not participate in seismic shaking. It is commonly thought that dead load participation of piping systems in structure inertia forces is overestimated in most designs.

Pipeways

Main pipeways are usually frames 20 to 25 feet (6 to 8 m) wide, spaced at 20 to 25 feet (6 to 8 m) longitudinally. They generally are longitudinally strutted and braced at every third to fifth bay. They often carry one to three levels of process and utility piping, conduit and cable trays. Many times air coolers are placed at the top of main pipeways. Structural steel is most often used for these structures due to the ease of erection. When pipeways need to be fire resistant, structural steel is encased in concrete or the pipeway is constructed of concrete. Concrete pipeways can be precast, if a sufficient quantity is required to justify establishing a jobsite casting yard. There should also be adequate mobile crane capacity for erection.

Secondary pipeways in process units, or offsite pipeways are usually single level unstrutted frames. These frames are 10 to 15 feet (3 to 5 m) wide, spaced at 15 to 20 feet (5 to 6 m) longitudinally. The material is almost always steel and often not fireproofed.

R_W values for both main and secondary pipeways are included in Chapter 4.

Chevron bracing or cross bracing systems should be used in braced bays and designed in accordance with the *UBC*, but K-bracing should not be used. The

SEAOC (1990) Commentary to Sect. 4G.3.b. states, "The K-bracing configuration is undesirable for seismic resistance. Deformations of the bracing system due to tensile yield and/or buckling may cause lateral deformations of the connected column sufficient to cause column buckling and subsequent collapse."

Knee-bracing can be used as an alternate method of creating a beam-to-column moment connection. However, the column or beam length used for calculating Kl/r ratios should ignore the presence of the knee brace unless the combined buckling behavior of the column and knee brace is evaluated. The presence of the knee brace should not be used to reduce the beam or column design moment.

Equipment Support Structures

Equipment support structures are usually open frame structures supporting elevated vessels (horizontal and vertical), heat exchangers, other miscellaneous mechanical and electrical equipment, and piping. For operation and maintenance reasons, these structures also include significant platform areas, stairways and ladders. Equipment is elevated either for process reasons, lack of plot space or a combination of both. Materials used are usually fireproofed structural steel.

Steel structures usually utilize moment-resisting frames in one direction and braced frames in the other direction. The cost effectiveness of braced frames suggests that whenever possible, braced frames in both directions should be used. However, access requirements quite often lead to the use of moment-resisting frames. R_W values for moment-resisting frames and braced frames, and the issues related to bracing systems, are discussed in Chapter 4. Rigid equipment is generally treated as lumped masses for analysis purposes.

Equipment anchorage loads should be carried to the main lateral load system by horizontal bracing. Checker plate platforming can be treated as a diaphragm to also carry equipment loads to the main lateral load system. Often, certain checker plate areas are detailed to allow removal of the plate during maintenance operations. In such cases the diaphragm may not be present during a seismic event occurring in an extended maintenance operation and horizontal bracing should be provided.

Another category of equipment structure supports rotating equipment such as compressors or generators, or equipment with intermittent significant vibrations such as coke structures. Materials used are usually concrete, to provide sufficient mass and stiffness to limit vibrations to a permissible level.

Concrete structures which support large rotating equipment or other equipment which generate sustained impactive loads are usually quite massive. Three feet square columns and three to four feet thick concrete decks are common. These structures can be designed with little concern for ductility, and therefore with low R_W

values. Such a structure can be designed on the basis of $R_W = 1$, in which case ductile detailing specified in the *UBC* can be relaxed.

5.3.3.4 Nonbuilding-Like Structures

There are a number of nonbuilding-like structures in common use which have special characteristics. The following guidelines address some of the issues to be taken under consideration when designing these structures. Other structures are essentially defined in *UBC* Table 16-P.

a. Tanks can be supported at grade, on pedestals or on braced or unbraced legs. Chapter 7 addresses the design and evaluation of tanks at grade. This section addresses tanks on pedestals or on braced or unbraced legs.

   All tanks should be anchored to the foundation or main structure. Tank legs and the tank-to-leg connection should be checked for stress and buckling effects.

b. Vessels, both horizontal and vertical, are designed to satisfy ASME code requirements (ASME, 1992). The design of the pressure portion of the vessel is generally not governed by seismic effects. The attachments to foundations and structures, are the elements directly affected by seismic loads. These elements are usually skirts or legs for vertical vessels and saddles for horizontal vessels. For seismic load resistance, attention should be given to welding and bolting, and bracing or plate buckling effects. Most often vessels are designed by mechanical engineers. Occasionally structural engineers are asked to give guidance in calculating appropriate seismic loads.

c. Bins and silos are structures used for storing solids, e.g. powder and granular materials. Silos are by definition tall bins. In bins and silos the lateral forces are mitigated by friction in the material stored in the bin. Research has shown that equivalent viscous damping may be as much as 20 percent. Also, the center of gravity can be considered at the center of mass rather than at the centroid of the more familiar triangular distribution. Good guidance exists for bin and silo design in *ACI 313*.

d. Storage racks are typically mass produced elements which are assembled on site. The geometry and strength requirements are quite varied, and standard components are mixed appropriately to provide the required performance. Many racks are made of relatively slender or cold formed elements, which require special evaluation procedures. Good guidance exists for storage rack design from the Rack Manufacturers Institute (RMI, 1990).

e. Skid-mounted equipment systems are usually very rugged, since layout and design criteria should take into consideration forces imposed by crane lifting, and truck, rail or ship transportation. The skid is usually a base frame constructed of structural steel shapes and the equipment includes pumps, compressors, small vessels and exchangers, and piping. The skid should be anchored to the foundation to resist horizontal seismic forces.

5.3.4 Elements of Structures, Nonstructural Components and Equipment

5.3.4.1 General ✓

UBC Section 1630 and Chapter 4 herein specify the lateral force to be used for design of parts and portions of structures and their attachments, permanent nonstructural components and their attachments, and the attachments for permanent equipment supported by a structure. In general, these items are most often found in buildings and not in the typical refinery structure. The SEAOC (1990) Commentary to Section 1G provides definitions to better distinguish the various categories of items which are covered by this section. A review of these definitions will show that "attachments for permanent equipment supported by a structure," are the items most often found in petrochemical plants. It should be noted that *UBC* Section 1630 applies only (in the words of the commentary), "to elements, components, and equipment attached to buildings whose dynamic behavior does not substantially alter the building's response." This implies that the elements, components and equipment are relatively small in relation to the supporting structure. Where this is not true, design is governed by *UBC* Section 1632 (Nonbuilding Structures). Also, some large grade-mounted equipment such as boilers and turbines may be constructed within a structure. In such cases the equipment should be considered as a nonbuilding structure.

Another approach is given in the *NEHRP* (1994) provisions which provide a more comprehensive treatment of this subject than the *UBC*. A number of additional factors which affect the response of equipment are addressed in *NEHRP* (1994). *NEHRP* (1994) also has a simplified approach similar to the *UBC*. Additional guidance is also given in Section 5.5 herein, which discusses physical interaction.

"Parts and portions of structures" and "permanent nonstructural components" in the *UBC* are building elements rarely found in refineries. Parts and portions of structures refer to miscellaneous assemblies or portions of structures having a structural function related to the structure and include exterior walls, interior bearing walls, penthouses (except where framed by an extension of the main building frame), and prefabricated structural elements other than walls and diaphragms. Permanent nonstructural components are permanent assemblies not having a structural function and include parapets, nonbearing walls and partitions, masonry and concrete fences over 6 feet high, exterior and interior ornamentation and appendages, signs and billboards, cabinets, book shelves, and storage racks, including contents, over 5 feet high, access floor systems, suspended ceilings and light fixtures.

5.3.4.2 Typical Supported Equipment

The common permanent equipment supported by structures in petrochemical plants include the following groups of items.

Cantilever Structures

Cantilever structures include chimneys, stacks and towers. Design concerns for these items in petrochemical plants, are generally no different than supported items in buildings. For these cantilever structures, it is especially important to recognize that in many cases, the support level is a flexible structural floor system. If horizontal deflections near the top of the cantilever item is a concern, it may be necessary to increase the rigidity of the support level to achieve the desired performance. Once the loads have been determined and support flexibility issues have been addressed, design procedures for a chimney, stack, tower or any other similar cantilever structure are the same as if they were supported at grade.

Vessels and Tanks

Vessels and tanks include boilers, heat exchangers, fired and unfired pressure vessels, and miscellaneous tanks. Design concerns for these items in petrochemical plants, are generally no different than supported items in buildings. Since these items should be relatively small to be included in this section, support flexibility is relatively unimportant, unless the item is quite long. If the item is long, relative vertical support movement may need to be addressed. Design aspects of vessels and tanks are discussed in Section 5.3.3.4.

Mechanical Equipment

Mechanical equipment include turbines, chillers, pumps, motors, and air-handling units. Design concerns for these items in petrochemical plants, are generally no different than supported items in buildings. These items are usually very rigid compared to the support level. Since these items generally have a low profile, seismic loads rarely, if ever, cause tension forces in the anchorage. However, it has been observed that the connecting structure between the component and the supporting structure is sometimes designed without due consideration for seismic loads. The engineer should review the adequacy of any connecting structures provided by component vendors to assure that adequate lateral load capacity exists. Anchorage acceptability is evaluated by comparing seismic forces to bolt shear and tension capacity, without frictional resistance from dead load of the item.

Vibration isolators are often utilized with rotating equipment to minimize vibration in the equipment and its supporting structure. The isolators, while solving a difficult vibration problem, may create problems during an earthquake unless care is exercised to restrict horizontal and vertical movement at the isolators. This is often accomplished with snubbers, guides or stops.

In some cases, mechanical equipment needs to be reviewed. Although specific guidance is not provided herein, seismic design of mechanical equipment should be performed by qualified structural/mechanical engineers. The design should take into consideration inelastic behavior as well as potential interaction with the supporting structure. These and other factors are considered in *NEHRP* (1994), Chapter 3.

For additional guidance, refer to the SEAOC (1990) Commentary to Section 1G.1.

Electrical Equipment and Control Systems

Electrical equipment and control systems include transformers, switch-gear, control panels, standby power equipment, and computer equipment. Design concerns for these items in petrochemical plants, are generally no different than supported items in buildings. These items are similar to cantilever structures, mechanical equipment, or something in between. Depending on the size and shape of the item, follow the appropriate guidance in the paragraphs above on cantilever structures and mechanical equipment.

Distributive Systems

Distributive systems include piping, ducts, conduits, cable trays and conveyors. Design concerns for these items in petrochemical plants, are generally no different than supported items in buildings, except that the pipe sizes in piping systems are usually larger in petrochemical plants. The major design concern for the item itself is the effect of relative movement between points of anchorage.

Leakage at equipment and piping flanges is often due to underdesign of the flange, i.e., designing the flange for only operating pressure-temperature conditions. By increasing the flange class, the seismic moments may be accommodated without leakage.

NEHRP (1994) has developed specific guidelines for the seismic design of distributive systems, such as those noted above. These guidelines include references to codes and standards, specific to given types of systems. It is recommended that these guidelines be used for the design of distributive systems in petrochemical facilities.

5.3.5 Foundations

5.3.5.1 General

Except for certain types of equipment (horizontal vessels, heat exchangers and vertical vessels), foundations in petrochemical facilities are similar to foundations in most other industries. Therefore, the design of foundations should satisfy the requirements of appropriate building code provisions.

Foundations should be designed for seismic loads calculated for the overall structural system. The loads generated by individual elements, e.g. braces designed for 150% of brace load, should be considered for anchor bolt design but should not be used for foundation design.

5.3.5.2 Anchor Bolts

Two design approaches for anchor bolts should be used for petrochemical facilities. Using *UBC* terminology, the first approach, Service Load Design, follows the requirements of the *UBC*. This should apply to grade mounted equipment such as heat exchangers and horizontal vessels, vertical vessels, pots and drums with a height to diameter ratio less than 3, pumps, compressors, generators, transformers, and other skid-mounted equipment. Here the requirement is to prevent the supported items from sliding during a seismic event. The second approach, Strength Design, should follow the requirements of *ACI 349*, App. B, with the exception that the concrete pull-out capacity should develop the bolt's yield strength (not its ultimate tensile strength) multiplied by 1.25. This should apply to vertical vessels with a height to diameter ratio greater than 3, and building-like structures, where ductility is figured into the R_W values.

5.3.5.3 Overturning

The *UBC* does not require a check for foundation overturning. If resistance to overturning is checked, a factor of safety of 1.0 should be used, considering only 0.9 times the dead load for resistance. The 0.9 factor for vertical loads accounts for uncertainty of the dead load and upward vertical acceleration.

ACI 318 requires that the reinforced concrete of footings be proportioned to resist factored loads. This requires applying load factors to the loads and calculating a fictitious soil pressure. The reinforced concrete is then proportioned to resist this fictitious soil pressure. When the factor of safety against overturning approaches 1.0, it may not be possible to calculate a fictitious soil pressure because the eccentricity is outside the footing. In this case, it is recommended that a point load at the edge of the footing be calculated to replace the fictitious soil pressure, by dividing the factored overturning moment by one-half the footing width in the direction of the moment (see Figure 5.1).

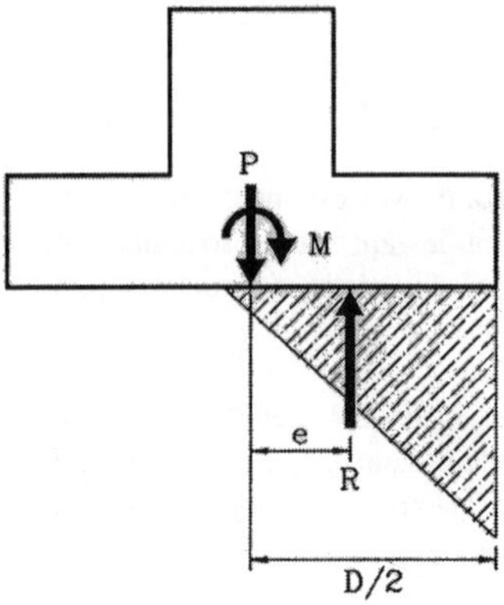

When S.R. $\cong$ 1.0
Then $M/P = e \cong D/2$

For Service Loads

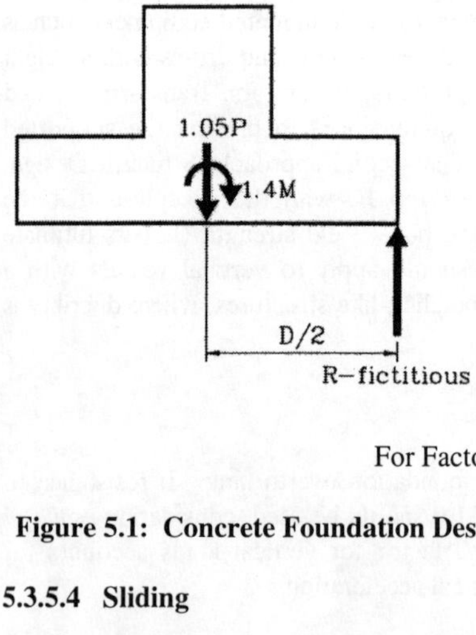

$$\frac{1.4M}{1.05P} > \frac{D}{2}$$

$$\text{R-fictitious} = \frac{1.4M}{D/2}$$

For Factored Loads.

Figure 5.1: Concrete Foundation Design When Stability Ratio Approaches 1.0

5.3.5.4 Sliding

The *UBC* does not require a check for foundation sliding. If resistance to sliding is checked, a factor of safety of 1.0 should be used, considering only 0.9 times the dead load for resistance. Lateral loads on spread footings and mats are resisted by friction between the footing and soil, and passive pressure on the footing.

5.3.5.5 Pile Foundations

Lateral loads on pile foundations are resisted by passive pressure on the piles and pile cap.

The lateral load capacity of a pile or pile group is essentially based on permissible horizontal deflections. Geotechnical consultants will often set lateral load capacity based on a pile deflection at ground level varying between 1/4 to 1 inch. The structural engineer should determine from the geotechnical consultant, whether lateral pile load capacity is based on deflection or soil strength. If deflection is the governing criterion, the engineer should then evaluate whether a larger horizontal deflection is acceptable for the particular facility being designed, to avoid unnecessary conservatism.

Most petrochemical facilities operating units are paved with 4 to 6 inches (10 to 15 cm) of concrete, reinforced with welded wire fabric to minimize shrinkage cracking. Consideration should be given to taking credit for the presence of the concrete paving in resisting lateral seismic loads to reduce the number of piles required for individual foundations. While this may increase the paving thickness to create the necessary mass, this may be a cost effective solution. Care should be exercised when combining lateral pile resistance, passive pressure on the pile cap and frictional resistance of paving. It may not be appropriate to take the maximum value of each mode of resistance when used as a combination. This subject should be discussed with a geotechnical consultant. Asphalt paving should not be considered as performing in the same manner as concrete paving. Asphalt paving is unreinforced and has low shear strength, and therefore is unable to contribute to resistance.

The *UBC* requires that pile caps of every structure subjected to seismic forces be interconnected by ties (e.g. grade beams), which are capable of resisting a minimum horizontal force equal to 10 percent of the larger column vertical load. Other approved methods may be used where it can be demonstrated that equivalent restraint can be provided. In petrochemical plants, it is desirable to minimize the use of grade beams to avoid interferences with underground piping systems and underground electrical duct systems. Adequate lateral restraint can, in many cases, be provided by passive soil resistance against the sides of the piles and pile caps. Adequate lateral resistance is also provided when the structure being supported can acceptably tolerate the lateral deflections and rotations at the structure/pile cap interface. The determination of acceptability can be investigated for critical structures by including the lateral and rotational stiffness of the pile and pile cap in the structural analysis model.

5.3.5.6 Pier and Tee Support Foundations

Pier and tee support foundations are typically used to support grade-mounted horizontal vessels and heat exchangers. These foundations are treated as "inverted pendulums". The vessel or exchanger is anchored at one pier and allowed to slide at the opposite pier to relieve thermal expansion forces. The anchor pier is designed to resist all longitudinal seismic forces. For simplicity, both the anchor pier and sliding pier are designed the same. When this approach creates excessively large pier foundations, two alternatives should be considered. For vessels with low design temperatures, less than about 150°F (65°C), the vessel can be anchored at both ends. Here each pier would be designed for one-half the vessel expansion and one-half the seismic load. When thermal expansion cannot be accommodated without allowing the vessel to slide, the piers can be tied together with structural steel struts, so that again, each pier foundation resists one-half the seismic load.

Longitudinal seismic loads on some analytical models have been studied (Richter, unpublished) which indicate that a significant amount of energy is absorbed at the sliding end pier, depending on the friction coefficient. This effectively reduces the load applied to the fixed end pier. In the study, a series of calculations were performed to investigate the seismic force distribution to pier foundations including nonlinear time history analyses on a two-dimensional model of a typical pier foundation. Table 5.1 gives tentative recommendations for load distribution to the fixed and sliding ends, as a fraction of the total horizontal seismic load. Additional savings may be achieved by designing each pier separately, for the horizontal load distribution shown in the table.

TABLE 5.1: Recommendations for Load Distribution

Friction Coefficient At Sliding End	V_{FIX}/V_{TOT}	V_{SLIDE}/V_{TOT}
0.0 - 0.2	1.0	0.6
> 0.2	0.7	0.6

Transverse seismic loads are usually carried by both saddles and the loads are transmitted in shear to the anchor bolts. When it is not possible to determine the exact mass distribution at each saddle, some engineers apply 60% of the transverse seismic load to each saddle.

5.3.5.7 Vertical Vessel Foundations

Historically, the foundation anchor bolts for tall vertical vessels and stacks have tended to stretch beyond yield when subjected to strong ground motion. Yielding of anchor bolts probably prevented collapse of these vessels. Based on this experience, some engineers design to develop the full uncorroded tensile capacity of the anchor bolts. However, this is a conservative design practice (See Section 5.3.5.2). Special care should be taken to not oversize the anchor bolts. Excessively oversized anchor bolts could remain elastic during a seismic event, creating overturning moments in the foundation beyond that used in the design.

When the anchor bolts extend only into the pedestal, the pedestal dowels should transfer the overturning moment into the footing. The dowels should be able to develop an overturning moment equivalent to the overturning moment based on anchor bolt strength (i.e. 1.25 time bolt yield strength; see Section 5.3.5.2). If the anchor bolts extend into the footing, which is often the case for very tall vessels, pedestal dowels do not transfer overturning moment to the footing. In this case, it is only necessary to provide a nominal number of dowels to minimize concrete cracking.

There are at least three known calculation methods used by engineers to deal with the transfer of horizontal seismic forces from the vessel to the concrete pedestal.

a. The *UBC* prohibits the use of friction due to dead load to resist horizontal seismic forces. The code does permit the use of friction caused by the downward force from the seismic overturning moment. Some engineers approximate the downward force (see Figure 5.2) as the overturning moment divided by two-thirds the bolt circle diameter. If the downward force times a friction coefficient of 0.55 exceeds the horizontal seismic force, it is assumed that there is no horizontal force on the bolts. If the horizontal seismic force exceeds the friction force, the total friction force is applied to the bolts. To minimize the need for excessive bolt edge distance or shear reinforcement, the bolts on a 90-degree arc in the direction of the horizontal force are ignored. The horizontal force is then carried only by the bolts on the remaining 270-degree arc (i.e. three-fourths the total number of bolts).

b. The shear-friction concept of *ACI 318* is used by some engineers. The total size and number of bolts required to resist overturning is first determined and then the number of bolts not in tension (i.e. number of bolts that can function as normal reinforcement in a shear-friction design) is determined (N_c). In this method, the bolt area represented by N_c (i.e. N_c x A_b) must be greater than A_{vf} in the *ACI 318* shear-friction equations. In the shear-friction equation, ϕ=0.85 and μ=0.6 (for concrete cast against steel, or in this case, steel placed on concrete) is used.

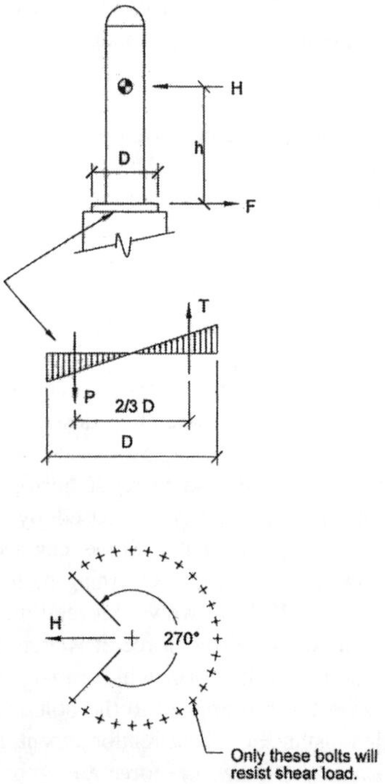

M = Overturning Moment
$= H \times h$

$$\frac{M}{2/3D} = P = T$$

$F = P \times \mu \qquad \mu = 0.55$

If $F = 0.55P > H$	Bolts do not carry shear
If $F = 0.55P < H$	Bolts carry all shear

Figure 5.2: A Method to Determine Transfer of Horizontal Seismic Force for Vertical Vessel Foundations

c. The third method is based on the same principles as the first method cited. The compressive force due to overturning moment is assumed to produce sufficient frictional resistance, such that the bolts do not need to be designed to resist the seismic shear if the vessel's height is more than three times the diameter of its bolt circle (i.e. when H/BC>3.0). If H/BC<3.0, the bolts are designed to resist the entire seismic shear. For the special case when H/BC<3.0, in Seismic Zones Nos. 1 and 2, friction is calculated as the downward force from the overturning moment plus 65 percent of the dead load times a 0.3 coefficient of friction. If this friction force is greater than the seismic shear, the bolts do not need to be designed to resist horizontal loads. If the friction force is less than the seismic shear, the bolts are designed to resist the entire seismic shear. Finally, for a vessel with H/BC less than 3.0 in Seismic Zones Nos. 3 and 4, supported on legs rather than a continuous base ring, anchor bolts are designed to resist the entire seismic shear.

5.3.5.8 Earth Retaining Structures

The most commonly used procedure for the design of gravity retaining walls is that proposed by Mononobe and Okabe, referenced in Seed and Whitman (1970). Mononobe and Matsuo (1929) and Okabe (1926) modified Coulomb's classical solution to account for inertia forces corresponding to horizontal and vertical accelerations, acting at all points of an assumed failure wedge. They expressed backfill thrust against a wall as function of the unit weight of the backfill, the height of the wall, and active stress coefficient. The stress coefficient is a function of the friction angle of the backfill, the friction angle between the backfill and the wall, and of the acceleration coefficients. Seed and Whitman (1970) provide a simplified version of the original equation, which is commonly used. A detailed description of the Mononobe-Okabe method can also be found in Dowrick (1987).

The Mononobe-Okabe equation is based on a number of assumptions. The backfill must be deformable enough to mobilize full shear resistance along the failure plane in the active sense, and that the accelerations must be constant throughout the failing wedge. Concerning the use of the Coulomb equation for static passive thrust apply to the dynamic case as well. This equation may overestimate the passive resistance in case wall friction is present.

Most earth pressure theories assume a constant horizontal acceleration over the height of the wall, with the movement of the wall controlled in some manner. In reality, neither condition may be satisfied. Depending upon the frequency of excitation and height of the wall, accelerations may increase significantly upward through the backfill. Furthermore, the non-linear behavior of the backfill has a significant influence. Unfortunately, there are few well-documented case studies from the field, with actual measurements of dynamic earth pressures. Several studies such as Lai (1979), Zarrabi (1973), Nadim (1980), Nadim and Whitman (1983 and 1984), and Anderson et al (1987) show the influence of various effects on dynamic lateral pressures, especially the role of residual pressure remaining after shaking. These studies have been summarized in Whitman (1990).

Many concepts developed for gravity retaining walls may be extended to other types of retaining structures. Whitman (1990) concludes that for design of relatively simple walls with heights of 30 feet or less, Mononobe-Okabe equation can provide reasonable results. For higher walls, and those restrained against outward movement, more careful analysis should be considered.

5.4 STRUCTURAL DETAILS

5.4.1 Introduction

Typical structures found in petrochemical plants are discussed in Section 5.3. In general, specific seismic details used in the building industry are also applicable to petrochemical plants. Most of the building industry practice can be found in Naeim, SEAOC (1990) and the *UBC*. This section discusses special seismic detailing requirements unique to petrochemical plants.

5.4.2 Steel

5.4.2.1 General

The general seismic requirements for steel structures can be found in Naeim, *SEAOC* (1990), *UBC*, *AISC ASD* and *AISC LRFD*. Special details that are not commonly encountered in the building industry will be discussed here.

Figure 5.3 shows a common connection detail which has been used in the building industry. In the aftermath of the January, 1994 Northridge, California earthquake, over 100 buildings were found where cracks occurred in connections based on this detail. The cause of these cracks is still under investigation. A number of causes have been postulated, such as poor welding and welding procedures, inadequate inspection, inadequately addressed thermal considerations, and the potential need to move the plastic hinge formation in the beam, away from the face of the column. At the time of writing of this document, the cause(s) are still under investigation, and until the industry has formulated a solution, it is prudent to avoid the connection. It is, in fact, currently prohibited in some jurisdictions. Further discussion of this, including some suggested details and retrofit details, is provided in SAC (1995).

The steel used in lateral force resisting systems should be limited to the following ASTM Specifications: A36, A441, A500, A501, A572 (Grades 42 and 50), and A588. Structural steel conforming to ASTM A283 (Grade D) may be used for base plates and anchor bolts.

In extremely cold regions, fine grained steels should be considered to reduce the likelihood of brittle failure under dynamic loads.

5.4.2.2 Requirements for Braced Frames

In the petrochemical industry, braced frames rely on diagonal members to resist horizontal forces and to provide stability. These extra members have a tendency to restrict access. Therefore, it is good practice to keep the number of braces to a minimum, and to properly locate those that are used. Generally, chevron or diagonal

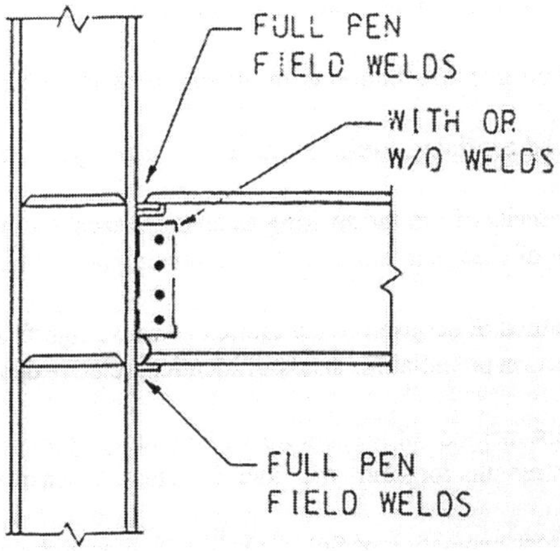

Figure 5.3: Former standard ductile moment connection detail. As a result of the Northridge Earthquake, this connection was shown to have major problems and is currently prohibited in many jurisdictions.

bracing is used in preference to X-bracing. Tees are preferred over double angles for ease of maintenance.

Quite often, it is necessary that the lower workpoint of the bracing to grade be kept above head room requirements to avoid blocking paths of egress in case of emergencies. Bracing should be located so as to avoid interferences with piping, ducts, electrical trays and conduits, and accessways. Also, diagonal bracing should be arranged so that it will not direct lateral load to only a few foundations.

5.4.2.3 Pipeways

To allow access under a pipeway, pipeways are generally designed as moment-resisting frames in the transverse direction, and are braced in the longitudinal direction. Longitudinal bracing transfers seismic and other longitudinal forces to the foundations. Normally, a long pipeway would require expansion joints (slotted strut connections) to allow for thermal movements and thus the longitudinal bracing is designed for the tributary segment between expansion joints (typically, 100 to 200 feet (30 to 60 m), but this depends on plant and site conditions).

5.4.2.4 Air Coolers (Finfans)

Typically air coolers are supported on pipeways. The air cooler is generally composed of a large box containing the fans and motors, supported on four or more legs. This generally creates a condition where a relatively rigid mass is supported on flexible legs on top of a pipeway. Whenever possible, the support legs should be braced in both directions. This however, may not always be practical due to the need for working platforms and access under the air coolers. Knee bracing and/or chevron bracing can be used as long as headroom is not compromised. Figure 5.4 illustrates a typical air cooler arrangement.

Though not a seismic design issue, care should be exercised to prevent possible resonance effects due to the operating frequency of the air cooler motors being too close to the natural frequency of the support structure.

5.4.3 Concrete and Foundations

5.4.3.1 Framed Concrete Structures

It has been observed that the connections of ductile moment-resisting frame concrete structures, when detailed and constructed properly, suffered little or no failure during a large seismic event. In petrochemical facilities, this includes structures such as table top structures and concrete structures supporting equipment or other steel structures,

However, it is clear that some of these items should be designed so that the connected elements can perform properly. This requires that the joints be proportioned and detailed to allow the elements framing into them to develop and maintain their strength as well as stiffness while undergoing large inelastic deformation.

5.4.3.2 Equipment Foundations

In general, most equipment foundations are designed with the equipment considered as rigid. Therefore, for seismic conditions, the anchorage should be designed for the code specified shear. Additional ties are usually required around the anchorage by the *UBC*. Special consideration should be given to vessels and exchangers as outlined below.

5.4.3.3 Horizontal Vessels and Exchangers

Horizontal vessels and exchangers are normally supported on two pedestals supporting saddles conforming to the vessel curvature. One saddle is fixed to the pedestal and the other is allowed to slide for thermal expansion.

For stacked vessels and exchangers where the anchor bolt capacity may not be adequate to carry the loads, the fixed foot plate can be welded to the bearing plate, or shear keys can be used. Shear keys and mechanical stops may be used on the sliding foot for transverse load resistance; however, this should be placed in such a way as not to impede the sliding of the foot, Figure 5.5. Note that shear capacity, either in

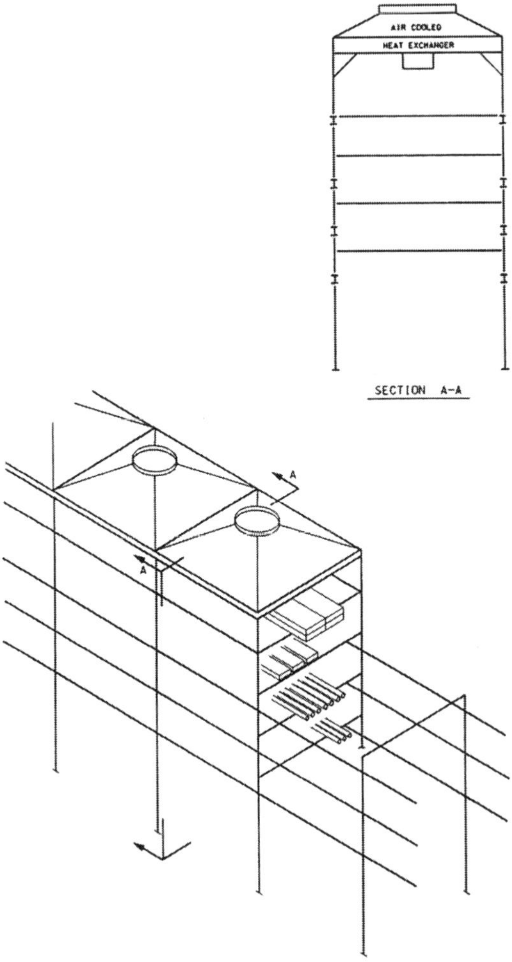

Figure 5.4: Typical Air Coolers Supported on a Pipeway

the transverse or longitudinal direction, may be governed by the concrete capacity. Special ties and details for seismic zones are shown in Figure 5.6.

For additional guidance, refer also to Section 5.3.5.6.

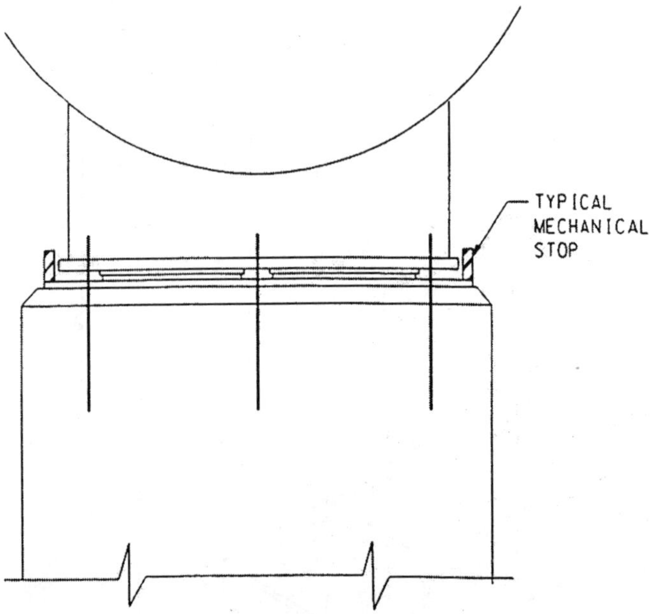

Figure 5.5: Transverse shear resisting elements. Where anchor bolts are not adequate to resist shear or are not appropriate, mechanical stops may be added.

5.4.3.4 Vertical Vessels and Stacks

Figure 5.7 illustrates some special details, particularly relating to the number and spacing of ties for vertical vessel foundations.

5.4.3.5 Foundations on Piles

Sometimes the pile cap/pile connection is designed to be fixed. A pile embedment of one pile diameter is recommended, but not less than 12 inches (5 cm). In general, the embedment need not exceed 2 feet (9 cm). The pile reinforcement should be anchored in the cap the appropriate embedment length. Whenever the pile cap/pile connection is designed as a pin, the pile embedment into the pile cap should be 3 to 6 inches (1 to 2 cm). Rebar development should be provided in the pile cap.

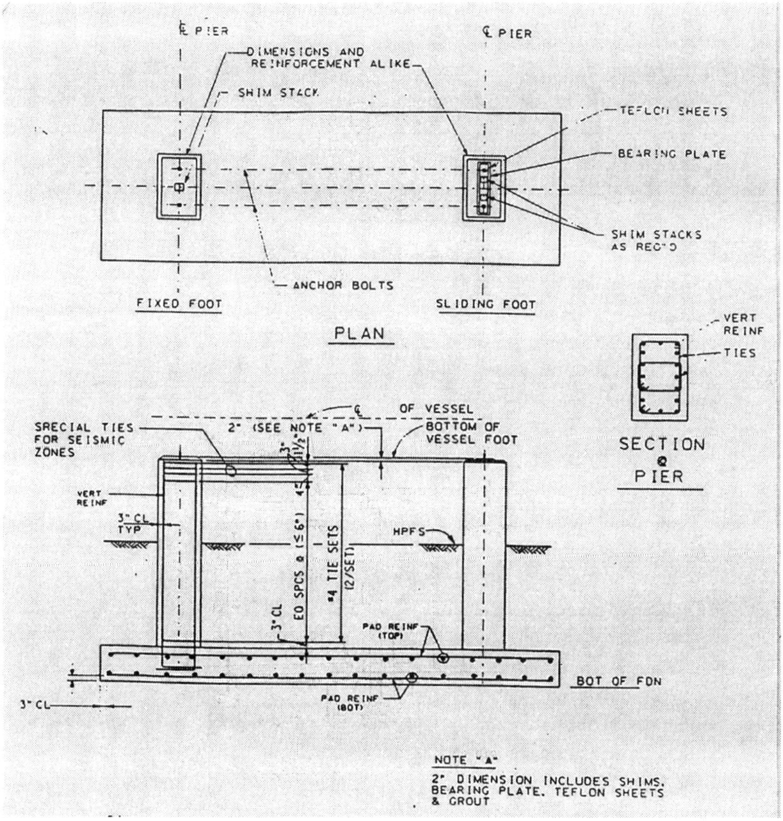

Figure 5.6: Typical horizontal vessel and exchanger foundation details. Note special seismic ties. Reinforcement is typical for both pedestals.

5.4.4 Masonry

Reinforced masonry structures are often an integral part of the landscape throughout a petrochemical plant. Masonry structures are limited to items such as retaining walls and barriers, operator shelters, auxiliary buildings and in some cases control buildings. Often, masonry is used for thermal linings in furnaces, heaters and other high temperature equipment. In an active seismic zone, connection details for the above items should comply with the *UBC* and related codes. However, care should be taken to ensure thermal growth compatibility of any ties with that of the masonry.

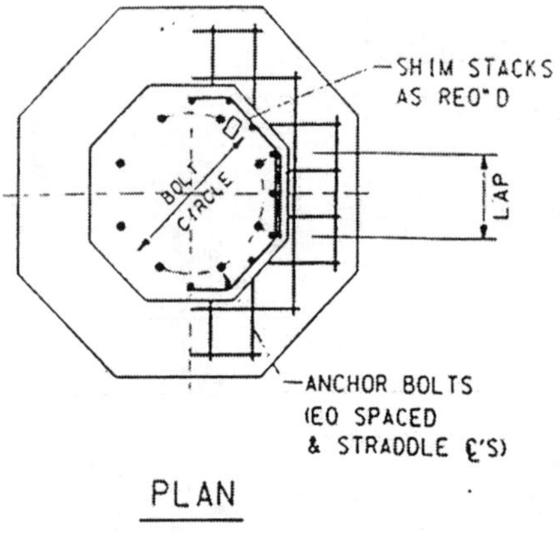

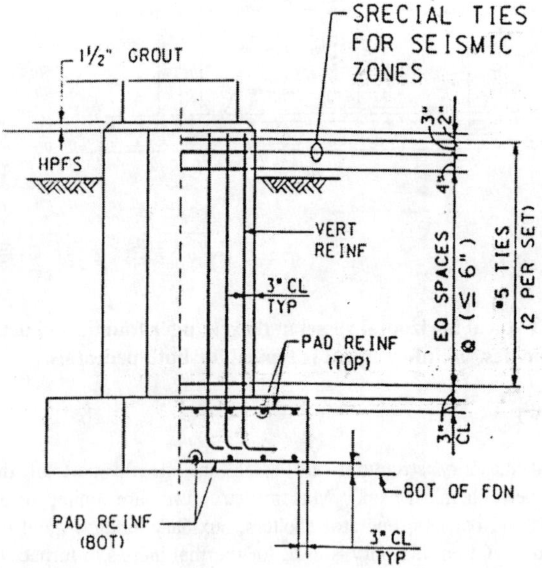

Figure 5.7: Typical Vertical Vessel Foundation Details

(Note special tie requirements)

5.4.5 Timber

In the petrochemical industry, most structures are built with materials other than timber, such as steel and concrete. However, when timber is used for the construction of buildings or supporting systems, connectors similar to commercially available seismic ties or with good seismic resistance, are recommended. In a high seismic zone these special connectors will provide excellent uplift and lateral load resistance to the structure.

5.5 PHYSICAL INTERACTION OF STRUCTURES AND COMPONENTS

5.5.1 Introduction

This section deals with physical interaction between structures and components, and the precautions that should be taken to minimize the negative effects.

5.5.2 General

The physical interaction between structures and components of a petrochemical plant during a seismic event is similar to those in the general commercial environment. The configuration of structures or components largely determines the ways in which seismic forces are distributed, and also influences the relative magnitude of forces and displacements.

The objective of a good petrochemical facility configuration is high operating efficiency and low capital cost. Process, mechanical and piping design requirements and the desire to minimize plot space encourage placing components close together. This inevitably creates the potential for damaging interaction of structures and components during an earthquake. It is incumbent upon the structural engineer to raise concerns about structure and component interaction.

Examples of potential structure and component interaction are:

a. Tall vertical vessels with platforms or pipe in close proximity to each other.

b. Vertical or horizontal vessels with shared working platforms.

c. Interconnecting pipeways.

d. Mobile equipment such as davits, cranes, etc.

e. Distributive systems which connect components supported on piles with components not supported on piles.

Some of the general concepts that are practiced to avoid or minimize physical interaction are as follows:

a. Layout all structures as regular structures whenever possible.

b. Provide adequate space between components.

c. Check the maximum displacement. Make sure there is enough room between the structure and component to match the displacement calculated.

d. Provide an appropriate support and restraint configuration for pipes to minimize transfer of load across flanges and couplings.

e. Make piping systems more flexible to mitigate the coupling effects of large pipes. Include loops in the pipes wherever needed.

5.5.3 Structure and Component Interaction

It is the general practice to layout all structures and components to minimize any physical interaction during a seismic event. When platforms or vessels are in close proximity to each other, the displacements and/or periods should be checked to insure that the spacing between such structures exceeds the sum of the absolute values of the displacements. The displacements (determined with code mandated forces) for this evaluation, should be increased by $3(R_W/8)$ to account for inelastic behavior. Also refer to Section 5.3.3.2 herein, for further information on dealing with inelastic behavior.

Often, piping in structures is routed vertically from a higher elevation to a lower elevation into flanges and couplings at the nozzles of turbines, pumps, vessels, etc. Large displacements of these pipes may cause leaks at the interface, thus causing fires and in some cases leading to explosions. All effort should be made to provide adequate system flexibility in the pipes to minimize load transfer across flanges and couplings due to seismic loads. This may be achieved by several methods, the most practical being proper support of the piping, and by limiting the displacement of pipes as specified below.

Where large pipe displacements caused by deflection of the supporting structure are unacceptable, limiting horizontal structure displacement on the order of H/240, where H is the height of the support point above the flange, may provide an acceptable solution.

5.5.4 Pipeways

Often, pipeways intersect each other, thus care should be taken not to transfer longitudinal seismic displacement and forces from one pipeway into transverse loads on another. Adequate longitudinal bracing or physical separation of pipeways can protect against such effects. Layout of piping and cable tray systems should be done in a manner to minimize such effects.

5.6 GEOTECHNICAL CONSIDERATIONS

Foundations for structures designed with the aid of modern building codes and seismic analysis techniques have generally performed well during major earthquake events. This satisfactory state of events is due to a combination of a good understanding of seismic loads, good construction and design procedures, and large safety factors used for static loads. Seed et al (1991) and Krintzsky et al (1993) provide some excellent background materials on seismic related foundation issues. The following sections provide additional discussion on selected geotechnical issues.

5.6.1 Piled Foundations

The ASCE Geotechnical Engineering Division recently published a number of papers reviewing the present understanding of dynamic pile response (Prakash, 1992). Among those papers was one by Hadjian et al (1992) that reviewed the state-of-the-practice as it relates to both code provisions and engineering practice. The following is largely abstracted from that paper and from Krinitzsky et al (1993).

Little effort is typically expended on pile-soil-structure interaction unless difficult soil conditions exists, or the capital expense or importance of the structure is great. However, a great number of procedures have been proposed and are in use for independent piles, pile groups, and linear and nonlinear soil response (e.g., Prakash, 1992; Gazetas, 1991; Nogami, et al 1991, 1992).

Piles inserted into sloping grounds, or adjacent to slumping materials, may experience lateral loading due to the transverse movement of soil during ground failure. Such conditions are difficult to design against.

Friction piles placed in loose sands, sensitive clays or high water content clays may experience loss of capacity or settlement during significant seismic events.

Battered piles offer a stiffer configuration to lateral loads than vertically oriented piles and therefore tend to increase seismic loads. Structures not appropriately designed or constructed for this response can experience severe damage. There are proposals to eliminate future construction with battered piles in seismic areas because of poor performance.

The seismic performance of piles can be improved by extending them to deeper, more competent soils, adding belled bases to improve tension and end-bearing capacity, or by adding a surface surcharge to increase the confining stress and strength at depth. Driving full displacement piles densifies the surrounding soil, thereby improving performance.

5.6.2 Soil Strength Considerations

Several codes allow the use of increased soil strengths under the action of seismic ground shaking. The increase is typically on the order of 1/3 or greater. The large factors of safety used in foundation engineering for static loads result in significant excess capacity that may be considered for the less frequently occurring transient loads due to seismic ground shaking. The general satisfactory performance of buildings and foundations designed under modern seismic codes would seem to validate this procedure. However, significant care must be exercised to insure that the foundation response under dynamic cyclic loading has been considered in an analysis attempting to characterize it with simple static load methods typically used in designs.

5.6.3 Geotechnical Site Investigations

Site investigations are required to acquire basic foundation design data. Zones of potential seismic activity require some additional considerations that are necessary to quantify local site response characteristics and seismic hazards. The following is a partial list of data required for conventional foundation analyses and seismic response and hazard analyses:

a. Depth to bedrock

b. Ground water table location

c. Soil stratification

d. Soil physical characteristics (grain size distribution, index properties, organic content, density, void ratio, water content)

e. Soil mechanical characteristics (elastic properties, consolidation properties, shear strength)

f. Seismic parameters

g. Unique conditions (sloping bedrock, surface grade, and proximity to faults, cliff areas, river fronts or coastal areas, arctic conditions)

h. Site investigation reports should include descriptions of drilling, sampling and in-situ testing methods, as this information in useful in aiding the comparison of results from different investigations.

Chapter 6
WALKDOWN EVALUATIONS OF EXISTING FACILITIES

6.1 INTRODUCTION

A "walkthrough" or "walkdown" evaluation is the term generally applied to an on-site, mostly visual, screening review where as-installed components are methodically "walked down" and evaluated for potential seismic vulnerabilities. Using this method, it is possible to rapidly and cost-effectively identify the highest risk areas and prioritize further, more detailed evaluations which might be appropriate. This section is intended to give practical guidance to engineers who will perform such evaluations.

6.2 BASIS FOR PERFORMING WALKDOWNS

Petrochemical facilities are increasingly being forced to demonstrate safety against toxic releases and pollution by mandates such as the California Risk Management Prevention Program (RMPP) requirements, the OSHA law (29 CFR 1910.119), and the proposed EPA law (40 CFR Part 68). There is currently no widely used and accepted standard for evaluating existing facilities for seismic loads. While some highly regulated industries, such as nuclear power plants, require conformance to new codes each time design standards change, when owners of petrochemical plants evaluate facilities, it is generally done voluntarily. Upgrade and acceptance decisions rely on cost-benefit considerations, with criteria set by the owners in agreement with local authorities as necessary.

Walkdown techniques along with limited analytical evaluations have been used extensively in California petrochemical facilities rather than a nuclear-type methodology to satisfy RMPP requirements since the early 1990s. This approach has been implemented because:

a. Very few existing facilities would be able to demonstrate conformance with current seismic codes. Seismic design codes change constantly in order to incorporate lessons learned from past earthquakes and ongoing research, and have usually become more restrictive and more conservative.

b. The walkdown method takes advantage of the lessons learned from the earthquake performance of industrial facilities, namely that most installations perform well, even when not designed specifically for seismic loads. The occurrence of damage can usually be traced to known causes which could have been mitigated by the evaluations described in this section.

c. The walkdown method is cost-effective. It is intended that all components of interest are looked at during the walkdown, but more costly detailed analyses are eliminated for all but the highest risk items. Obvious problems can be quickly identified and mitigated, as well as those areas where low-cost modifications or maintenance can significantly improve the seismic integrity of the equipment/structure (e.g. missing hardware).

d. The method is logical and defensible to regulators and owners. It considers the actual conditions of the plant; it relies on demonstrated performance in past earthquakes, backed up by performance observations and data; and it incorporates the experience, judgment, and common sense of the engineers performing the review. Several California regulators have accepted and recommended this approach for RMPPs.

e. The method is appropriate for regions of high and low seismicity. The level of seismic hazard can be accounted for in the walkdowns.

In summary, the walkdown methodology allows the owner to identify high risk items and assess potential safety, pollution, and economic exposure due to seismic events.

6.3 GENERAL METHODOLOGY

Walkdowns are generally performed by an engineer or team of engineers in a methodical, systematic manner, to assure consistency and completeness. The overall methodology may include several or all of the following elements:

a. Meetings with owners, operators, regulators, process safety engineers, or other appropriate parties to discuss objectives of the evaluation and to establish performance requirements of facility.

b. Identification of equipment, structures and piping of interest. If the review is being performed as part of a process hazards analysis or process related safety review, the walkdown engineers should review the assumptions used in the hazard analysis regarding the expected post-earthquake availability of critical systems. If the review is voluntary, for purposes such as evaluating insurance needs or overall risk quantification, the engineer may be asked to review all major equipment and structures in a facility.

c. Establishment of damage categories. Walkdown efforts are often required to be coordinated with a process safety team to establish requirements for use in the consequence analyses. For example, the process safety team may need an indication of whether, in a given earthquake, a vessel might:

- be undamaged
- suffer minor damage and leak
- fail catastrophically.

d. Collection of site data. Data of interest include seismic hazard data, fault locations, available soil borings, plot plans to locate items, and seismic design basis data applicable to the unit being evaluated.

e. Walkdown evaluation of components. This is done systematically, using checklists for each component, to document the evaluation and to serve as a reminder of the screening criteria. An example evaluation sheet is shown in Figure 6.1.

f. Review of drawings as necessary. This may be done to check adequacy of reinforced concrete structures, to verify anchorage details, or to identify configurations which cannot be visually reviewed due to obstructions, fireproofing, insulation, etc.

g. Identification of items for analytical review. These may include "worst-case" items or any items that appear to be seismically vulnerable. This is based on the potential for damage that would cause toxic release, pollution, or other unacceptable performance characteristics, such as damage that would cause significant business interruption.

h. Documentation of "poor" or "questionable" items for owners or regulators. Sufficient explanation must be provided such that corrective actions, maintenance, further evaluation, etc., will in fact address the engineer's concerns. The engineer must recognize that others may perform additional risk mitigation without further consultation with the engineer who performed the review.

i. Recommendation of structural or mechanical fixes or other efforts which would mitigate risk from items listed above. The engineer may be required to interact with process safety engineers and owners to evaluate the economic and technical feasibility of structural and process modifications.

FIELD DATA SHEET FOR EQUIPMENT	
EQUIPMENT ID: **DESCRIPTION:** **LOCATION:**	
SCREENING EVALUATION: SUMMARY	
Summary of Evaluation:	____ Adequate ____ Not Adequate ____ Further Evaluation Required
Recommendations:	
SCREENING EVALUATION: ANCHORAGE	
Noted Anchorage Concerns:	
_____ Installation Adequacy	_____ Weld Quality
_____ Missing or Loose Bolts	_____ Corrosion
_____ Concrete Quality	_____ Other Concerns
_____ Spacing/Edge Distance	
Comments:	
SCREENING EVALUATION: LOAD PATH	
Noted Load Path Concerns:	
_____ Connections to Components	_____ Missing or Loose Hardware
_____ Support Members	_____ Other Concerns
Comments:	

Figure 6.1: This example walkdown sheet shows how a simple checklist can remind the engineer of what to evaluate for a given piece of equipment.

FIELD DATA SHEET FOR EQUIPMENT (Cont.)

EQUIPMENT ID:

SCREENING EVALUATION:
STRUCTURAL INTEGRITY/EQUIPMENT SPECIFIC

Noted Structural Integrity/Equipment Specific Concerns:

_____ Maintenance
_____ Brittle Material
_____ Corrosion
_____ Functionality
_____ Ground Failure
_____ Lateral Load
_____ Other Concerns

Comments:

SCREENING EVALUATION: SYSTEMS INTERACTION

Noted Interaction Concerns:

_____ Failure and Falling
_____ Proximity and Impact
_____ Differential Displacement
_____ Spray/Flood/Fire

Comments:

ADDITIONAL NOTES

SIGNATURES

Name: ______________________________ Date: __________

Name: ______________________________ Date: __________

Figure 6.1 (Continued)

j. Identification of consequences due to failure of each of these items and the prioritization of any recommended risk mitigation actions according to the consequences of failure and the existing level of risk.

   A rating system may be appropriate, identifying:

   - major seismic vulnerabilities which should be fixed immediately

   - serious vulnerabilities which might require fixes, depending on economics

   - relatively simple fixes which might be performed in conjunction with routine maintenance or during the next scheduled turnaround.

6.4 SYSTEM CONSIDERATIONS

In most practical applications, walkdowns are performed on a component basis. Individual items, e.g. equipment items, vessels, specific pipelines, are generally identified as important because of hazardous materials, fire potential, potential interaction with other components, etc. and evaluated by the seismic walkdown team. Often, these evaluations are performed completely independent of any process hazards analyses (e.g. "What-ifs", HAZOPS, etc.) which may have initiated the seismic evaluations to be performed. In those situations, it is important that the walkdown team interact with teams performing process hazards analyses. A constructive information interchange greatly enhances the efficiency and potential benefits from the review.

The seismic review team should be able to describe to owners and to process safety engineers some of the general effects that can be expected in a scenario earthquake. For example:

a. The entire facility will be shaken simultaneously without prior warning.

b. The shaking may last 10 seconds or longer. Very large magnitude earthquakes (greater than magnitude 8) have caused shaking lasting on the order of 60 seconds.

c. Off-site power will likely be lost.

d. Several systems may be lost at the same time, such as phones, water, etc. and for long periods of time.

e. Underground piping may break.

f. Certain vulnerable equipment items and piping systems may be damaged and unable to function.

g. Offsite emergency services may not be available due to infrastructure problems (bridge or highway damage) or due to their required use in the general community.

h. Concerns about personal or family safety may be the priority of operator personnel, and operator action may not be a viable method of mitigating damage.

If the review is part of a hazard analysis, all of these issues may affect the hazard analysis results, and should be considered by the process safety team. The walkdown engineer should critically review what assumptions have been made in the process hazards analyses which might be inappropriate regarding post-earthquake capabilities of facilities and equipment.

The walkdown engineer should interact with operators, owners, process safety engineers, and other available specialists regarding consequences of damage. For example, a civil/seismic engineer might assume that the highest consequences of failed process piping are associated with pipes carrying the most toxic material. In reality, other considerations, such as whether the system will continuc to feed material through the line, or whether the pressure drop will shut down production of the material, may be more significant factors in the prioritization of the hazards.

This point is made to alert walkdown teams to be consistent in evaluations, calibrating judgment based on understanding of the systems, not on unfounded assumptions. It is also made to emphasize to the civil/seismic engineer that not all potential damage needs to be mitigated. The walkdown engineer will likely identify several concerns which are determined to not have significant safety or economic implications, a decision that will be made by others with input from the walkdown team. At that point, decisions regarding upgrades should be made by the owner on a cost-benefit basis.

6.4.1 Emergency Systems

During a damaging earthquake, it is very likely that off-site utilities will be disrupted and potentially lost for long periods of time. If the scope of the review has been limited to equipment and piping with hazardous materials, the civil/seismic engineers should question the process safety engineers to determine their assumptions on the availability of off-site utilities following an earthquake. It may be prudent to include items such as backup power supplies and water storage tanks in the seismic evaluation.

The walkdown team should also question whether other emergency systems are being counted on to function during a large earthquake to mitigate damage. In particular, it should be determined whether the fire protection system, telecommunications systems, and containment systems are required to perform active functions after the earthquake.

6.5 EVALUATION OF COMPONENTS

The following paragraphs are intended to give guidance for performing walkdowns of typical components in a petrochemical facility. Note that this guidance is not intended to be all inclusive; it would be impossible to list all of the possible situations that an engineer might encounter. Rather, the issues discussed below represent those that have been identified in the investigations of equipment performance in earthquakes throughout the world over the last two decades. In addition, it incorporates the in-plant experience of engineers who have performed seismic walkdowns of petrochemical facilities, primarily in California. In all cases, the walkdown engineer must use his or her common sense and fundamental principles of engineering mechanics, as necessary, in the identification of potential seismic vulnerabilities.

6.5.1 Major Considerations

Several major considerations should influence the focal points of the walkdown investigation and the relative effort spent on various aspects. Examples include:

a. Level of Ground Shaking Hazard: In areas of lower seismicity, major structures and vessels may be designed for sufficient lateral load capacity resulting from design for other criteria, such as wind. However, displacement-induced damage can occur at low levels of shaking.

b. Severity of Other Hazards (faulting, soil failure, and landslides): Known faults in the vicinity of the site should alert the walkdown team to be on the lookout for situations where imposed displacement could cause damage, such as buried piping, or equipment supported on different structural systems. Where known faults run through the site, a walkdown evaluation may need to be supplemented with additional geotechnical or other investigations. Soil failure such as liquefaction could also greatly impact the severity of damage.

c. Vintage of the facility and applicable codes at the time of construction: Applicable codes and seismic design methods may have changed considerably since a unit was designed. In particular, reinforced concrete design codes changed in the early 1970s, adding detailing requirements which would ensure ductile behavior in an overload condition. There should be more emphasis on evaluating overall structural capacity in older units than in newer units. In addition, engineers evaluating older facilities should be more alert for existing damage, such as dents in structural members, damaged concrete, corrosion, etc.

d. Overall quality of maintenance: Where overall maintenance appears to be poor or inconsistent, walkdown teams should be alert for missing nuts and bolts, unrepaired damage, field modifications, etc., especially in the primary load path and connections.

e. Priorities based on process safety considerations, pollution, regulatory needs, etc.: The process safety engineers and owners should identify to the walkdown team which components may warrant a more thorough initial review due to safety, pollution, or economic consequences of damage.

6.5.2 Generic Issues

The following issues are common to several types of electrical and mechanical equipment. Additional guidance is provided for several of these issues, as appropriate, in the discussion of specific equipment items.

6.5.2.1 Anchorage

Displacement resulting from inadequate or missing anchorage has probably been the most common source of damage to equipment in past earthquakes. Among the specific details noted to have caused problems are the following:

a. Vibration Isolators: Rotating equipment is often isolated from its supporting structure by the use of elastomeric pads or springs which do not transmit the vibrational loads from the equipment to the structure. Those isolators, which may appear on a quick visual review to be designed for lateral loads, often lack the strength and ductility to resist seismic loads without failing (Figure 6.2). One potential cause of failure is when the isolators are made of non-ductile material, such as cast-iron, which may fracture rather than deform under earthquake loading. Another potential cause of damage is a lack of vertical uplift restraints. The equipment may bounce out of the support and thereby lose its effective lateral support. A good detail on a vibration isolator commonly includes "bumpers" in the lateral direction (Figure 6.3), or stops which will not prevent motion, but will limit the displacement to tolerable levels. A good detail also includes uplift restraints. In general, it is recommended that any vibration isolated equipment be carefully evaluated. Isolators themselves should be evaluated, as well as the consequences of large displacements which may occur should that isolator fail.

b. Welds: Non-ductile failure may occur in situations where welds are overstressed. Situations of concern that might be identified during a walkdown evaluation include:

- corroded welds, a concern which should be evaluated wherever standing water accumulates or welds are constantly exposed to water;

- potentially undersized welds;

- situations where good quality welds may be difficult to install, such as a weld to checker plate which may not be of high quality (Figure 6.4);

- welds where they shouldn't be (e.g. anchor bolts welded to their "seats" on tanks); and

- welds over shim plates (Figure 6.5), an especially difficult detail to detect in a field review, and unlikely to show in drawings.

c. Bolted anchorages: Cast-in-place, grouted-in-place, and expansion anchor bolts may fail not only due to lack of strength, but due to details such as inadequate edge distance or cracks in the concrete (Figure 6.6). Factors such as spacing of the bolts may reduce the capacity of bolted anchorages due to overlapping shear cones. Spacing and edge distance may cause a reduction in capacity if distances between bolts or bolts and edges are less than 10 times the bolt diameter. Special attention should be given to inspection (e.g., bolt tightness checks) of grouted-in-place and expansion anchors, as their capacities are very sensitive to proper installation.

Figure 6.2: This is an example of a failed vibration isolator. In this case, the spring broke. Other times, the mounting may be made of brittle material, such as cast iron, and may fracture.

Figure 6.3: Bumpers should be included to limit the movement of vibration isolated equipment. Uplift restraints should also be provided.

6.5.2.2 Load Path

a. The load path of the major equipment masses down to the foundation should always be visually reviewed.

b. The engineer should be aware of unusual cutouts or modifications. Where those cutouts are obviously field modifications, the engineer should assess whether lateral capacity is significantly reduced. Cutouts are common in support saddles, especially for horizontal vessels and heat exchangers where the anchor bolts on the piers are not correctly aligned with the pre-drilled holes in the steel saddles. They may also be found in vessel support skirts, when piping does not align with prefabricated openings.

c. Load cells within the load path (Figure 6.7) may not be capable of resisting lateral loads. These are typically used for vessels.

Figure 6.4: Example of a poor quality weld, in this case a tank base plate to checker plate decking. Where welds may be difficult, the walkdown team should evaluate the quality closely.

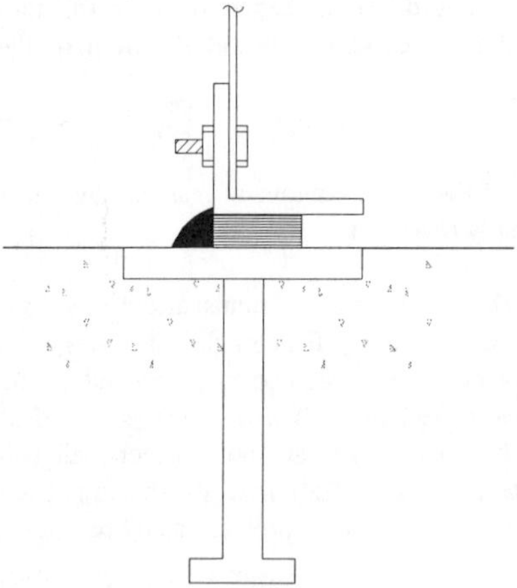

Figure 6.5: Shim plates are often used for leveling vessels. Welds over these shims may have severely reduced capacity. This poor detail is difficult to spot in drawings or in the site investigation. In this case, the walkdown team should notice the apparent thickness of the base plate.

d. A common problem is missing nuts and bolts on connections. This situation is especially prevalent where structural members must be removed to provide access for regular maintenance of equipment.

e. Attention must be given to cases where large eccentricities exist. This often occurs as a result of field modifications which have no engineering basis, such as a shifting of braces to allow for clearance for piping or other equipment. Eccentricities, if significant, can induce significant bending on structural members, such as columns, for which these members are not designed.

Figure 6.6: Large cracks within 10-bolt diameters could reduce the tension capacity of an anchor bolt. Cracks such as these through the anchor bolts could significantly reduce their tensile and shear capacity.

Figure 6.7: Load cells are commonly used in the support for vessels. These may lack capability of resisting lateral loads and should be carefully examined.

6.5.2.3 Maintenance

During walkdowns of facilities, engineers routinely observe conditions which compromise the seismic structural integrity of equipment, yet could be easily taken care of through routine maintenance. This occurs even in otherwise well-maintained facilities. As discussed above, this is primarily a load path/anchorage issue related to missing or damaged hardware.

6.5.2.4 Corrosion

The walkdown team should always be on the lookout for areas where corrosion may occur. The concern is not surface rusting, but a loss of structural strength which may be indicated by thinning, pitting, or flaking. Areas especially vulnerable would be where especially corrosive materials such as acid are present, and where water may accumulate.

Another area where corrosion may be a problem is where concrete cover is spalled and the reinforcement is exposed. This is generally a matter of maintenance.

Because corrosion is often a high priority general concern to a facility, the plant may have a corrosion group that can assist in identifying potential problem areas.

6.5.2.5 Construction/Installation Quality

During walkdowns, engineers may also observe consistently poor installation practices. This may be evident in welds, or in expansion anchor bolt installations. For example, expansion anchors may not be able to attain their tensile design capacity if embedment is inadequate. This could result from the use of shim plates or large grout pads. It may be evident by long studs protruding above the concrete surface, or exposure of part of a shell insert. Other examples of installation concerns would include connections, such as cotter pins not installed properly or fasteners missing positive locking devices for vibrating equipment.

6.5.2.6 Seismic Interaction

Seismic interaction refers to damage to a system or piece of equipment due to impact with or movement of another piece of equipment, system, structure, storage cabinets, furniture, etc. This is a particular aspect where the walkdown evaluation is the best way to identify potential interactions.

For the purposes of this document, seismic interactions are divided into four primary categories:

a. Proximity and Impact: This occurs when there is not adequate clearance between two items to prevent impact. This may occur from sliding of unanchored equipment; swinging of rod-hung piping, ducts, or cable trays; or cantilevered deflection of electrical cabinets causing pounding with adjacent cabinets, walls, or structural members. Another example would be the hazard of walkway platforms with sharp ended beam supports, if the walkways are capable of movement relative to the tank such that the tank wall can be punctured.

b. Structural Failure and Falling: This usually occurs when inadequately restrained components fall from above, impacting the equipment in question. This can also occur when a large item nearby structurally fails and impacts with the equipment being evaluated by the walkdown engineer.

c. Differential Displacement: This is a particular concern for the walkdown team wherever items are supported by different structural systems. The engineer should be aware of potential situations where the different systems can displace, such that connecting piping, ducts, conduit, tubing, etc. do not have adequate flexibility to survive the motion. Flexibility is the key feature to resist damage. This is also a specific concern when different foundations act as supports for one piece of equipment, or where equipment is unanchored.

d. Waterspray and Flooding: This may be of concern inside buildings, where damage to sprinkler systems could affect the operability of electrical equipment. Of particular concern should be sprinkler heads on fire piping which might impact hard structural members and open, spraying water on electrical equipment below.

6.5.2.7 Process Changes

Process changes may result in operating conditions which have been changed from the design conditions without consideration of the effect on seismic vulnerability. The walkdown team should make appropriate process engineers and operators aware of this possibility and investigate where such changes may have occurred.

6.5.2.8 Inadvertent Relay Actuation / Functionality

Functionality of equipment may be affected by the action of electromechanical relays during an earthquake. This cannot be evaluated during a walkdown and requires a system evaluation. Walkdown engineers should be aware of the potential for relays chattering, tripping, or changing state due to earthquake shaking and that certain types of relays, such as switches utilizing mercury filled vacuum tubes, have been demonstrated to be vibration sensitive. Walkdown engineers should notify process engineers and operators of this possibility and investigate further when this condition is a concern.

6.5.2.9 Ground Failure

Ground failure has led to severe damage and collapse of many otherwise well-designed structures and equipment in earthquakes.

a. Walkdown engineers should always review soil reports to identify the potential for faulting, liquefaction and settlement. Special caution should be exercised whenever one or more of these situations is encountered, since even well-engineered structures and equipment can be severely damaged. Walkdown evaluations generally must be supplemented with additional studies whenever these types of ground failure are possible.

b. Steep slopes with potential stability problems should be identified, and if questionable, slope-stability studies should be recommended.

6.5.2.10 Design Interface

In general, the walkdown team should always be alert when investigating areas of design interface, where connecting structural elements may have been designed by different engineering groups. Examples include vessels on supports, where the vessel and saddle design may be by the vendor, while the attachment to the support and the support may be by others; or finfan units, where the pipeways may be designed by one group and the finfan and support framing by the vendor.

In these situations, the walkdown team should be alert for inconsistent design practices, an indication that one or more elements may not have been properly designed for seismic loads.

6.5.3 Evaluation of Specific Components

The following sections list considerations in the evaluation of several specific types of equipment and structures found in petrochemical facilities. Again, it should be emphasized that the following guidance is not all inclusive and cannot possibly address all situations that might be encountered. It simply indicates observed causes of damage and observed vulnerabilities from past walkdowns.

6.5.3.1 Mechanical Equipment

Many types of equipment consist of complex assemblies of mechanical and electrical parts that typically are manufactured in an industrial process that produces similar or even identical items. Such equipment may include manufacturer's catalog items and are often designed by empirical (trial and error) methods for functional and transportation loads. One characteristic of this equipment is that it may be inherently capable of surviving strong motion earthquakes without significant loss of function. Equipment that may fit into this category include most air handlers, compressors, pumps, motors, engines, generators, valves, pneumatic, hydraulic and motor operators, fans, chillers, evaporators, and condensers.

The engineer performing the walkdowns should review each of these items looking for possible fragile parts of the components and for specific configurations and details that have been shown to be potential problems, such as the following:

a. Anchorage of the unit. In particular, vibration isolators may be found on air handlers, compressors, and small pumps.

b. Compressors, generators, and pumps may have engines and motors located on separate skids or foundations. In those cases, the units should be investigated for potential damage due to differential displacement, such as binding of a shaft. This is a functionality issue, and may not be an issue for toxic material, flammable material, or product releases.

c. Attached piping must be flexible enough to withstand differential motion between its two anchor points. This may be particularly important when it is attached to unanchored equipment or tanks.

d. Valves are generally very rugged seismically. However, there have been cases where they have been damaged due to impact of the operator with a structural member. This is a special concern when the valve yoke is constructed of cast iron. The walkdown team should also investigate those situations where a valve and its operator are independently supported on different structural systems.

e. Additional investigation will also be appropriate where in-line components are large relative to the size of the piping.

f. Non-ductile materials, such as PVC or cast iron.

6.5.3.2 Electrical Equipment

Similar to mechanical equipment, much electrical equipment is designed and manufactured for functional and transportation loads and has characteristics of ample construction that make it inherently able to survive strong earthquakes. Well anchored electrical equipment has typically performed well in past earthquakes. This includes motor control centers (MCCs), low and medium voltage switchgear, transformers with anchored internal coils, inverters, battery chargers, batteries, and distribution panels.

When electrical equipment is required to function during or after an earthquake, the walkdown engineer should review each of these equipment items, looking for potential vulnerabilities. Examples of concerns for electrical equipment items include the following:

a. Verify anchorage of electrical equipment. The anchorage may be bolts to concrete, fillet welds to embedded steel, or plug welds to embedded steel. Of particular concern are plug welds, which will not have the same capacity in tension as they will in shear. If there is a potential for overturning, the plug welds should be checked with a reduced capacity. To check weld capacity, use 25% of the capacity of an equivalent fillet weld around the perimeter of the hole.

b. Cabinets that are not bolted together may pound against each other. This is a particular concern if the cabinets need to function after an earthquake, and there are trip-sensitive devices, such as switches and relays inside the cabinet.

c. Cabinets which are adjacent to structural columns or walls may experience a cantilever deflection, causing an impact. Except for extremely flexible cabinets, this should not be an issue where there is more than approximately 1 inch (25 mm) clear space. Again, this is a concern where trip-sensitive devices are present. This is not an issue if the cabinet is stiff due to top bracing, or rigidly supported conduit coming from the top of the cabinet.

d. The front to back shear panels should not have unusually large cutouts in the side, near the bottom, which may compromise the structural integrity of the cabinet. This does not refer to manufacturer's installed and reinforced cutouts, or cutouts and doors in the front and back panels.

e. Internal devices should be secured to the cabinet structure or internal framing. For example, bolts connecting transformer coils to the cabinet are sometimes removed after transporting the unit to a site and installing the equipment.

6.5.3.3 Battery Racks

Emergency battery racks are identified separately because they have failed several times in earthquakes, often leading to a lack of emergency power. Walkdown engineers should evaluate the following:

a. The battery rack should be structurally sound, capable of resisting transverse and longitudinal loads.

b. The batteries themselves should be restrained from falling off the rack. This is typically done by installing wrap-around bracing around the batteries (Figure 6.8).

c. Where batteries have gaps between them, some form of spacer should be present to prevent sliding of the battery and impact or damage to bus bars.

d. Falling of overhead equipment should be avoided to prevent possible electrical short circuits or damage to the batteries. Of particular concern would be fluorescent tubes in lights, which have been observed to fall from fixtures and drop to the floor if there is not safety grating. All emergency lights, horns, speakers, etc. in the vicinity of batteries should be looked at to ensure that they will not slide, fall, or otherwise move such that they can hit the batteries.

e. If the engineer is reviewing the batteries to ensure their functionality after an earthquake, related electrical equipment should also be included in the review and given special attention (e.g. inverters, control panels, etc.).

Figure 6.8: Batteries must be kept from sliding off the racks. This is commonly done with wraparound bracing, as illustrated here.

6.5.3.4 Control and Instrumentation Equipment

Control panels should be viewed with the same concerns as electrical cabinets. Of particular concern will be the presence of trip-sensitive devices, such as relays. When relays are present, the walkdown engineers should question process safety personnel or operators as to whether those relays are required to function during or after an earthquake.

Instruments on racks generally perform well, provided that they are secured to the rack and the rack is anchored. Instrumentation such as thermocouples and gauges are not an issue except where they can be damaged by impact or excessive motion pulling out cables.

A few other issues that are particular to control and instrumentation equipment are as follows:

a. Control panels often contain components on rollers or slides. These drawers may not have stops, and have been observed to roll out and fall to the floor during an earthquake. The walkdown engineers should check for stops or other restraints on components on slides or rollers.

b. Circuit cards often slide in and out of panels with no restraining devices. These circuit cards have been observed to slide out and fall to the floor during earthquakes. The engineer should look for restraining devices. Some cards are restrained by tight friction and will not have latches. Retrofits may be impractical.

c. Control panels often have doors left open or unlatched. The swinging of doors and resulting impact may be a concern if trip sensitive devices are present.

6.5.3.5 Pressure Vessels

Vertical pressure vessels are often mounted on steel skirts and anchored to a concrete foundation. The vessels themselves are usually designed for high pressure and perform well in earthquakes. Tall vessels and columns are also often designed for wind loads and have significant lateral capacity. Of special concern for vertical vessels are the following issues:

a. Unreinforced cutouts in skirts. Of special concern should be cutouts that appear to be field constructed.

b. Flexibility of attached piping. Rigid, separately supported piping can experience damaged nozzles or failed pipes as a result of differential displacement.

c. Strength and ductility of the anchorage, such as anchor bolts with no chairs.

Horizontal pressure vessels are typically supported on steel cradles which are anchored to concrete piers. Where thermal expansion can occur, one end will be fixed, with the other end using slotted holes to allow for axial thermal growth. As with vertical vessels, the vessels themselves are designed for pressure loads and would be expected to perform well in earthquakes. The following concerns have been noted for horizontal pressure vessels:

a. Piers which are unusually tall may not be capable of resisting transverse or longitudinal loads.

b. Narrow piers may have cast-in-place anchor bolts with edge distance problems.

c. Walkdown teams should be particularly aware of field modifications in the supports, such as cutouts to modify alignment of the bolts and bolt holes.

d. Flexibility of attached piping.

e. For stacked horizontal heat exchangers, the walkdown team should check connection bolts between the exchangers. It is common that the nuts or bolts are not replaced after maintenance or a turnaround.

f. Actual condition of a "sliding" support. While the supports may be designed such that the "fixed" end is intended to take all of the longitudinal load, actual conditions, such as a corroded and fused slide may cause the sliding support to resist half of the longitudinal load, even though it may not be designed for that load.

Pressurized spheres are typically supported on several legs evenly spaced around the circumference of the sphere. The legs may or may not be braced, typically with X-bracing between adjacent legs. Failures that have been observed in past earthquakes have been caused by failure of the support system. In the 1952 Kern County Earthquake, failure of the support legs led to breaking of attached piping. The butane that escaped the spherical tank eventually ignited, causing explosions and fires. The structural adequacy of the legs and bracing should be the primary focus in evaluating spherical tanks. Drawings should be reviewed to ensure that legs are tied together with grade beams.

Small tanks and pressure vessels on legs are found throughout petrochemical facilities. The tanks and vessels themselves have not been observed to be significant problems in earthquakes. The following areas should be emphasized:

a. The structural adequacy of the support legs to resist overturning must be considered. These have failed in many instances in earthquakes.

b. Flexibility of attached piping should be checked. This is especially true if the piping is connected to unanchored equipment or vessels that can move.

6.5.3.6 Finfans

Finfans are air coolers which are typically mounted on top of pipeways. The following considerations should be given to the seismic evaluation of these units:

a. The structural adequacy of the support framing and the attachment to the pipeway should be evaluated. Further investigation is warranted if the framing shows signs of distress, such as buckling or bowing of members, under operating conditions. Attachments should be investigated where they are eccentric, or do not frame into primary structural members.

b. Coil bundles are removed at regular intervals for maintenance purposes. These units may be positively attached to the support frame at one location or on one end only. Reinstallation of the coils may be incomplete, with missing bolts, misalignments of structural framing, etc. The walkdown team should investigate those interfaces.

6.5.3.7 Heaters

Boiler and heater structures are generally thick walled steel vessels, supported on several low concrete piers. They may also be cylindrical, supported on skirts similar to other horizontal pressure vessels. Horizontal heaters are almost always fixed at one pier with slotted bolt holes at other piers to allow for thermal expansion.

The main focus on a boiler structure will be the support system. Reinforced concrete piers should be checked for adequate strength and stiffness, so that they do not create a "soft story" effect.

The walkdown team should be aware of the possible presence of refractory brick inside a heater or boiler structure. This will add weight to the equipment and may be an additional source of internal damage to the equipment.

6.5.3.8 Support Frames and Pedestals

Many equipment items will be located above grade, supported on reinforced concrete or steel frames. These frames may be irregular and are typically open at one end to allow for installation and removal of the vessels.

The failures of freeway structures in the 1989 Loma Prieta and 1994 Northridge Earthquakes illustrate the potential for catastrophic collapse of older reinforced concrete structures without adequate shear reinforcement and confinement. A common configuration in refineries is to install large vessels, elevated high above the ground on pedestal supports (Figure 6.9). The support system typically has no redundancy. Reinforced concrete frames and pedestals should be carefully evaluated, especially if constructed prior to the mid 1970s, when changes in building codes added ductile detailing requirements. The walkdown team should review available structural drawings to verify adequacy of concrete structures. In many cases, some form of numerical evaluation may be necessary to determine adequacy of the reinforced concrete structures.

The walkdown team should also be on the lookout for damaged and cracked concrete, especially where reinforcement is exposed. Steel reinforcement in cracked concrete could be susceptible to moisture and corrosion, with subsequent loss of strength.

6.5.3.9 Steel Frames

Steel frames have traditionally performed well during earthquakes. However, there have been a number of surprises noted in the 1994 Northridge Earthquake (EERI, 1996). Over 100 steel frame buildings were damaged as a result of that earthquake. The damage has been on moment resisting frames and has been, for the most part, concentrated in beam to column connections (cracks have been found in welded beam flanges to the column) and in some cases, in fracture of column base plates.

This is of particular concern to the structural community because these types of structures have been thought of to be the most ductile and because of the potential implications to the vast number of existing steel frame structures. It must be noted however, that none of the damaged structures collapsed and most remained functional.

At the time of this writing, there are a number of studies and investigations under way on this issue and more information will be known in the future. For now, the walkdown engineer is alerted to pay additional attention to the connections in steel frame structures, in light of recent experience.

Figure 6.9: Vertical vessels are often supported on each end by a single reinforced concrete pedestal. These vessels may be 30 feet (9 meters) above the ground or more, creating a large moment on the pedestal. Drawings may need to be reviewed for this type of configuration. Special caution should be given to supports designed prior to building code changes in the mid 1970s.

The walkdown team should be aware of sign of distress due to dead load conditions or corrosion. Particular attention should be given to cases where drawing modifications (brace relocation/removal) may have taken place subsequent to the original design of the structure. These modifications may be related to piping clearances, etc., and may have taken place without the consultation of a structural engineer. Brace relocation and removal can result in load paths being different than originally designed and potential structural inadequacy.

Most often, the weakest links, where failures can be expected, are in the connections. The connections should be looked at for signs of insufficient stiffening, indirect load path, potential prying action, etc.

Finally, in cases where non-structural elements are attached to structural frames (platforms, guard rails, etc.), the walkdown engineer should check that these do not act to significantly alter the dynamic response of the structure in an earthquake, or to change the primary load path.

6.5.3.10 Buildings

This document will not detail the evaluation of existing buildings. That topic is covered in great detail elsewhere.

The engineer should be cognizant of the types of building construction which may have a higher potential for complete or partial structural collapse. While minor damage or even collapse of some buildings may be acceptable, suspect buildings should be identified to the process safety group. The following items are not uncommon in petrochemical facilities and should be evaluated by the walkdown team:

a. Unreinforced masonry buildings are susceptible to partial or complete collapse.

b. Masonry infill in walls are susceptible to collapse.

c. Tilt-up buildings are susceptible to partial collapse if they are poorly tied together.

d. Structures having vertical or plan irregularities may perform poorly in an earthquake.

e. Reinforced concrete frame buildings which lack ductile details may be susceptible to failure.

Attention should be given to the level of functionality required of specific buildings following an earthquake. For example, when evaluating a firehouse, the walkdown engineer should make an evaluation to ensure that the operability of the facility remains intact, such as the ability to open doors for fire engines to exit.

6.5.3.11 Stacks

Although unreinforced concrete stacks and chimneys have failed in earthquakes and tall steel stacks have buckled, stacks generally perform adequately in earthquakes. The walkdown engineer should be aware of significant changes in building codes over the years relative to tall, flexible structures, such as stacks. For example, the 1991 *UBC* would require a minimum lateral force of 0.20g in Zone 4. However, the same structure may have been designed to 1/3 that load in the early 1960s. This discrepancy may be a special concern in evaluating a spread footing for overturning, as the footing may appear to be underdesigned. However, because of the cyclic nature of dynamic loading, foundations have not been observed to suffer gross overloading such that a stack could tip over in an earthquake. This should not be a concern unless soils are liquefiable or very weak.

It should be noted that past experience has shown that other structures attached to furnace stacks may be overstressed, such as trusses supporting ducts feeding to chimneys high above the ground. The walkdown team should be alerted to look for situations where flexible, or sliding type connections are not present, as these connections would tend to preclude significant interaction between stacks and other structures.

6.5.3.12 Gas Cylinders

Chemical releases have occurred in earthquakes due to gas cylinders toppling and rolling. Toppling of cylinders also has the potential to create a missile hazard. The following guidance applies to gas storage cylinders:

a. Gas cylinders are often chained to prevent falling during normal operations. Single chains do not necessarily prevent falling. Chains supporting both the upper and lower portion of the cylinder are necessary to prevent the cylinders from falling and sliding or rolling.

b. The engineers should ensure that cylinders that appear to be secure are, in fact, secured to structural members. This is particularly true inside buildings, where straps may be tied to non-structural elements.

c. Horizontal cylinders should be secured so that they cannot roll and fall off of supports. An example of a good detail is shown in Figure 6.10, where removable hold down bolts are used to secure chlorine cylinders. Where hold-down devices are present, but appear to be ignored or incorrectly used, the walkdown engineers should question operators regarding typical procedures for restraining cylinders.

6.5.3.13 Chemical Storage Areas

Chemicals have fallen from shelves, reacted with other spilled chemicals, and caused fires in past earthquakes, as well as concern for explosions (Reference 4). The following concerns should be investigated by walkdown engineers:

a. The engineers should determine whether cabinets are secured to prevent falling.

b. Engineers should determine whether restraints prevent contents from being spilled off of shelves.

c. Where a potential for chemical spill is identified, the engineer should question the operators as to the potential consequences of spills. Note that several mitigation methods may be available, such as physical restraints or separation of incompatible chemicals.

Figure 6.10: Cylinders that are removed when empty often sit unrestrained on vertical saddle shaped supports. In this photo, a simple hold-down bolt prevents motion while the cylinder is in use. The presence of a mechanism like this can be judged to reasonably prevent overturning or sliding of the cylinder.

6.5.3.14 Piping

Process piping runs throughout petrochemical facilities, running directly between pieces of equipment, or often supported on overhead pipeways. In many situations, the piping of interest will be particular lines containing specified quantities of hazardous material. There are several difficulties in evaluating individual piping runs:

a. With several lines on congested overhead racks it becomes extremely difficult to initially locate and then to follow specific piping runs.

b. Piping may be difficult to locate, even with P&IDs or flow diagrams. These drawings do not adequately represent physical locations or distances of piping runs. Layout drawings are usually not available.

c. It may be difficult for the walkdown engineer to identify the boundaries of concern, especially considering bypass lines, injection lines, valves, etc.

Given these difficulties, it is often more practical and efficient to evaluate all piping in a given area. That method does require additional interaction with the process safety engineers to determine the consequences of postulated damage.

In evaluating process piping, stresses due to inertial loads are not the primary consideration, except in certain circumstances. Rather, the focus is on vulnerable details, fragile attachments, and connections which may experience severe displacements. The following observations should be considered when performing the evaluation:

a. Welded steel piping generally performs well in earthquakes and is typically not susceptible to damage from inertial loading. Inertial loads may be a concern for non-ductile materials, such as cast iron or PVC. Note that materials such as cast iron are probably used because of their non-corrosive properties, and changing the material on the pipeline is not a reasonable option. In these cases stress analysis may be necessary.

b. Lack of lateral supports will not necessarily lead to failure of the pipe. Piping often spans very long distances without lateral supports with no damage or failure. Rather, the emphasis should be on ensuring that the piping system will not lose vertical support. For example, the walkdown engineers should look for situations where the pipeline is near the edge of the support and could slide off (Figure 6.11).

c. Where there is a lack of lateral support, making the pipe very flexible, the walkdown team should also be aware of situations where the pipeline may be effectively "anchored" by a rigid connection of a branch line (Figure 6.12). If the branch line is significantly smaller than the header (less than one half the diameter), the pipe could be overstressed at the connection.

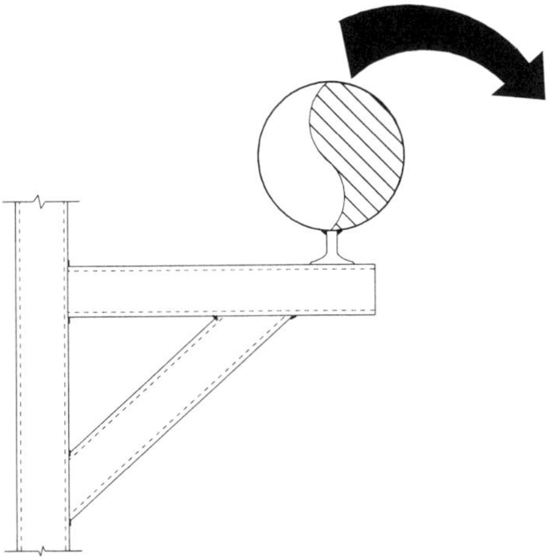

Figure 6.11: Pipes that are near the edge of a support without lateral stops may slide off. Loss of vertical support is the primary concern in these situations, not the length of span without lateral support.

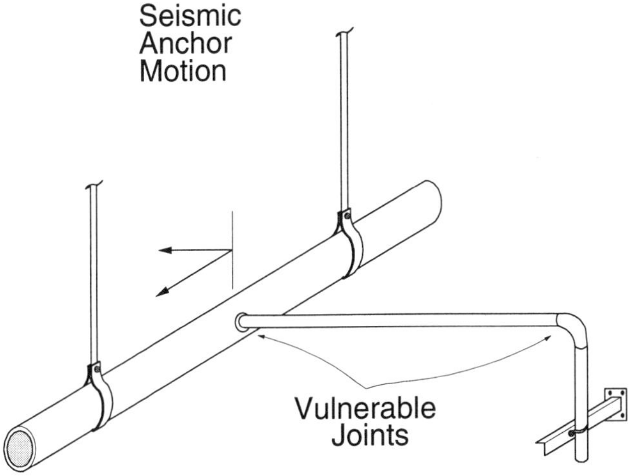

Figure 6.12: Rigid or restrained branch lines may be vulnerable to unrestrained motion of the header.

d. The walkdown team should look for situations where vulnerable appurtenances or portions of a pipeline could be impacted and damaged due to motion of the pipeline or the impacting object. Examples would include drain taps or sampling lines that could be impacted by valve diaphragms on adjacent lines. Of special concern are sprinkler heads on fire lines that might impact hard sharp structural members (Figure 6.13). This has occurred several times in past earthquakes.

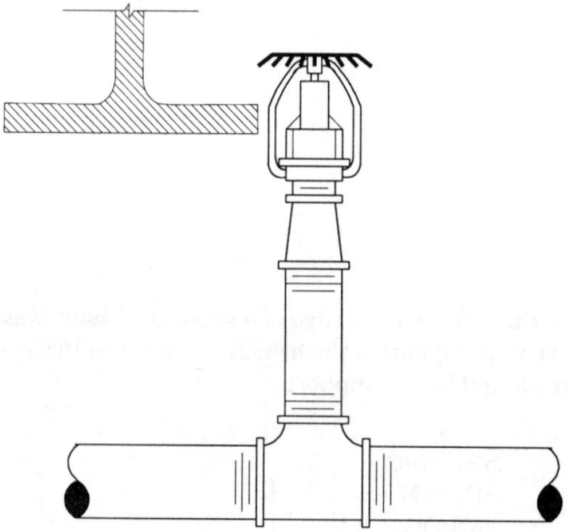

Figure 6.13: Fusible sprinkler heads are sensitive to impact.

e. Mechanical couplings could fail due to excessive displacement or impact.

f. Rod hung systems, particularly fire protection systems within buildings, can fail and fall when supported by short rod hangers configured such that moments can be developed at the top connection. This is a low cycle fatigue failure.

g. Buried piping could fail where ground failure can occur.

h. Piping attached to unanchored tanks or equipment can fail if there is inadequate flexibility in the pipe to withstand large displacements (Figure 6.14).

i. In many instances, a relatively short span of large diameter (8" or more) pipe connects elevated vessels supported by independent structural systems such as concrete frames. The stiff pipe may affect the interaction of the two structures and can result in overstress at the flanges or elbow areas, particularly when stress concentrations are taken into account. The walkdown engineer should take this into consideration, and if in doubt, recommend a proper coupled analysis of the entire system.

Figure 6.14: Piping damage is common where it is rigidly restrained at unanchored tanks.

6.5.3.15 Cable Trays and Conduit

Cable trays and conduit are generally very rugged seismically. It is important to note that damage to the trays and conduit themselves do not necessarily imply damage to the cables contained within them. The most important consideration for cable trays and conduit is to ensure that vertical support capacity will be maintained during a seismic event.

6.5.3.16 Ductwork

Ducting is often used in petrochemical facilities to transport hazardous gasses, and may be identified by the process safety engineers as requiring review. Duct construction can range from thin gage sheet metal to steel pipe sections. Sheet metal ducting has failed during past earthquakes in certain circumstances. Failure of sheet metal ducting generally is caused by corrosion, poor connections, loss of structural support, or differential displacement concerns. Large diameter, thick ducting, such as plate steel construction, should follow the general considerations presented earlier on piping, especially concentrating on overall support systems and adequate flexibility to accommodate differential motions.

6.5.3.17 Air Tubing

Tubing is very ductile and is usually installed with substantial flexibility. However, tubing can be damaged by large displacement or impact, and the consequences of loss of air to instruments should be considered.

6.5.3.18 Substations

Substation equipment may be especially susceptible to damage in earthquakes. Ceramic insulators often fail. Transformers which are unanchored, or lightly anchored with friction clips, may slide and damage connections.

6.5.3.19 Cooling Towers

Wood cooling towers have generally performed well in earthquakes. The following have been the primary causes of damage:

a. The primary cause of damage to wood cooling towers in earthquakes has been a deteriorated condition prior to the earthquake.

b. Cooling towers have also been damaged due to poor structural configurations at connections. For example, Figures 6.15 and 6.16 show an eccentric joint which failed during an earthquake. This figure is added to emphasize that the engineer should focus on details first, rather than strength, when performing walkdown evaluations.

6.5.3.20 Platforms / Walkways

An extensive number of elevated platforms and walkways can be found in a refinery. In many instances these platforms surround tall vessels and are supported on a structural system that may not be directly connected with the vessels. In cases like these, differential displacement is the primary concern, with the potential for damage in the following ways:

a. Pounding between the vessel and catwalks, potentially resulting in either rupture of the vessel wall or sufficient damage to the platforms themselves such that they may be inaccessible in an emergency following the earthquake. The walkdown engineers would look for not only the proximity of the platforms to the vessels, but also for sharp ends of supporting beams that could increase the potential for damage.

b. Walkways spanning different structures without adequate flexibility, such that differential motion could cause collapse and falling of the walkways.

6.6 LIMITATIONS

Because the walkdown review is intended to be a screening process, it is important that all concerned parties understand that it is impossible to identify all sources of seismic risk in such a mostly visual review. Items identified as potential hazards in a walkdown may survive an earthquake; likewise, items which appear to be adequate could fail for reasons not apparent during a visual or analytical review.

The engineer must always caution both owners and regulators to understand that seismic risk can never be completely eliminated. Even with a more thorough review, some level of seismic risk will always exist, no matter how much time, effort, and money are spent evaluating and upgrading a facility. The risk can be better understood and reduced, but there are never any guarantees.

Figure 6.15: Eccentrically loaded connection in a wood cooling tower. The cross member above is a retrofit.

Figure 6.16: Identical joint in the same wood cooling tower as shown in Figure 6.15.

Chapter 7
DESIGN AND EVALUATION OF TANKS AT GRADE

7.1 INTRODUCTION

The purpose of this section is to provide the user with guidelines for designing new tanks and evaluating existing tanks for seismic loads. Emphasis is given, however, to evaluation of existing tanks. The information contained herein is mostly applicable to unanchored flat-bottomed storage tanks at grade in zones of higher seismicity, with requirements to be de-rated for lower seismic zones. Some guidance is also provided for anchored storage tanks.

Oil storage tanks are typically designed according to the industry standard *API 650* (API, 1993). Seismic design provision located in Appendix E of *API 650* first appeared in the 3rd revision of the 6th edition, dated 10/15/79. Although the general theory was developed earlier, few tanks were designed for earthquakes before the code provisions came into effect. Since then, there have been several experimental programs and numerous field observational data that suggest that *API 650* Appendix E is conservative in most cases. The conservatism may be appropriate for design of new tanks but not necessarily for assessment of existing tanks.

Because only recently constructed tanks have been designed to resist earthquakes, there may be several potentially damageable tanks in any given tank population. To limit a facility's exposure to earthquake damage, potentially damageable tanks should be identified, evaluated and, if required, retrofitted.

Since seismic design provisions were only introduced into the API code in the late 1970's (Wozniak and Mitchell, 1978), tanks that are older than this may be considered vulnerable to damage by large earthquakes. However, it should be noted that many liquid storage tanks built before these provisions were introduced have been able to withstand strong ground shaking with minimal or minor damage and were able to continue functioning.

The steps involved in undertaking a seismic hazard mitigation program for existing tanks are discussed in this section and include:

a. Quantification of the site-specific seismic hazard.

b. Walkthrough inspection to assess piping, stairway and walkway attachments, and other potential hazards.

c. Analytical assessment of tanks to evaluate the potential for overturning and shell buckling.

d. Mitigation of seismic hazard. The most commonly used hazard mitigation measures include addition of flexibility to rigid attachments, reduction of safe operating height and, as a last resort, anchorage of the tank.

7.2 PAST EARTHQUAKE PERFORMANCE OF FLAT-BOTTOMED TANKS

The following discussion on earthquake response of tanks is generally extracted from material presented in ASCE (1984) and Dowling and Summers (1993).

Flat-bottom vertical liquid storage tanks have sometimes failed with loss of contents during strong earthquake shaking. In some instances, the failure of storage tanks has brought about disastrous consequences. Some examples include: fires causing extensive damage to oil refineries in the 1964 Niigata, Japan earthquake and the 1991 Costa Rica earthquake; polluted waterways in the 1978 Sendai, Japan earthquake; fires and failure of numerous oil storage tanks in the 1964 Prince William Sound earthquake in Alaska; and failure of numerous liquid storage tanks, both above and below ground, in the 1971 San Fernando, the 1980 Livermore, the 1985 Chilean, the 1991 Costa Rica and the 1992 Landers earthquakes.

The response of unanchored tanks, in particular, during earthquakes is highly nonlinear, and much more complex than implied in available design standards. The effect of seismic ground shaking is to generate an overturning force on the tank. This, in turn, causes a portion of the tank baseplate to lift up from the foundation. The weight of the fluid resting on the uplifted portion of the baseplate, together with the weight of the tank shell and roof, provides the restraining moment against further uplift. While uplift, in and of itself, may not cause serious damage, it can be accompanied by large deformations and major changes in the tank wall stresses. This is especially apparent when the seismic loading reverses and the (formerly) uplifted segment moves down impacting the ground and introducing high compression stresses into the tank shell. Tank uplift during earthquakes has been observed many times, but the amount of uplift has rarely been recorded. A 100 ft (30.5 m) diameter, 30 ft (9.1 m) high tank uplifted 14 inches (350 mm) during the 1971 San Fernando earthquake. During the 1989 Loma Prieta earthquake, two 42 ft (12.8 m) diameter, 28 ft (8.5 m) high tanks uplifted 6 to 8 inches (150 to 200 mm); and a tank uplifted 18 inches (450 mm) in the 1964 Alaska earthquake (EERL, 1971; EERI, 1990; and National Research Council, 1973). While tank uplift is very common, sliding of tanks is rare and generally need not be considered a credible failure mode for storage tanks at grade.

In general, tanks, especially unanchored tanks, are particularly susceptible to damage during earthquakes. This is because all of the mass contributes to the overturning moment, but only a small portion of the mass contributes to the overturning resistance (the reason for this is that the contained fluid and the relatively flexible tank shell and bottom plate cannot transfer the lateral shear induced by the earthquake to the foundation). Some examples of tank damage that has occurred in past earthquakes include:

a. Buckling of the tank wall, known as "elephant foot" buckling. Essentially, this occurs because the vertical compressive stresses in the portion of the tank wall remaining in contact with the ground (i.e., diametrically opposite the uplifted portion) are greatly increased when uplift occurs. More precisely, that portion of the tank shell is subjected to a biaxial state of stress, consisting of hoop tension and axial compression. In addition, the baseplate prevents the radial deformation which would normally occur under internal pressure. As a result, bending stresses are introduced into the shell wall, further increasing the tendency to buckle. The photograph in Figure 7.1 (taken after the 1992 Landers earthquake in Southern California) shows a classical example of elephant foot buckling and accompanying failure of overconstrained piping. This buckling mode is normally associated with larger diameter tanks having height to diameter (H/D) ratios of about 1 to 1.5.

Figure 7.1: Elephant Foot Buckling and Failure of Rigid Piping

County of San Bernardino, Water Storage Tank, Landers, CA

Landers Earthquake, Richter Magnitude 7.4, June 28, 1992

Another common buckling mode, normally associated with taller tanks having H/D ratios about 2, is "diamond shape" buckling. In contrast to elephant foot buckling, which is associated with an elastoplastic state of stress, diamond shape buckling is a purely elastic buckling.

A feature of tanks which experience either elephant foot or diamond shape buckling is that the buckled tank often does not rupture and continues to fulfill its function of containing fluid. However, all buckled sections of the tank should be replaced.

b. During tank uplift, the baseplate may not be able to conform to the displaced shape of the tank and the weld between the baseplate and the tank wall may not be able to accommodate the tension stresses that develop as a result of the fluid hold-down forces which are mobilized to resist uplift. In this case, fracture at the junction between the baseplate and the shell wall may result. This was observed, in particular, in the Chilean earthquake of 1985, where some tanks experienced failure of the baseplate or of the weld between the wall and the baseplate (EQE, 1986a). Good welding practices may preclude such failures, which can lead to rapid release of the tank contents; further, the differential pressures created within the tank by the rapidly evacuating fluid may also lead to damage to the upper shell courses and roof.

c. Seismic shaking causes the surface of the tank fluid to slosh. If insufficient freeboard is provided to accommodate this sloshing, damage to the tank's floating roof or fixed roof, followed by spillage of fluid over the tank walls, may result. This type of damage is usually considered only minor but may be important for some stored products.

d. Support columns for fixed roof tanks have buckled in past earthquakes from the impact of sloshing fluid and their own inertial force in combination with the vertical loads they support. Collapse of several columns, while often not a catastrophic failure, can be a significant damage item.

e. Breakage of piping connected to the tank as a result of relative movement between the tank and the nearest pipe support. This is one of the most prevalent causes of loss of contents from storage tanks during earthquakes. Failures of this type are typically due to inadequate flexibility in the piping system (termed "overconstrained piping") between the nozzle location at the tank shell and the adjacent pipe support. Failures have also occurred due to relative movement between two different tanks connected by rigid piping.

f. Tearing of tank wall or tank bottom due to overconstrained stairways anchored at the foundation and tank shell.

g. Tearing of tank wall due to overconstrained walkways connecting two tanks experiencing differential movement.

h. Anchored tanks, with non-ductile connection details have performed poorly in past earthquakes. Non-ductile connection details can lead to tearing of the tank's shell and release of its contents. Details that do not allow for full development of anchor bolts have led to anchor bolt pullout and failure of the tank.

i. Tank failures have been found to occur as a result of severe distortion of the tank bottom at or near the tank side wall due to a soil failure. This failure may be associated with soil liquefaction, slope instability, excessive differential settlement, bearing failure or washout due to pipe failure. A failure of this type occurred during the Miyagi Earthquake of 1978.

j. Tensile hoop stresses due to shaking-induced pressures between the fluid and the tank walls can become large and can lead to splitting and leakage. This has been observed during earthquakes, but appears to be a problem only for bolted or riveted tanks. For welded tanks, material ductility appears to accommodate these high hoop stresses.

Figures 7.2 through 7.5 present some examples of tank failures in recent earthquakes including overturning of a tank during the 1991 Costa Rica earthquake.

7.3 WALKTHROUGH INSPECTION

A walkthrough is an on-site visual screening, whereby “as-installed” components can be evaluated for seismic vulnerabilities. Walkthroughs in general are discussed in more detail in Chapter 6 of this document. The purpose of the walkthrough is to identify a variety of seismically vulnerable details. In this section, walkthrough evaluation guidance is given specifically for tanks.

The principal feature which distinguishes the seismic response of unanchored tanks from that of anchored tanks is the large uplift displacements commonly observed around the edge of unanchored tanks. As described earlier, this uplift may induce large tension or compression forces and bending moments in the tank wall, baseplate, and at the intersection of the two. Such forces may lead to severe damage or failure of the tank. Furthermore, the adverse effects of excessive tank uplift can be greatly exacerbated by a variety of commonly encountered tank details. Walkthrough inspection of individual tanks or tank farms should focus on the identification of such details. In many cases, while the tank itself may be found to be structurally adequate, retrofit of a number of these seismically vulnerable details may be deemed necessary. The following material, which describes the walkthrough process, is taken from Dowling and Summers (1993) and Summers and Hults (1994).

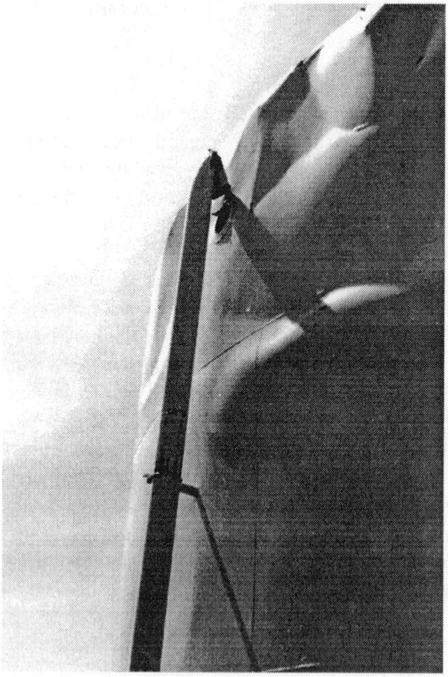

Figure 7.2: Elephant Foot Buckling, Failure of Rigid Piping and Tank Wall Failure at Manhole Access

Bighorn Desert View Water Agency, Water Storage Tank, Landers, CA

Landers Earthquake, Richter Magnitude 7.4, June 28, 1992

Figure 7.3: Above: Tank Wall Failure at Tank Manhole Access Bighorn Desert View Water Agency, Water Storage Tank, Landers, CA

Below: Overall View of Failed Water Storage Tank, Landers, CA, County of San Bernardino, Water Storage Tank, Landers, CA`

Landers Earthquake, Richter Magnitude 7.4, June 28, 1992

Figure 7.4: Above: Overturned Oil Storage Tank, RECOPE Oil Refinery, Costa Rica

Below: Spilled Oil and Ruptured Piping, RECOPE Oil Refinery, Costa Rica

Costa Rica Earthquake, Richter Magnitude 7.4, April 22, 1991

Figure 7.5: Above: Damaged Roof, Seals, and Sloshing of Oil over Tank Walls, RECOPE Oil Refinery, Costa Rica

Left: Severe Elephant Foot Buckling, Transmerquim Tank Farm, Costa Rica

Costa Rica Earthquake, Richter Magnitude 7.4, April 22, 1991

Poor Details	Retrofit Recommendations
(a) 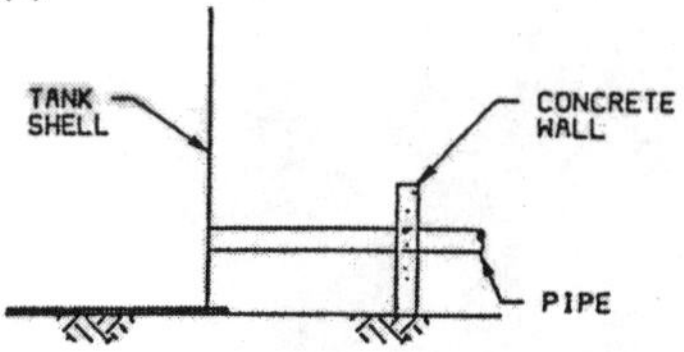	• Add flexibility to pipe
(b) 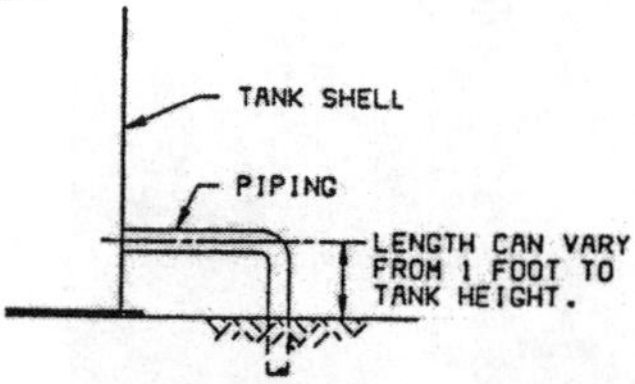	• Add flexibility to pipe
(c) 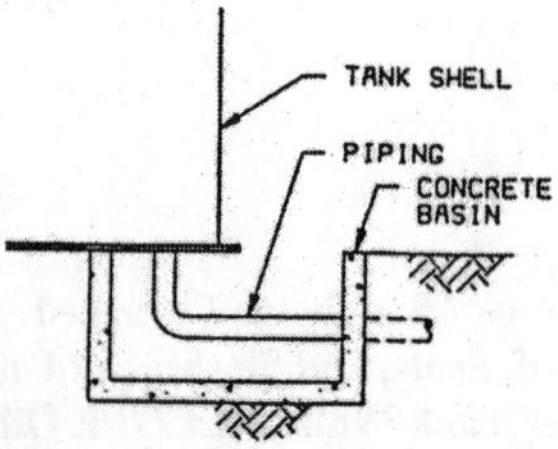	• Add flexibility to pipe
(d) 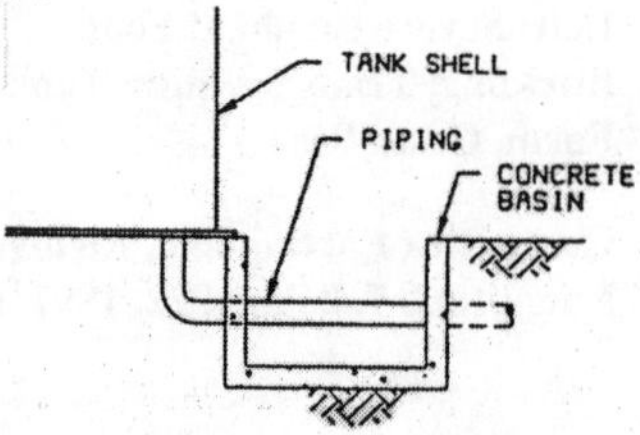	• Reroute piping to center of tank or extend inner wall of concrete basin beyond pipe/tank connection

Figure 7.6: Poor Details at Unanchored Tanks and Retrofit Recommendations

<table>
<tr><th>Poor Details</th><th>Retrofit Recommendations</th></tr>
<tr><td>(e)
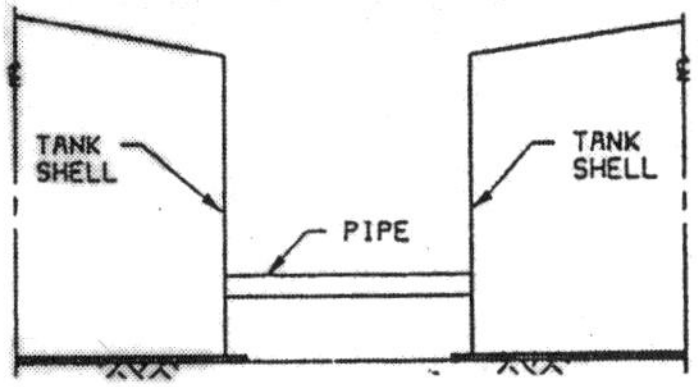
</td><td>• Increase flexibility by providing horizontal or vertical bends</td></tr>
<tr><td>(f)
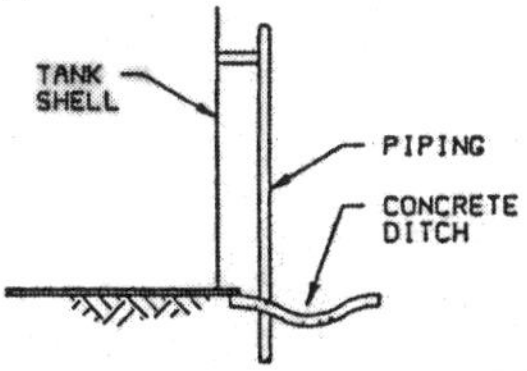
</td><td>• Anchor pipe at roof instead of along shell wall</td></tr>
<tr><td>(g)
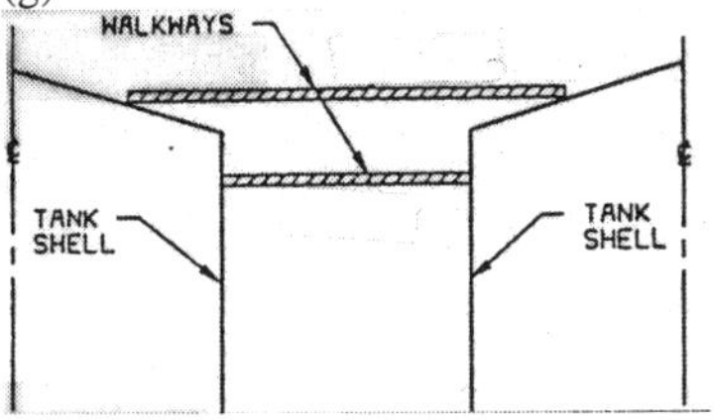
</td><td>• Increase walkway flexibility to accommodate relative displacements</td></tr>
<tr><td>(h)
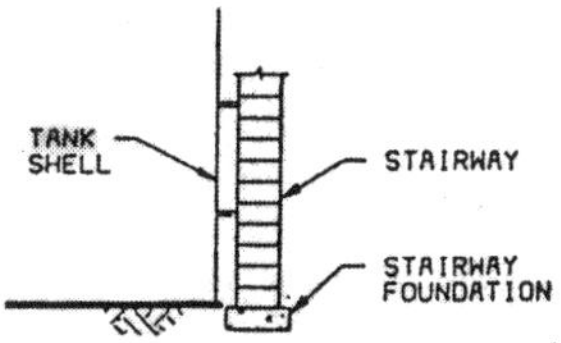
</td><td>• Support stairway exclusively on tank shell</td></tr>
<tr><td>(i)
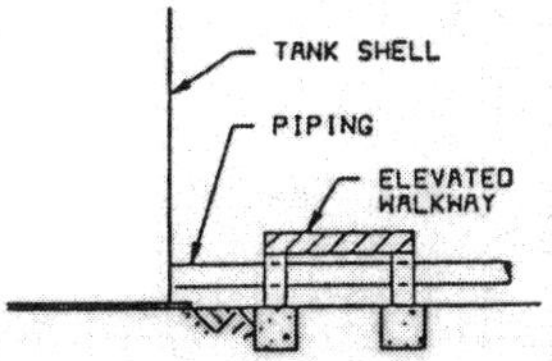
</td><td>• Increase piping flexibility, attach walkway exclusively to tank shell, or provide more piping clearance</td></tr>
</table>

Figure 7.6 (Continued)

The most frequently encountered hazardous details are listed below, together with appropriate retrofit recommendations, and illustrated in Figures 7.6 and 7.7.

a. A common failure mode in tanks has been breakage of piping connected to a tank as a result of relative movement between the tank and the nearest pipe support. Alternatively, if the piping is stronger than the tank wall or baseplate to which it is connected, tearing of the wall or baseplate may result. Piping should not pass directly, with little or no flexibility, from the tank shell or tank bottom to the ground or to rigid concrete walls, basins, pumps rigidly fixed to the ground, etc. Failures of the type described above are typically caused by the details shown in Figures 7.6(a) through 7.6(d). In the first three cases, additional piping flexibility should be provided by adding horizontal or vertical bends, or by installing a length of flexible piping. In the fourth case, piping should be rerouted to the center of the tank or, if the piping is flexible enough, the concrete basin may be extended beyond the pipe/tank connection.

b. Similar failures have also occurred due to relative movement between two tanks connected by a rigid pipe, as shown in Figure 7.6(e). Again, additional piping flexibility should be provided as described above.

c. Partial loss of contents may result from the type of detail shown in Figure 7.6(f), where a vertical pipe is rigidly connected to the ground or foundation and also supported rigidly along the wall of the tank. A detail offering a lesser level of risk, but present in many cases, is a tank wall support that consists of a large U-bolt which might appear to be capable of sliding up and down the pipe as the tank lifts and falls. However, it is possible that the U-bolt will "bind" with the pipe, thereby also forming an essentially rigid connection, and leading to tearing of the tank wall. Any connection along the tank shell judged to be rigid should be replaced by a connection near the shell/roof intersection, coupled with sliding connections or "guides" along the shell wall. In many cases, simply loosening the U-bolts will suffice.

d. Roof access is frequently facilitated by walkways spanning between the tanks. Typical walkway arrangements are shown in Figure 7.6(g). In both cases, relative movement between tanks may lead to rupture or tearing of the tank wall or roof. However, whereas the lower walkway arrangement shown in Figure 7.6(g) may lead to partial loss of tank contents, the upper walkway arrangement will, at worst, lead to damage to the walkway itself and/or to the roof; hence, no loss of contents will result. The distinction between the two arrangements is important since the lower walkway represents a concern that could result in release of product, whereas failure of the upper walkway will likely only lead to a release of fumes and a much lower level of economic loss. In either case, the required retrofit would take the form of increased walkway flexibility.

Elevated walkways also represent falling hazards for tanks located in plants with significant adjacent pedestrian traffic or sensitive equipment. Where necessary, walkways should be attached to the tanks by cables as a secondary means of support to prevent them from falling.

e. Stairways should not be attached to both the tank shell and the foundation; see Figure 7.6(h). However, only in thin-shelled tanks is such a detail likely to lead to failure of the tank wall and to loss of contents. Again, therefore, a distinction should be drawn between this case and the case of a thick-shelled tank, where such a detail would only result in damage to the stairway itself. In either case, the hazard may be eliminated by attaching the stairway to the tank shell or by eliminating the connection which prevents the stairway from displacing vertically.

f. Tank piping is usually concentrated in one area, often with an access walkway spanning over the piping, as shown in Figure 7.6(i). If the walkway is rigidly attached to the ground and if insufficient clearance is provided between the piping and walkway, then tank uplift may lead to impact between the piping and the walkway, resulting in damage to one or the other. However, only with small diameter pipes or thin shelled tanks is loss of tank contents likely to occur. Otherwise, damage is likely to be confined to the walkway itself. In both cases, the hazard may be mitigated by increasing the piping flexibility, attaching the walkway exclusively to the tank shell, or providing more piping clearance. Another potentially seismically vulnerable detail is the case of a walkway attached to both the tank shell and foundation, as in Item (e) above for stairways.

g. Tanks anchored with anchor bolts having poor connection details may tear the bottom plate or tank shell resulting in a loss of product. Poor details (see Figure 7.7) include anchors which are clipped to the bottom plate, chairs which are unusually short so as not to permit adequate transfer of forces in the bolt to the tank shell, or any detail which will result in the tearing of the tank shell before the anchor bolt yields. This hazard can be mitigated by replacing the connection with one that will exhibit more ductility.

When performing walkthrough inspections, experienced engineers familiar with seismic design and the effects of earthquakes should be utilized in order to answer the questions as to "how much flexibility is sufficient." The assumed value of tank uplift is critical to answering this question. Values of 6 to 8 inches (150 to 200 mm) have commonly occurred in the past. Using a value of on the order of 6 to 12 inches (150 to 300 mm) of vertical displacement, and on the order of 4 to 8 inches (100 to 200 mm) of horizontal displacement (at least in zones of highest seismicity) would be considered prudent and conservative. Actual expected values are a function of tank size, fill height, aspect ratio, and local seismicity and soil type. Additional discussion of uplift is given in Section 7.4.5.

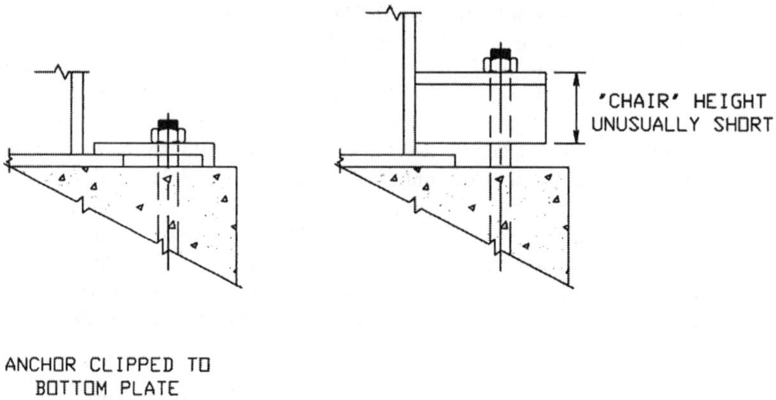

Figure 7.7: Poor Anchorage Details

7.4 ANALYTICAL EVALUATION

7.4.1 Methods for Analysis of Unanchored Tanks

There is extensive literature on the seismic analysis of flat-bottomed tanks. The literature includes a number of methods available for analyzing unanchored tanks. Some of these analysis methods are:

a. *API 650* Appendix E (API, 1993) - This method is the standard for design of new tanks for the petrochemical industry. It is simple to use and its provisions generally match those of the Uniform Building Code (ICBO, 1994).

b. *AWWA D100* (AWWA, 1985) - This method is very similar to the *API 650* method, and is used primarily for design of water storage tanks.

c. Earthquake Tank-Wall Stability of Unanchored Tanks (Manos, 1986) - George Manos has developed an alternative method of assessing tanks which is significantly different to the previous two methods, and is based on observed performance of tanks during past earthquakes.

d. Seismic Design of Storage Tanks (Priestley, et al, 1986) - This method was proposed as the tank design code for New Zealand. Presently, it has not been adopted. Of all the methods listed, it is the most involved and has the most detail.

More discussion of the above assessment methodologies is given in subsequent sections.

7.4.2 Methods for Analysis of Anchored Tanks

Past performance of anchored tanks during earthquakes has indicated that such tanks generally experience very few problems. This is partially because very few tanks were anchored before the seismic provisions of *API 650* were introduced in the late 1970's (Wozniak and Mitchell, 1978), and those that were subsequently anchored were designed to those very same provisions.

Anchored tanks should be considered as adequate unless anchorage details are judged to be capable of tearing the tank shell or bottom plate, causing loss of contents. Anchorage details should be assessed during walkthrough inspection to ensure that there is an adequate load path for the hold-down forces developed in the anchor bolts to be transferred from the tank shell to the foundation.

If an anchored tank needs to be evaluated analytically, the methods in API (1993), ASCE (1984), or Housner and Haroun (1980) may be used.

7.4.3 Stability

API Evaluation Methodology

The seismic design methodology for welded steel storage tanks presented in *API 650* Appendix E (API, 1993) is based on the simplified procedure developed by Housner (1977). Details of the development of the API methodology are described in Wozniak and Mitchell (1978). The procedure considers the overturning moment on the tank to be the sum of:

a. The overturning moment due to the tank shell and roof, together with a portion of the contents which moves in unison with the shell, acted on by a horizontal acceleration. The value of the acceleration is usually taken as the peak of the 2% damped site response spectrum, divided by a factor that accounts for the ductility and reserve capacity of the tank. Alternatively, the code allows a value of 0.24g to be used for the highest seismic zone. This is termed the impulsive component.

b. The overturning moment due to that portion of the tank contents which moves in the first sloshing mode (i.e., independently of the tank shell), acted on by a horizontal acceleration equal to the 0.5% damped spectral acceleration corresponding to the period of that mode, again divided by a ductility/capacity factor. Alternatively, the code provides simplified formulas to determine the acceleration to be used. This is termed the convective component.

Resistance to the overturning moment is provided by the weight of the tank shell and roof and by the weight of a portion of the tank contents adjacent to the shell. The structural adequacy of the tank is determined by a "stability ratio," which is a measure of the ratio of the overturning moment to the resisting moment. The stability ratio is defined as the quantity $M/[D^2(w_t + w_L)]$ where M is the overturning moment at the bottom of the tank shell (ft - lbs); D is the nominal tank diameter (ft); w_L is the maximum weight of tank contents that may be used to resist shell overturning (lbs per ft of circumference); and w_t is the weight of the tank shell and the portion of the fixed roof supported by the shell (lbs per ft of circumference). The value of the stability ratio must not exceed 1.57 (no metric equivalent is provided). Further, *API 650* provides a methodology for calculating the compressive stress at the bottom of the tank shell together with the maximum allowable value of shell compression; the latter corresponds to approximately one-third to one-half of the theoretical buckling stress of a uniformly compressed perfect cylinder. If the stability ratio exceeds 1.57 or the compressive stress exceeds the allowable value, retrofit of the tank or reduction of the liquid height is necessary.

Extensive experimental studies and observations during past earthquakes have demonstrated that the radial length of uplifted bottom plate, and hence, the actual liquid weight resistance which is mobilized during an earthquake is substantially underestimated by the API uplift model. The reasons for this are that the API model does not account either for the in-plane stress in the bottom plate, or for the dynamic nature of the tank response. The model also calculates an unrealistically narrow compression zone at the toe of the tank, thus leading to large compressive stresses in the tank shell for relatively low overturning moments. Finally, the API approach does not account for the effect of foundation flexibility on the tank wall axial membrane stress distribution.

Although the API methodology is known to be somewhat conservative and condemning existing tanks for failing to meet the API criteria may not be deemed appropriate, the criteria are the basis of the current seismic design practice and serve as a good benchmark. Large exceedance of specific provisions should be taken as an indication that retrofits may be necessary.

Unlike the method developed by George Manos, presented next, the *API 650* criterion is relatively insensitive to the tank's wall thickness. This is because tanks usually fail by exceeding the "stability ratio" and not by exceeding the shell's allowable stresses. *API 650* then becomes more of an overturning check rather than a stress check. Thus, while *API 650* is conservative for tall tanks, it may be unconservative for broad tanks with very thin shells due to the use of high strength steels. Care should be taken when assessing these tanks.

Alternative Methodology

There are several alternatives to the API methodology described above; one that might be considered for use in evaluation of existing tanks is a modified version (Dowling and Summers, 1993) of a method developed by George Manos (Manos, 1986) presented herein. Manos' method is based on experimental studies, as well as on observed behavior of unanchored tanks during past earthquakes. Instead of trying to model the complex uplifting plate behavior, Manos assumes a stress distribution at which the shell will buckle and solves for the resisting moment produced by the sum of the stresses. This resisting moment can then be compared to the overturning moment and the resisting acceleration solved for.

The assumed compressive stress is maximum at the toe (opposite the point of maximum uplift), and decreases to zero at an empirically determined distance from the toe. The maximum compressive stress is limited to 75% of the critical buckling stress of a uniformly compressed perfect cylinder. The model ignores the effect of hoop stress on buckling stress, but correlation of the method with actual test results validates the results obtained. Integration of the assumed axial stress yields a resultant compressive force which must be balanced by an equal tensile force due to the weight of the fluid resting on the uplifted portion of the bottom plate. Using an empirical formula for the lever arm between these two forces, an expression for the resisting moment against uplift of the tank is developed. Additional resistance provided by the weight of the tank shell, the bending moment distribution in the tank wall, and other sources are ignored.

The overturning moment on the tank is calculated in a manner similar to that used in the API methodology, except that the convective component of the overturning moment is neglected, in the interests of simplicity. This is felt to be appropriate since, because of phase differences between the impulsive and convective components, the convective portion is not believed to contribute much to the peak tank wall stress response, especially for very tall tanks. This omission is balanced somewhat by ignoring some portion of the overturning resistance, as described above, and by the use of an expression for the height of the center of mass of the fluid which is slightly conservative.

The tank is deemed to be stable if the resisting moment, M_{RES}, is greater than the overturning moment induced by the earthquake, M_{OT}. Expressed alternately, the tank is stable if the limit impulsive acceleration, C_{eq}, calculated by equating M_{OT} with M_{RES}, is greater than the earthquake-induced peak spectral acceleration at 2% of critical damping.

The method for evaluation of unanchored storage tanks included herein is based on that of Manos, but includes some important variations. The most notable of these are:

a. Tank anchorage is recommended in zones of high seismicity whenever the ratio of safe operating height to tank diameter exceeds two (Dowling and Summers, 1993). Based on the data presented in Manos (1986), and the higher level of risk for taller tanks, this is believed to be the upper limit of applicability of the Manos method.

b. The allowable compressive stress in the tank shell should not exceed 75% of the theoretical buckling stress, as presented in Manos (1986), nor should it exceed the material yield strength. This last requirement is significant for thicker-walled tanks. Note that under certain circumstances an increase in the allowable compressive stress beyond 75% of the theoretical buckling stress may be justified (Dowling and Summers, 1993). Examination of the experimental and observational data presented by Manos indicates that an increase may be justified for the types of tanks encountered at petrochemical facilities. In any event, the compressive stress should never exceed the material yield strength.

c. The compressive force in the tank shell should not exceed the total weight of the fluid contents (Dowling and Summers, 1993). This has the effect of imposing an upper bound on the resisting moment.

A final note of caution: The critical formula for term C_{eq} (the limit impulsive acceleration), as presented by Manos in Equation (9) of his paper (not shown below), should include the term (m_t/m_1) not (m_1/m_t), as originally presented, where m_1 is the liquid impulsive mass and m_t is the total liquid mass. Correction to this formula was made in the form of an erratum to the original paper (Manos, 1986).

The expression for overturning moment, M_{OT}, from Manos (1986) in English units is given by:

$$M_{OT} = 1.29\rho_w G H^2 R^2 C_{eq} \frac{m_1}{m_t}\left(\frac{H}{R}\right)^{0.15} \tag{7.1}$$

where

ρ_w = mass density of water (=62.4/g)
G = specific gravity of contained liquid
H = tank liquid height
R = tank radius
C_{eq} = limit impulsive acceleration (in g's)

and a curve for the ratio (m_1/m_t) is given in *API 650*, Appendix E for the ratio (W_1/W_T), where W_1 is the impulsive liquid weight and W_T is the total liquid weight. The expression for resisting moment, M_{RES}, is given by:

$$M_{RES} = 0.48 S E R t_s^2 \left(\frac{t_s}{t_p}\right)^{0.1}\left(\frac{R}{H}\right)^{n-0.15} \tag{7.2a}$$

where

t_s = shell thickness

t_p = bottom plate thickness
n = 0.1 + 0.2 (H/R) ≤ 0.25
E = Young's modulus
S = Foundation deformability coefficient

However, from Item (b) above, an upper bound on the resisting moment assuming the compressive stress in the tank shell just equals its yield stress, F_y, is given by:

$$M_{RES} = 1.06 S F_y R^2 t_s \left(\frac{t_s}{t_p}\right)^{0.1} \left(\frac{R}{H}\right)^{n-0.15} \tag{7.2b}$$

Also, from Item (c) above, an upper bound on the resisting moment when the compressive force in the tank shell just equals the weight of the fluid contents (assuming a lever arm of 1.25 $R(H/R)^{0.15}$, as expressed in Manos (1986)), is given by:

$$M_{RES} = \pi R^2 H g \rho_w G \times 1.25R \left(\frac{H}{R}\right)^{0.15} \tag{7.2c}$$

As can be seen from the above, the resisting moment, M_{RES}, should be taken as the smallest of the expressions given in Equations (7.2a), (7.2b) and (7.2c).

An important feature of the modified Manos methodology is the use of a foundation deformability coefficient (S). This should be taken as 1.0 for tanks founded on more rigid materials, such as concrete, asphalt rings or pads, and 1.2 for materials founded on more pliable materials, such as crushed rock, sand, wood planks or soil. The effect of this is that the size of the compressive stress zone is larger for a soft foundation than for a rigid foundation. This enables the development of a larger limit resisting moment (subject to the limitation imposed by the total weight of the fluid, as described above) and, consequently, enables the tank to withstand a larger seismic acceleration. This contrasts with the API methodology, where the soil type has no influence on the resisting moment, but where a softer soil leads to a larger convective acceleration and hence an increased overturning moment.

A comparison of the results of an evaluation of a 35 ft (10.7 m) diameter, 30 ft (9.1 m) high tank, filled to a height of 26 ft 4 in (8.0 m), using the modified Manos and API methodologies, is given in Table 7.1. As can be seen, the API approach would require either a reduction in fill height by about 40% to 16 ft 6 in (5.0 m) or tank anchorage, whereas the modified Manos method indicates that the seismic safe operating height can be increased to 20 ft 1 in (6.1 m). Hence the required reduction in fill height is reduced from 9 ft 10 in (3.0 m) to 6 ft 3 in (1.9 m).

TABLE 7.1: Comparison of API and Modified Manos Results
(from Dowling and Summers, 1993)

Typical Tank			
Diameter	35'	Product:	Vinyl Acetate
Height	30'	Fill Height:	26' 4"
		Roof Weight:	14.2 kips
Shell Properties: All courses - 0.18" thick			
Bottom Plate: 0.22" thick			
Specific Gravity:	0.93		
Site Amplification Factor:	1.5		

Site-Specific API Approach		Modified Manos Approach	
Instability Ratio:	2.79	Limiting Acceleration:	0.74g
Therefore, unstable.		Earthquake-Induced Acceleration:	1.29g
		Therefore, unstable.	
Seismic Safe Operating Height:	16' 6"	Seismic Safe Operating Height:	20' 1"

Note: Metric units not presented, since both API (1993) and Manos (1986) only present results for English units.

It is possible that a situation may be encountered where loss of contents of a single critical tank (or a number of critical tanks) is of concern. In this case, the structural integrity of the nearby tanks, containing relatively harmless materials, may only be of concern in so far as their failure could adversely impact the adjacent more critical tank(s). While an elephant foot buckling type of failure of one of the surrounding tanks would not pose a threat to the integrity of the critical tank, a gross failure, such as overturning, could lead to an impact with the critical tank, possibly leading to rupture of the tank wall and release of its contents. In such cases, the surrounding tanks need to be evaluated to ensure that they have an adequate margin of safety against overturning or collapse (but not necessarily against buckling). For such a situation, the modified Manos criteria could be relaxed still further (Dowling and Summers, 1993). Examination of the data on which the Manos methodology is based (Manos, 1986) suggests that failure/collapse may be less likely in cases where the ratio of overturning moment to restoring moment is less than two. Further, since local buckling of the tank wall is less a concern, it may be appropriate to increase the allowable compressive stress in the tank shell by 33% from that presented earlier, i.e., up to the theoretical buckling stress, with the caveat to remain that the compressive stress should not exceed the material yield strength. Again, however, the compressive weight in the tank shell should not exceed the total weight of the fluid contents. These recommendations are based on limited data and should be used with care (Dowling and Summers, 1993) but are supported (in principle) by research presented by Peek and El-Bkaily (1990), which suggests that the ultimate seismic overturning moment which was resisted by a subject 100 ft (30.5 m) diameter by 40 ft (12.2 m) high tank was 31% higher than the overturning moment at which elephant's foot buckling began.

7.4.4 Freeboard Requirements

Tanks with insufficient freeboard may have their fixed or floating roofs damaged by sloshing fluid. In fixed roof tanks, the sloshing fluid can impact and damage rafters, as well as buckle the tank shell. Floating roofs can tilt with the sloshing wave and, if insufficient freeboard exists, the roof's seal can be damaged or the roof may impact the access platform. In order to prevent this damage, sufficient freeboard may be provided to accommodate fluid sloshing. The height of the sloshing wave can be calculated using methods described by Wozniak and Mitchell (1978) and Housner and Haroun (1980).

7.4.5 Uplift Calculations

When assessing the vulnerability of a tank's piping, walkway and stairway attachments (as shown in Figure 7.6), one should consider that the tank may be subject to uplift. Using a value on the order of 6 to 12 inches (150 to 300 mm) of uplift in the zones of highest seismicity can be considered prudent and conservative. Actual expected values are a function of tank size, aspect ratio, fill height, and local seismicity and soil type. In lieu of justifying other values, a value of 12 inches (300 mm) is proposed in the latest *NEHRP* provisions for certain tanks. If explicit calculation of tank uplift is required, the only analytical method known to this committee is found in Priestley, et al (1986).

It should be pointed out that *AWWA D100-84* (AWWA, 1985) indicates that uplift does not occur when the term $M/[D^2(w_t + w_L)]$ is less or equal to 0.785. This committee feels that this criterion should not be used for assessing piping and other attachments. One of the reasons for this, aside from the ever-present risk that an unanchored tank will uplift, is that the term w_L, which is the resisting liquid component, only occurs when there is uplift and, therefore, should not be used to determine whether uplift occurs.

The method in Priestley, et al (1986) was proposed by a study group for the design of storage tanks. The group did an extensive review of the available literature at the time to come up with their proposed methodology. It includes provisions for rectangular and concrete tanks. Some differences between this and other methods include:

a. The impulsive and convective components are combined by the SRSS method instead of algebraically.

b. The tank bottom uplift is based on a model that incorporates both the bending and the in-plane forces in the bottom plate.

c. The method is iterative, equating the overturning moment with the resisting moment.

d. The analysis is based upon ultimate loads rather than working loads.

As mentioned earlier, this method is more involved than either *API 650* or the method developed by Manos. As stated in Priestley et al (1986), the calculated displacements become less accurate as the displacements increase. Good engineering judgment should be used in these cases.

7.4.6 Riveted and Bolted Tanks

Riveted and bolted tanks have the additional failure mode of tank shell splitting, which does not occur in welded tanks. Tank shell splitting is believed to occur from excessive hoop tension and poorly proportioned joints. A quick assessment of this failure mode would be to compare the cross-sectional strength of the bolts or rivets to the steel plate. If the bolts or rivets are stronger than the surrounding plate, the shell should behave with ductility. If additional analysis is required, the bolted/riveted section strength can be compared to the hoop tension predicted by AWWA (1987) or Priestley, et al (1986). Capacities of riveted sections are provided in *API 653* (API, 1991).

7.4.7 Fiber Reinforced Plastic (Fiberglass) Tanks

Fiberglass does not have the ductility typically associated with the steel. Fiberglass properties are also anisotropic, that is, the strength in a direction parallel to the grain is different to that perpendicular to it. Presently, there is no standard for designing or assessing fiberglass tanks for seismic loadings. Guidance on non-seismic design is found in ASME (1992) and ASTM (1988). Many variables are involved in determining the strength and ductility of the fiberglass composite material, including the properties of the resin matrix and the angle of winding of the fibers. Seismic loads should be determined from *API 650* (API, 1993), with due consideration given to expected tank performance and ductility, and allowables obtained from manufacturers' recommendations or test results.

7.5 MITIGATION OF SEISMIC EFFECTS

Mitigating a seismic hazard can be quite involved or relatively simple. For overconstrained piping, additional bends or a flexible section of piping may be added. Stairs and walkways can be solely supported by the tank shell. Tank wall stability can be more difficult to correct. No one method will work all the time and operating as well as construction economics should be considered.

Where the tank is found to be structurally inadequate (as determined by exceedance of the modified Manos criteria or gross exceedance of the API criteria), any of the following retrofits may be implemented:

a. Reduction of the fill height; this is the simplest and most commonly recommended retrofit, and should also be considered in cases where the available freeboard is found to be inadequate. Note that reduction of fill height can have a significant effect on the economics of tank storage.

b. Increase the shell thickness and/or the bottom plate or annular ring thickness.

c. Anchor the tank in accordance with the provisions specified in *API 650.*

d. In lieu of anchorage, prevent uplift of the tank by stiffening the tank base through the installation of a concrete slab within the tank shell, or by other methods. This method is relatively untried but may have the same effect as anchoring the tank.

7.6 CONSIDERATIONS FOR FUTURE INVESTIGATION

This committee did not review all aspects of seismic tank performance. Three areas which would warrant further evaluation include:

a. Investigation as to applicability of New Zealand code (Priestley, et al, 1986) for use in the U.S.

b. Development of a method to predict tank uplift.

c. Development of seismic design and evaluation procedures for fiberglass tanks.

7.7 DESIGN OF NEW TANKS

Seismic design of new tanks is covered in *API 650* Appendix E (API, 1993) which, usually being conservative, is a good candidate for design. As discussed in Section 7.4.3, *API 650* may be unconservtive for very broad tanks with thin shells when using high strength steel and/or thickened annular rings. The following modifications or additions are proposed to address other shortcomings.

Sloshing Fluid

Earthquakes cause the upper portion of the contained fluid to slosh. The height of the sloshing fluid can be calculated by an equation found in Wozniak and Mitchell (1978). This height should be used for freeboard requirements if the owner is concerned with floating roof damage or with spillage of product in floating roof or open roof tanks. The sloshing fluid can also impact and damage rafters and supporting columns of fixed roofs. Wozniak and Mitchell (1978) also shows how to calculate this wave force.

Overturning Moment on the Foundation

The hydrodynamic forces which create the overturning moment on the tank walls also act on the tank bottom and, hence, also on the foundation. This additional overturning moment (ASCE, 1984) should be included when designing the structural portion of the foundation and piles.

Tank Movement

Tank uplift during earthquakes can damage attached piping and other appurtenances. The same provisions discussed in Section 7.4.5 may be used in design. Additionally, anchored tank appurtenances may be designed for some level of anchor bolt stretch. A value of 2 inches (50 mm) is proposed in the latest *NEHRP* (1994) provisions.

API 650 states that piping attached to the tank bottom that is not free to move vertically shall be placed a radial distance from the shell/bottom connection of 12 inches (300 mm) greater than the uplift length predicted by the *API 650* uplift model. The *API 650* uplift model, however, may underpredict the amount of radial uplift (Manos, 1986; Dowling and Summers, 1993). It may be prudent to consider changing this requirement to that predicted by Priestley et al (1986), twice the *API 650* model, or an interaction of allowable vertical movement with the distance placed radially from the shell.

Walkways between tanks should be designed to accommodate relative movement of the tanks. There is no reference known to this committee which calculates the predicted movement. In lieu of a more rigorous analysis, a walkway should be designed to accommodate a total of 12 to 18 inches (300 to 450 mm) of movement, at least in the zones of high seismicity. This is based upon limited experience data from past earthquakes and is thought to be conservative for tanks with small height-to-diameter ratios. For anchored tanks, this movement should be reduced further.

Anchored Tanks

API 650 or other methods may be used for design. Attached ringwalls should be designed appropriately. Anchoring a tank to a small ringwall and not developing the forces into the soil by the weight of the ringwall or with piles should be viewed with caution. Anchor bolts need to be designed such that they behave in a ductile manner, both in terms of the force transfer to the shell and pullout from the concrete foundation.

Chapter 8
EARTHQUAKE CONTINGENCY PLANNING

8.1 INTRODUCTION

Although not explicitly a part of petrochemical facility design, a section on contingency planning was included due to the importance of the topic. This section does not give specific guidance on how to author contingency plans, rather it merely outlines some general points that should be addressed by in-place contingency plans.

8.2 PURPOSE

It is expected that every facility located in a seismic region should have its own contingency plan in place. It is imperative that all parties involved in the response to a seismic event be familiar with the response plan in order to utilize it to its fullest potential. This section merely offers suggestions that such a plan should include.

The primary purpose for assembling an earthquake emergency contingency plan is to have a rapid, rational and structured response to a seismic event. A contingency plan will allow the following do be done in an efficient and safe manner:

a. Emergency response to maintain public, personnel, and plant safety

b. Organized inspection of facilities for earthquake structural damage and conveyance of results to management so as to minimize business interruption

c. Focusing of critical resources for recovery effort

8.3 SCOPE OF RESPONSE PLAN

This guideline is intended to cover the organization of personnel and resources for performing structural damage assessment and damage control after a seismic event. An effective response plan should cover all of the following elements:

a. Pre-earthquake Preparation

b. Event Recognition
c. Command & Control System / Mobilization of Inspection Team
d. Roles & Responsibilities of Team Personnel
e. Inspection Methodology
f. Assembling Inspection Data / Reporting Results

This section will concentrate mainly on Items a-d, with e and f covered in more detail in Chapter 9 of this document

8.4 PRE-EARTHQUAKE PREPARATION

The key to effective response to any disaster situation is organization and planning before the event actually occurs. As likely scenarios could entail loss of water, loss of communications, loss of firefighting ability, inability to reach site, release of hazardous materials, etc., it is imperative to take a proactive role in planning for any emergency. Some of the most critical areas to address would be:

a. Pre-Event Assessment of Seismic Risk

A key component in planning response to an earthquake emergency is having insight into what type of damage may be expected and where it may occur. Performing a seismic assessment of a facility is an ideal way to assess the inherent risk at the facility. Another benefit of performing a seismic assessment is that it allows structures to be prioritized according to risk. This risk hierarchy can then be implemented into the response plan and allow the highest risk structures to be inspected first. This risk hierarchy list needs to be a 'living' document and must have an owner to maintain it.

b. Formal Response Plan

Another key component of effective response to a disaster is a written response plan which outlines:

- Organization of Inspection Teams
- Command Structure of Teams
- Listing of Key Contacts
- Risk Prioritized Listing of Structures

The response plan must effectively outline the team's organization, command structure, and role in the assessment process in order to be useful. Its contents must be effectively communicated to and understood by personnel who will be involved in the assessment effort. Drills are an excellent method to help implement the intents of the document.

It is often useful to set up standing agreements with support resources such as local engineering firms, local emergency response agencies, and professional organizations such as ASCE. Having standing assistance agreements in place can help streamline the response process.

c. Pre-Earthquake Training

In order for inspection personnel to perform effectively, they must be trained in post-earthquake damage assessment. It is suggested that all inspection personnel undergo *ATC-20* or similar training for building assessment as well as similar training geared toward inspection of industrial structures.

d. Inspection Materials

For quick response, inspection materials (i.e., paper, pencils, clipboards, film, etc.) as well as structural priority information and posting materials should be kept in a secure location that is to be accessed only in the event of an earthquake. The post-event scenario is inherently confusing without having the problems of finding inspection materials. It may be desirable to include search and rescue equipment. Water and food supplies should be kept in the secured location additionally, as shelter in place conditions may occur.

8.5 INCIDENT RECOGNITION

Before any response or assessment effort can begin, there must be some formal recognition of the event that has occurred. Recognition of the event will allow response plans to be put into effect. It is advisable to set up a matrix or classification system to describe the extent of the event (i.e., low, moderate, severe). This matrix could be based on the extent of the observed damage. By doing this, each level of alert can then be paired with an appropriate level of response. The obvious benefit is that the appropriate amount of response is employed for the size of event that has occurred. For additional information, please refer to Chapter 9.

8.6 COMMAND & CONTROL / MOBILIZATION SYSTEM

In order to effectively respond to an emergency, a clear command and control structure must be maintained. Key contacts and decision makers must be clearly identified, and a hierarchy of authority must be clearly understood. The response plan should specifically designate key contacts and decision makers, as well as backups in case the primary contacts are unavailable. It should also describe how and to where inspection results should be communicated to the decision makers. Finally, the emergency operations center (EOC) should be located in a safe area, preferably on the perimeter of the site.

After an earthquake, there will be a short term (rapid assessment) and a longer-term (detailed assessment) response necessary. Immediately following an event, rapid assessment teams will need to be sent out to identify obvious or immediate problems. These problems might include failures, environmental releases, fires, etc. Concurrently, the incident commander will need to start mobilizing structural expertise to: a) advise plant personnel on the course of action to stabilize immediate failures or crises; and b) begin performing a detailed inspection.

Once the rapid assessment teams have reported to the incident commander and the seriousness of the incident has been determined, the appropriate level of response must be mobilized. The incident commander must have trained personnel available to make decisions regarding short term stabilization of failures or crises. Examples may include advising on temporary bracing/shoring, coordination of multidisciplinary problems, advising on plant shutdown, etc.

The response plan must contain instructions for the team members once the level of response needed has been determined. These instructions must include where and when to report. Additionally, details instructing the team members who to report to once they have reached the facility need to be included. Some contingencies need to be addressed to account for the inability of team members to get to the site, difficulty in communications, etc. or any foreseeable difficulties that may be encountered.

8.7 ROLES AND RESPONSIBILITIES OF TEAM PERSONNEL

After the inspection team has been assembled, it is imperative that they know what is expected of them, and what responsibility each of them will be held accountable for. A model team structure should be laid out within the response plan to show what role each will play. The desired qualifications for each role in the inspection effort should be outlined in the response plan, with the realization that circumstances may not allow a perfect matching of skills to positions. It is advisable to have an operating representative as part of the inspection team. The plan should also clearly outline lines of communication and authority within the team structure as well. See Chapter 9 for additional information.

8.8 INSPECTION METHODOLOGY

It is desirable that the response plan address the methodology to be employed for damage assessment. Things that should be specified include:

a. Inspection Criteria to Use (*ATC-20* / Other)
b. Posting Criteria for Buildings / Structures
c. Authority of Postings
d. Dealing with Aftershocks
e. Repair Authority

This item is addressed in more detail in Chapter 9.

8.9 ASSEMBLING OF INSPECTION DATA / REPORTING RESULTS

After performing the field inspections, posting buildings, and making structural evaluations, data and results must be assembled in order to report it to the incident commander. It is desirable to have pre-designed forms to help standardize the data collected and make it easier to assemble after the inspections. These forms should be stored in a secured cabinet, such as the one discussed in Section 8.4. It also allows documentation of damage to be kept for future review and/or analysis. Using the standard forms makes the task of assembling and transmitting the information to the appropriate decision maker much more efficient. Also, these forms should include some method of incorporating secondary inspections after the inevitable large aftershocks. Additional information is contained in Chapter 9.

Chapter 9
POST-EARTHQUAKE DAMAGE ASSESSMENT

9.1 INTRODUCTION

This section provides guidance with respect to post-earthquake damage assessment of those facilities considered to be in need of structural investigation after the occurrence of an earthquake. After every significant seismic event, an immediate and complete walkdown of the petrochemical facility in question would be the optimum response. However, although such action is strongly advised, it is also realized that this is impractical due to cost and manpower constraints. For these reasons, two factors need to be considered with regards to the scope of, and necessity for, post-earthquake damage assessments: (1) prioritization of items to be assessed after an earthquake; and (2) determination as to what "size" of an event warrants an assessment.

9.1.1 Assessment Priorities

The major safety/operational concerns of operators of petrochemical facilities fall under the following three priorities:

First Priority:	Health and human safety.
Second Priority:	Damage to the environment.
Third Priority:	Other items with significant economic impact.

Under the first priority item, the major risks to health and human safety associated with earthquakes (in no particular order) are the following:

a. Fires.
b. Explosions.
c. Collapsed and damaged structures.
d. Release of hazardous materials.

Under the second priority item, the major risk to the environment associated with earthquakes is the release of environmentally sensitive products. Such releases are generally related to the following occurrences:

a. Storage tank failure.

b. Pipeline rupture or failure.

c. Failure or collapse of other vessels containing environmentally sensitive products.

Note that failure in the above discussion also refers to significant leakage of tanks, pipelines, and vessels, and is not limited to complete collapse.

Under the third priority item, the major additional cause of significant economic impact to a facility operator is a loss of production capability. Occurrences that contribute to loss of production capability (in addition to those listed in the first two priority items) are the following:

a. Loss of power.
b. Loss of communications.
c. In-place emergency shut-down procedures activated by earthquake.

Auxiliary structures that also require investigation following an earthquake include the following:

a. Utility systems that would be required to operate following an earthquake to maintain the facility in a safe condition, e.g., firewater and emergency power systems.

b. Adjacent systems, structures, or components whose structural failure or displacement could result in the failure of systems that pose a risk to health and human safety, contain hazardous materials or environmentally sensitive products, or are particularly valuable from an operations point of view.

c. Any structures, systems, or components that, from an operator viewpoint, are required to remain functional during and after a major earthquake.

9.1.2 Assessment Triggers

No absolute quantitative measure of earthquake severity can be given as a guideline as to when a post-earthquake damage assessment should be performed. Much depends on whether there has been any reported significant damage at the facility, and whether the earthquake event was serious or damaging. Ideally, a post-earthquake damage assessment should be undertaken after a seismic event of any significant magnitude. The following examples (either occurring at the facility or in the immediate vicinity of the facility) should trigger the need for a post-earthquake response:

a. Injury to personnel
b. Structural collapse
c. Release of hazardous materials or environmentally sensitive products
d. Fire
e. Explosion
f. Automatic system shut-down
g. Loss of power, utilities, or communications.

Any of the above occurrences may indicate more serious problems, and a post-earthquake damage assessment should be initiated immediately. In addition to the structural investigation, mechanical and systems assessments may also be required.

9.2 PRE-INVESTIGATION ACTIVITIES

The performance of a post-earthquake damage assessment should be preceded by the following safety-related actions, which should take place immediately after a significant seismic event:

a. Accounting for the safety and welfare of all persons on the site (employees, contractors, and visitors)

b. Control of all immediate dangers, such as fires, collapsed structures, etc.

c. Determination of safety for non-emergency response trained personnel, i.e., the engineers performing the post-earthquake damage assessment, to enter the facility.

Pre-planning of inspection activities is essential, and should include a meeting with plant personnel familiar with the facilities under review. To help ensure that all pertinent topics are addressed, a list of questions should be prepared before this meeting. One individual should be appointed to write notes for a record of conversation, or instead, it is permitted, a tape recorder may be used. Topics to be discussed with plant personnel include the following:

a. Plant operating history before and after the earthquake.
b. Corrective action taken by the operators during or after the earthquake.
c. Maintenance or repairs that may have been made before the inspection.
d. Any problems experienced with operability and functionality.
e. Any equipment failures during or after the earthquake.
f. Equipment accessibility.
g. Hazardous areas.

h. Safety precautions.
i. Existence of any instrumentation on site that recorded the earthquake motion.

Particular attention should be given to corrective actions, maintenance, and other repairs made at the facility due to seismic activity. The adequacy of such repairs should be checked, and the location of these corrective activities may indicate additional areas of concern.

During pre-investigation activities, the inspection team should also discuss and determine what areas of the plant, equipment, or components will be inspected and in what order. Plant arrangement drawings should be obtained and marked with the location of specific components selected for evaluation. If more than one inspection team is involved, areas of responsibility should be divided as needed.

A prudent reminder for all those involved with the inspection is that the plant has experienced a seismic event. Before beginning inspections, plant personnel should visually inspect the plant for any existing hazardous condition (for example, areas contaminated by chemical spills). If any hazardous condition is found, this area should be noted and inspection team members advised accordingly. Inspection of these areas should be performed only if precautions to protect the safety of the inspection team members can be and have been taken.

One of the most important functions of the pre-investigation phase is to thoroughly question operators as to the extent of the damage. Usually, the operators will have already performed a quick inspection of the facility and will be able to provide exact locations of known damage. Such areas should be the first priority of the inspection team. If a seismic hazard mitigation program has already been undertaken at the facility, then the structures known to be seismically vulnerable, and their weak links, should be the second priority of inspection. If no such program has been previously undertaken, then the vulnerable structures will not be known a priori, and the assessment team should sweep the entire facility in a systematic manner, while concentrating on the assessment priorities as discussed previously in Section 9.1.1. Attention should be given to types of items that have performed poorly during past earthquakes, such as older structures. In any event, plant operators will be the key to prioritizing the assessment.

9.3 PERFORMING FIELD INSPECTIONS

Inspections of the facility should be documented with field notes and accompanying photographs. Checklist-style forms may be used; see Chapter 6 for examples. Although inspection team members may prefer taking notes to filling out checklists, using these forms can provide a greater measure of consistency.

Measurements should be made with a tape measure as much as is practical. For components that are inaccessible, a visual estimate of dimensions should be made.

When visual dimensions are used, the documentation provided should reflect this fact. For some items, an as-found sketch may be needed to identify all of the parameters investigated. Complete information, as required, should be provided on the sketch regarding dimensions, sizes, component types, etc. At least one photograph of each structure or component investigated should be taken. A labeling system should be implemented to match the photographs to the inspection notes. If permissible, a video camera can be used. The video camera will generally provide a better visual aid for historical data, and the voice recording unit of the camera can be used to narrate condition and type of equipment being inspected.

Above all, any damage which resulted from the seismic event should be described in detail. Damage should be assessed immediately at each individual location, and some engineering basis to explain the failure should be provided and noted, if possible. The inspection team should try to come to a consensus as to any remedial measures that may be required.

9.4 EVALUATION OF LOAD-CARRYING SYSTEMS

Of paramount importance when performing a post-earthquake damage assessment is the ability to determine what exactly constitutes a given structure's gravity and lateral force resisting systems. A structure whose gravity system has been damaged, and its ability to continue to carry vertical (dead) loads is in question, is a very hazardous condition since collapse may be imminent. This becomes even more critical when the likelihood of aftershocks is included. Such a structure should be immediately flagged, and suitable measures taken, such as barricades, evacuation, immediate stabilization, demolition, etc.

Structures that have intact gravity systems, but have substantial damage to their lateral force resisting system, e.g., buckled or damaged braces, should also be regarded as potential hazards, due to the possibility of future aftershocks. Although such structures are generally not as significant a hazard as those with damaged gravity systems, immediate steps should be taken to restore the integrity of the original lateral force resisting system.

In deciding whether a structure has a damaged vertical and/or lateral force resisting system, the question as to the ability of the structure to withstand an aftershock of equal or greater magnitude is often asked. If an experienced damage assessment team does not believe the structure is capable of surviving such an event, immediate steps should be taken, and entering the structure or its immediate vicinity should only be done on a limited as-needed basis. Continued operation should be justified on a case-by-case basis. Some items of particular concern include the following:

a. Loss of integrity of vertical and/or lateral force resisting systems.

b. Steel structures -- yielding, hinging (top and bottom of columns), web buckling and crippling, brace buckling, weld cracks, etc.

c. Concrete structures -- excessive cracking, spalling, exposed rebar, damaged rebar, hinging, crushing, etc.

d. Anchors and foundations -- anchors and/or bolts pulled out of footings, large depressions around column bases, etc.

e. Equipment -- visible punctures, leaks, cracks, toppled items, loose fittings and valves, contents under high pressure, weld cracks, enclosed areas where build-up of explosive gases may occur (confined spaces), etc.

f. Roadways -- clear of large debris, downed power lines, "continuous surface" (no faulting), etc.

g. Evidence of liquefaction, fault rupture, significant settlement, landslides, and tsunami/seiche.

9.5 IDENTIFICATION OF DAMAGED STRUCTURES

It is recommended that a facility-specific “tagging” system be considered in order to identify systems, structures, or components judged as being vulnerable by the inspection team. A system developed for post-earthquake evaluation of buildings and used relatively successfully following recent major earthquakes is described in ATC-20. That system essentially involves placing green (safe), yellow (enter with caution for restricted use), and red (do not enter) tags on inspected buildings. Such a system may require modification for use in a petrochemical facility setting, due to the congestion and (often times) indistinguishability of different structures, and it should be understood that multiple tags or tape may be required to rope off those sections deemed unsafe by the assessment team.

9.6 DOCUMENTATION

The objective of the inspection team's effort at each facility should be to collect all information needed to document equipment and structural performance during the earthquake. Figure 9.1 shows, in the form of a recommended table of contents, the organization and content of a report that can be produced for each facility visited (EQE, 1986b). Note that the contents of this report can be separated between those sections that should be substantially completed during the field inspection and those that can be completed later.

The final report should reference published information on the earthquake severity in discussions of the ground motion at each facility, summarize information of the inspected equipment and structures at each facility, discuss generally the performance of each type of inspected equipment, and describe in detail any damage that was noted during the inspections, along with any required or recommended retrofits.

TABLE OF CONTENTS

1. INTRODUCTION AND PURPOSE. Generic description of purpose of report, which is to document post-earthquake inspection of facility after earthquake event. This section can be completed after inspection.

2. FACILITY DESCRIPTION. A brief overview of facility, including function. Description of major structures, age, exact location, operating history, etc. During the plant visit, collect information necessary to include in this section: plant literature, drawings, tape recordings of interview with personnel, etc.

3. GROUND MOTION AT FACILITY. Unless records during the plant visit can be obtained, expect to write this section later using published reports of records throughout the area (e.g., those published by USGS).

4. OPERATIONAL IMPACT OF EARTHQUAKE ON FACILITY. Interviews with plant personnel will form the basis for this section. If possible, obtain copies of operator logs during the plant visit.

5. EARTHQUAKE PERFORMANCE. This section will form the main body of the report, and should be completed during the field inspection. This section should include recommendations for remediation, if required. Responsibility for originating various subsections should be divided up among walkdown team members.

6. CONCLUSIONS/RECOMMENDATIONS. Briefly summarize the primary findings of the team, including recommended actions. This section may be written later.

7. APPENDIX A. The appendix should contain photographs, plans, drawings, etc., which are referenced within the body of the report.

Figure 9.1: Example Report Table of Contents

9.7 INSPECTION TEAM

Each inspection group should consist of a minimum or two (2) individuals with the following qualifications:

a. Petrochemical facility walkthrough inspection experience.

b. Experience in seismic design and analysis of equipment, systems, and structures found in petrochemical facilities.

Inspection team members should have undergone training in post-earthquake damage assessment and in the procedures to document such assessments at the facility in question.

The structural portion of a post-earthquake damage assessment should be conducted by experienced engineers familiar with seismic design and the effects of earthquakes. They should be able to readily identify areas of weakness, and prioritize remedial measures to correct severe damage and to ensure continued safe operation of the facility.

9.8 RECOMMENDED EQUIPMENT

The following items are recommended while performing post-earthquake damage assessments:

a. Flashlight

b. Tape measure or folding rule

c. Compass

d. Clipboard

e. Hard hat

f. Safety glasses

g. Hearing protection

h. Safety mask (particularly after a major seismic event and/or in areas of known hazardous material or environmentally sensitive product release)

i. Construction boots

j. Plumb bob or level

k. Photo camera (Polaroid or 35mm)

l. Long sleeve shirt or any protective clothing as mandated by site personnel

m. Plot plans and facility road map

n. Hand-held video camera (optional)

o. Tape recorder (optional)

Note: Check camera, flash, video, and tape recorder use with facility operators prior to their use at the facility. This should be done not only for confidentiality purposes, but also because some camera equipment is considered an ignition source in certain hazardous areas or could trigger certain fire detection systems.

Chapter 10
RETROFIT DESIGN

10.1 INTRODUCTION

The guidelines presented in this section are intended to assist an engineer in performing pre-earthquake seismic upgrading and modification of existing structures. These guidelines are not intended to perform as a code document; rather, they are intended only to give guidance to the engineer faced with a task of retrofitting seismically deficient structures.

10.2 UPGRADE SITUATIONS

Generally, structures need seismic upgrading and modification for one or more of the following reasons:

a. Existing structures may be identified to be potentially hazardous to public safety after a walkthrough and an initial screening evaluation process (see Chapter 6). The initial evaluation procedure is a cursory review of existing seismic resisting framing structures, systems, and equipment, to determine if they are categorized to be "safe", "unsafe" or "need further study". For structures and systems that are classified as "safe", no further action is required. However, for those that are classified as "unsafe" or "need further study", a more rigorous evaluation should be performed.

b. Additions to and modifications of existing structures often trigger the need to upgrade structures to current code requirements. Upgrading may be to the code of record if approved by the local building official. However the entire structure may not need to be checked against the current seismic code; for example if the following conditions exist:

   1. Addition is designed to the current code.

2. Addition does not increase seismic forces, stresses, and displacements in the entire modified structure by more than a set percentage of the design values from the code of record. Values of 5% to 25% have been used by local building officials.

3. Deteriorated conditions do not reduce the capacity of the existing structure by more than a set percentage.

4. Addition does not decrease the seismic resistance of any structural elements of existing structures unless the reduced resistance is equal to or greater than that required for new structures.

c. Owners often will upgrade existing facilities to reduce the risk of business interruption losses.

10.3 CRITERIA FOR VOLUNTARY SEISMIC UPGRADING

The intent of voluntary seismic upgrading and modification of existing structures is not to bring them up to the current codes. Rather, the goal is to provide reasonable assurance to the public, owners, and state building officials that structures and systems will survive a major earthquake without catastrophic failure, though they may suffer extensive damage. Business owners may desire to retrofit to a higher performance level in an effort to minimize business interruption losses. Additionally, there are situations where regulatory agencies set the retrofit standard. See Chapter 2 for additional background.

10.4 GUIDELINES / PROCEDURES

Criteria for design of new structures and systems are well defined in building codes such as those discussed in Chapter 1. However, criteria for assessing and/or upgrading existing structures are poorly defined. Currently, there are no code documents that specifically outline retrofit standards. Suggested guidelines for pre-earthquake seismic upgrading and modifications are presented in the following:

1. Obtain an up-to-date geotechnical / seismological report.

2. Collect the existing design calculations and drawings.

3. Review the initial evaluation report, verify the vertical and lateral seismic force resisting systems, and identify any special loads for determining the potential weak links in the structural systems.

4. Use *FEMA-178* R factors (in lieu of R_w factors from the *UBC*) for buildings and Q factors from the RMPP criteria (see Appendix 4F) for plant structures in calculating the seismic forces for analysis.

5. When dynamic analysis is required, use either of the following design response spectra:

   a. For buildings, use the *FEMA-178* seismic acceleration spectral shape or a site specific spectrum, if available, modified per *FEMA-178*.

   b. For plant structures, use a site-specific acceleration response spectrum based on mean estimates of occurrence for representing the mean values of spectral accelerations. These values should consider the remaining life of the structure and the consequences of failure.

6. Use actual dead and live loads in the analysis, not design basis loads.

7. Use in situ member strengths for calculating the member capacities. Non-destructive testing may be required to obtain the as-built strength of structural members.

8. Check the existing seismic capacities (C) of structural members, connections, and equipment supports versus the seismic demand (D). If C > D, no further action is required. Otherwise, seismic upgrading and modification should be initiated. It is recommended that strength design methods be used to calculate capacities.

9. When deformations and drift limits need to be checked against the allowable, they should be consistent with those discussed in Chapter 5.

10. Alternate procedures using rational analyses based on well established analysis principles may be used. Methods such as non-linear inelastic time history analyses would be acceptable.

10.5 STRENGTHENING CRITERIA

To ensure that proper corrective actions are implemented in seismic upgrade programs, engineers should be fully aware of the latest developments in earthquake engineering. The Applied Technology Council (ATC) is currently finalizing a guideline specifically addressing seismic retrofitting. A 75% complete draft of "Guidelines for the Seismic Rehabilitation of Buildings" (*ATC 33.03*) has been issued for review, and is expected to be completed some time in 1996. This document is the first code-like guideline to address seismic retrofit work, and while focused primarily on buildings will be an important resource for petrochemical facilities. Additional resources would include several organizations and programs mentioned throughout this document, such as the American Concrete Institute (ACI), the American Institute of Steel Construction (AISC), the American Society of Civil Engineers (ASCE), the National Earthquake Hazard Reduction Program (*NEHRP* (FEMA)), the Earthquake Engineering Research Institute (EERI), the Structural Engineers Association of California (SEAOC).

When retrofitting a structure, the main objective is to provide reasonable assurance that the retrofitted structure will perform in an acceptable manner when subject to strong ground motion. It must be kept in mind that the intent of retrofitting in not to bring the structure up to the letter of current code. However, in all situations, it is necessary to meet the intent of the code, i.e., non-collapse, as a minimum criteria. It may be advisable to strengthen beyond these minimum requirements if minimized business interruption or prevention of hazardous material release is the performance objective.

Another important point to consider when performing retrofit design is the concept of proportioning within the structure. Overstrengthening areas of a structure that are currently deficient in strength can force the weak link(s) to other elements that are perhaps even weaker or more brittle. If this occurs, the impact upon the overall structural performance is often undesirable. Therefore, care must be taken so that a currently weak, but ductile, structure is not modified such that it becomes a structure with a brittle failure mode.

Finally, there are some additional issues that must be considered when retrofitting a structure. Issues such as access, functionality, detailing, and constructibility must be addressed. In some cases, access requirements may be the determining factor in selecting a retrofit scheme. A typical example is the use of chevron braces as opposed to cross bracing. In addition, the retrofit must be functional and not create any additional problems. An example is that of air-cooled heat exchangers, or fin-fan structures, atop elevated pipeways. The supports for the exchangers are often not designed for seismic loads and may lack proper detailing. When retrofitting, the structure should not be stiffened such that its new structural period approaches that of the fan motors. Detailing is also a key consideration in retrofit design. One of the primary goals of retrofitting is to provide a ductile system. An example is retrofit of anchor bolts on tall process columns. Retrofit design should ensure that the mode of failure will be a ductile, i.e., yielding of the anchor bolts, and not brittle, i.e., pullout from the concrete or buckling of the support skirt. Finally, constructibility of the retrofits is a key consideration. Knowledge of whether bolting or welding is preferred, structure accessibility, potential interferences, etc., all will have bearing on the selected retrofit option.

NOMENCLATURE

C = Numerical coefficient representing potential amplification of seismic forces due to resonance effects

C_{eq} = Limit impulsive acceleration (in g's)

Cp = Numerical coefficient representing potential amplification of ground motion through the structure into the subsystem

D = Dead load is the total weight of materials forming the permanent part of a structure, including structural framing, platforms, walls, fixed equipment, vessels, piping, insulation and fireproofing.

D = Tank diameter

D = Resultant displacement

De = Elastically computed displacements

DP = Piping operating load includes weight of any liquids or solids within piping and on line equipment during normal operation

DV = Vessel operating load, including the weight of any liquids or solids within the vessel, attached equipment, and piping during normal operation

E = Earthquake load

E = Young's modulus

F_y = Yield stress of tank shell

g = Acceleration due to gravity

G = Specific gravity of contained liquid

H = Soil loads, including the effects due to weight and lateral pressure of soil and water in soil

H = Tank liquid height

I = Importance factor

L = Live load is the weight of all movable loads such as personnel, tools, stored material, movable partitions, cranes and hoists, maintenance loads, snow and ice loads, impact, surge forces, vibration, and longitudinal and transverse horizontal forces from moving equipment.

M = Overturning moment at bottom of tank shell

m_I = Liquid impulsive mass

M_{OT} = Overturning moment

M_{RES} = Resisting moment

m_t = Total liquid mass

n = Coefficient = $0.1 + 0.2\,(H/R) \leq 0.25$

p = Probability of exceedance

Q = Ductility based reduction factor for evaluation of existing facilities using the RMPP guidance document (RMPP, 1992)

R = Tank radius

R_w = Ductility based reduction factor for design of new facilities

S = Foundation deformability coefficient for tank analysis

S = Snow loads

S = Site coefficient for soil characteristics

T = Return period

T = Thermal loads are the loads caused by a change in temperature and may result from both operating and environmental conditions, including those caused by vessel, piping, and structure expansion and contraction.

T = Fundamental period of structure under consideration

t = Number of years

TE = Test loads, including all loads in the empty condition and the weight of test fluids

TL = Longitudinal Pipe Thermal Loads, including pipe anchor force, if any

t_p = Bottom plate thickness

t_s = Shell thickness

V = Base shear

W = Wind loads

W = Weight of the structure

W_I = Liquid impulsive weight

w_L = Maximum weight of tank contents that may be used to resist shell overturning

Wp = Weight of subsystem

W_T = Total liquid weight

w_t = Weight of tank shell and portion of fixed roof supported by tank shell

Z = Seismic zone factor

π = Constant = 3.14159

ρ_w = Mass density of water = 62.4/g

GLOSSARY

Acutely Hazardous Material - Material considered hazardous to health of general public if released to atmosphere, defined by Federal/State/Local agencies

Attenuation - Decay of ground motion with distance

Building-like Structures - Nonbuilding structures whose structural characteristics resemble those of a building

Convective Component - That portion of the tank contents which accelerates independently of the tank shell when subjected to seismic shaking; the convective component of the liquid is in the upper portion of the tank and responds in a sloshing mode

Davit - A small crane that projects over the side of a platform to lift small relatively light items, such as tools, manhole covers, etc.

Diamond Shape Buckling - A form of buckling of the tank shell, often found in the upper courses of slender tanks, in which the shell wrinkles in "diamond-shaped" patterns

Drift - Lateral displacement between floors or segments of a structure under earthquake loading

Ductility - Maximum deformation divided by elastic deformation; routinely refers to a measure of energy absorbing capability

Ductility Based Reduction Factor - A factor representing a measure of energy absorbing capability of a structure

Elephant Foot Buckling - A form of buckling of the tank shell near its connection with the bottom plate that resembles an "elephant's foot," in which the shell bulges outward near the bottom, but is constrained at its base by the bottom plate

Event - Occurrence of an earthquake

Fill Height - Height to which a tank is filled

Finfan - Air cooled heat exchangers, often located on top of pipeways

Freeboard - Vertical distance between the free surface of liquid contained in the tank and the top of the tank shell or underside of tank roof

HAZOPs - Hazard and Operability studies; a particular structured method of process hazards analysis commonly used in petrochemical facilities to identify process safety concerns

Importance Factor - A factor representing the importance of a structures depending on usage category

Impulsive Component - That portion of the tank contents which accelerates in unison with the tank shell when subjected to seismic shaking

Intensity - Measure of effects or strength of an earthquake at a particular site

Intermediate Moment Resisting Frame - A concrete moment resisting frame with certain design features to provide ductile post yield behavior, but not containing all of the design features of a special moment resisting frame

Magnitude - Measure of total energy released during an earthquake

Maximum Credible Earthquake - Maximum earthquake potential of a source

Moment Resisting Frame - A frame in which members and joints are capable of resisting forces primarily through flexure

Near field - Area in close proximity to active faults usually taken as within 5 to 10 kilometers of the fault trace

Nonbuilding-like Structures - Nonbuilding structures whose structural characteristics do not resemble those of a building

Overconstrained Piping - Piping exhibiting a lack of flexibility between the nozzle location on the tank shell and the nearest pipe support or ground penetration

Prying Action - Increase in load on a component or fastener caused by the bending of attached members

P-Δ Effects - Secondary effect on shears, axial forces, and bending moments in frame members induced by the vertical loads acting on the laterally displaced structure

Redundancy - Commonly refers to structures with multiple elements and load paths in the lateral force resisting system

Resonance - Amplification of earthquake motion due to similarity in frequency content of the applied motion and the structure under consideration

Response Spectrum - Response of a single degree of freedom oscillator subject to vibratory motion

Ringwall - A circular "ring" foundation beneath the tank shell

Rugged - Commonly refers to structures or equipment that are capable of surviving strong ground shaking with minimal damage

Seiche - Large waves generated by local submarine earthquakes in enclosed bodies of water, such as lakes, bays, reservoirs, or estuaries

Seismic Interaction - Interaction, such as impact or differential displacement, between adjacent structures, systems, or components during an earthquake

Seismic Weight - Total weight of the structure that gets excited by an earthquake

Seismic Zone Factor - A factor representing the severity of earthquake motion depending on seismic zonation

Sloshing - Relative movement of the free surface of liquid contained in the tank as a result of seismic shaking

Soft story - One in which the story stiffness is less than about 70% of that of the story above

Soil-Structure Interaction - Interaction effects between soil and structure under seismic loading

Special Moment Resisting Frame - A moment resisting frame specially detailed to provide ductile post yield behavior through member proportioning and connection detailing

SRSS - Square root of the sum of the squares; a method for combining modes

Stability Ratio - The quantity $M/[D^2(w_t + w_L)]$ in the API 650, Appendix E code check (API, 1993), as used in Chapter 7. The stability ratio is a function of overturning moment and resisting moment.

Subsystems - Nonstructural elements and components

Time History - Time variation of response such as acceleration, velocity, or displacement

Tsunami - Long period waves (also referred to as "tidal waves") typically generated by large, sometimes distant, submarine earthquake

Weak story - One in which the story strength is less than about 80% of that of the story above

REFERENCES

ACI 313, 1983, *Recommended Practice for the Design and Construction of Concrete Bins, Silos and Bunkers for Storage of Granular Materials (ACI 313R-77(R83))*, American Concrete Institute, Chicago, IL.

ACI 318, 1995, *Building Code Requirements for Reinforced Concrete and Commentary*," American Concrete Institute, Chicago, IL.

ACI 349, 1990, *Code Requirements for Nuclear Safety Related Structures*, American Concrete Institute, Chicago, IL.

ACI 530, 1992, *Building Code Requirements for Masonry Structures (ACI 530-92)"* American Concrete Institute, Chicago, IL.

ACI 530.1, 1989, *Specifications for Masonry Structures*, (ACI 530.1/ASCE 6), American Concrete Institute, Chicago, IL.

AISC, 1989, *Manual of Steel Construction - Allowable Stress Design*, American Institute of Steel Construction, Chicago, IL.

AISC, 1993, *Load and Resistance Factor Design Specification for Structural Steel Buildings*, American Institute of Steel Construction, Chicago, IL.

AISI, 1973, *The Criteria for Structural Application for Steel Cables for Buildings*, American Iron and Steel Institute, Washington, DC.

AISI, 1986, *Specification for the Design of Cold-Formed Steel Structural Members, SG-673*, American Iron and Steel Institute, Washington, DC, 1989 Addendum.

Andersen, G.R., R. V. Whitman, and J. T. Germaine, 1987, "Tilting Response of Centrifuge-Modeled Gravity Retaining Wall to Seismic Shaking: Description of Tests and Initial Analysis of Results," Rpt. R87-14, Dept. of Civil Engineering, MIT, Cambridge, MA.

API 650, July 1993, *Welded Steel Tanks for Oil Storage*, 9th Edition, American Petroleum Institute.

API 653, January 1991, *Tank Inspection, Repair, Alteration, and Reconstruction, First Edition*, American Petroleum Institute.

ASCE 7, 1995, *Minimum Design Loads for Buildings and Other Structures, ANSI/ASCE 7-95*, American Society of Civil Engineers, New York, NY.

ASCE 8, 1990, *Specification for the Design of Cold-Formed Stainless Steel Structural Members, ANSI/ASCE 8-90*, American Society of Civil Engineers, New York, NY.

ASCE, 1984, *Guidelines for the Seismic Design of Oil and Gas Pipeline Systems*, American Society of Civil Engineers, Committee on Gas and Liquid Fuel Lifelines, New York, New York.

ASME B31.3, 1993, *Chemical Plant Petroleum Refinery Piping* (*ASME B31.3*), American Society of Mechanical Engineers.

ASME RTP-1-92, 1992, *Reinforced Thermoset Plastic Corrosion Resistant Equipment* (*ASME RTP-1-92*), American Society of Mechanical Engineers, New York, NY.

ASME, 1992, *Boiler and Pressure Vessel Code*, American Society of Mechanical Engineers, New York, NY.

ASTM D32.99-88, 1988, *Standard Specification for Filament-Wound Glass-Fiber-Reinforced Thermoset Resin Chemical-Resistant Tanks*, American Society for Testing and Materials, Philadelphia, PA.

ATC-14, *Evaluating the Seismic Resistance of Existing Buildings,* Applied Technology Council, Redwood City, CA.

ATC-20, 1988, *Procedures for Postearthquake Safety Evaluation of Buildings (ATC-20),* Applied Technology Council, Redwood City, CA.

ATC-3-06, 1978, *Tentative Provisions for the Development of Seismic Regulations for Buildings,* Applied Technology Council, Redwood City, CA.

ATC-33.03, 1995, *Guidelines for the Seismic Rehabilitation of Buildings*, 75% Complete Draft, Applied Technology Council.

Atkinson, G. M., and D. M. Boore, 1995, "Ground Motion Relations for Eastern North America," *Bulletin of Seismological Society of America*, Vol. 85, pp. 17-30.

AWWA D100-84, 1985, *AWWA Standard for Welded Steel Tanks for Water Storage (ANSI/AWWA D100-84)*, American Water Works Association.

AWWA D110-86, 1987, *AWWA Standard for Wire-Wound Circular Prestressed-Concrete Water Tanks* (*ANSI/AWWA D110-86*), American Water Works Association.

Bechtel Power Corporation, 1980, "Seismic Analyses of Structures and Equipment for Nuclear Power Plants," Bechtel Design Guide C2.44, Rev. 0.

BOCA, 1994, *The BOCA National Building Code* , Building Officials and Code Administrators International.

Boore, D. M., and W. B. Joyner, 1991, "Estimation of Ground Motion at Deep-Soil Sites in Eastern North America," *Bulletin of Seismological Society of America*, Vol. 81, pp. 2167-2185.

Boore, D. M., W. B. Joyner, and T. E. Fumal, 1993, "Estimation of Response Spectra and Peak Accelerations from Western North American Earthquakes: An Interim Report," Open File Report 93-509, 94-127, and 1995 Addendum, U.S. Geological Survey, Menlo Park, CA.

California Building Code - Title 24, 1991, California Building Standards Commission, Sacramento, CA.

Campbell, K. W., and Y. Bozorgnia, 1994, "Near-Source Attenuation of Peak Horizontal Acceleration from Worldwide Accelerograms Recorded From 1957 to 1993", in *Proceedings, Fifth U.S. National Conference on Earthquake Engineering*, Vol. III, Chicago, IL.

Cornell, C. A., 1968, "Engineering Seismic Risk Analysis," *Bulletin of the Seismological Society of America*, Vol. 58, no. 5, pp. 1583-1605.

Cornell, C. A., and E. H. Vanmarcke, 1969, "The Major Influences of Seismic Risk," In *Proceedings of the Fourth World Conferences on Earthquake Engineering, Santiago, Chile*, Vol. 1, pp. 69-83.

Crouse, C. B., 1991, "Ground Motion Attenuation Equations for Earthquakes on the Cascadia Zone," *Earthquake Spectra*, Vol. 7, No. 2, pp. 201-236, and Errata to Crouse (1991a), *Earthquake Spectra*, Vol. 7, No. 3, pp. 506.

Crouse, C., B, and J. W. McGuire, 1994, "Site Response Studies for Purpose of Revising NEHRP Seismic Provisions," In *Proceedings of Strong Motion Instrumentation Program (SMIP94)*, California Division of Mines and Geology, Sacramento, CA.

Der Kiureghian and Ang, August 1977, "A Fault -Rupture Model for Seismic Risk Analysis," *Bulletin of Seismological Society of America*, Vol. 67, No. 4, pp 1173-1194.

DOE 1020, 1994, "Natural Phenomena Hazards Design and Evaluation Criteria for Department of Energy Facilities," DOE-STD-1020, U.S. Department of Energy, Washington D.C.

Dowling M. J., and P. B. Summers, June 21-24, 1993, "Assessment and Mitigation of Seismic Hazards for Unanchored Liquid Storage Tanks," Presented at the Independent Liquid Terminals Association Bulk Liquid Transfer and Above-Ground Storage Tank Terminals Conference, Houston, TX.

Dowrick, D. J., 1987, "Earthquake Resistance Design for Engineers and Architects," (Second Edition), John Wiley & Sons, New York, NY, 519 p.

EERI, 1994, *Liquefaction*, Earthquake Basics Brief No. 1, Earthquake Engineering Research Institute.

EERI, May 1990, *Loma Prieta Reconnaissance Report*, Earthquake Engineering Research Institute, El Cerrito, CA.

EERL, June 1971, *Engineering Features of the San Fernando Earthquake, February 9, 1971*, Earthquake Engineering Research Laboratory, Pasadena, CA.

Egan, J. A., F. I., Makdisi, and D. Rosidi, 1994, "Near-Field Vertical Ground Motions from the 17 January 1994 Northridge Earthquake: Where they Unusual?," Poster Presented at SSA-94, 89th Annual Meeting of the Seismological Society of America, April 5-7, Pasadena, CA, Abstract No. 46 in Program for Northridge Earthquake Abstracts.

EQE, 1986a, "Affects of the March 3, 1985 Chile Earthquake on Power and Industrial Facilities," San Francisco, CA.

EQE, 1986b, "Post-Earthquake Investigation: Planning and Field Guide," (NP-4611-SR), Prepared for the Electric Power Research Institute, Palo Alto, CA.

Esfandiari, S., and P. B. Summers, 1994, "Seismic Analysis and Load Determination in Support of Seismic Evaluation and Design of Petrochemical Facilities," American Power Conference, Chicago, IL, April 24-27, 1994.

FEMA-178, 1992, *Handbook for the Seismic Evaluation of Existing Buildings*, Building Seismic Safety Council, Washington, DC.

Gazetas, G., 1991, "Chapter 15 - Foundation Vibrations," *Foundation Engineering Handbook*, H. Y. Fang (editor), Van Nostrand Reinhold, NY.

Gutenberg, B., and C. F. Richter, 1956, "Earthquake Magnitude, Intensity, Energy, and Acceleration," *Bulletin of the Seismological Society of America*. 46:105-145.

Hadjian, A. H., R. B. Fallgren, M. R. Tufenkian, 1992,. "Dynamic Soil-Pile-Structure Interaction; The State-of-the-Practice," *Piles Under Dynamic Loading*,

Geotechnical Special Publication No. 34., S. Prakash (editor), pp. 1-26, ASCE, NY.

Hanks T. C., and H. Kanamoria, 1979, "A Moment Magnitude Scale," *Journal of Geophysical Research*, 84:2348-2350.

Heaton, T., F. Tajima, and A. W. Mori, 1986, "Estimating Ground Motions Using Recorded Accelerograms," *Surveys in Geophysics*, 8:25-83.

Housner, G. W., and M. A. Haroun, 1980, "Seismic Design of Liquid Storage Tanks," ASCE Convention and Exposition, Portland, Oregon, April 14-18, 1980.

Housner, G. W., October 1977, "Dynamic Pressures on Accelerated Fluid Containers," *Bulletin of the Seismological Society of America*, Volume 47, pp. 15-35.

Houston, J. R., and A. W. Garcia, 1978, "Type 16 Flood Insurance Study: Tsunami Predictions For Pacific Coastal Communities," U.S. Army Corps of Engineers Waterways Experiment Station Technical Report H-78-26, 38 p.

Itasca Consulting Group, Inc., 1995, *Fast Lagrangian Analysis of Continua, User's Manual*, FLAC Version 3.3.

Joyner, W. B., and D. E. Boore, 1988, "Measurement, Characterization, and Prediction of Strong Ground Motion," In *Proceedings of the ASCE Geotechnical Division Specialty Conference on Earthquake Engineering and Soil Dynamics*, Park City, Utah, pp. 43-102.

Krinitzsky, E. L., J. P. Gould, P. H. Edinger, 1993, "Fundamentals of Earthquake Resistant Construction," John Wiley, NY.

Lai, C. S., 1979, "Behavior of Retaining Walls Under Seismic Loading," ME Report 79/9, Dept. Of Civil Engineering, University of Canterbury, Christchurch, New Zealand.

Ledbetter, R. H.,1985, "Improvement of Liquefiable Foundation Conditions Beneath Existing Structures," *Technical Report REMR-GT-2*, U.S., Army Corps of Engineers, Washington, DC.

Manos, G. W., August 1986, "Earthquake Tank-Wall Stability of Unanchored Tanks," American Society of Civil Engineers, *Journal of Structural Engineering*, Vol. 112, No. 8, including Erratum in *Journal of Structural Engineering*, Vol. 113, No. 3, March 1987.

McCulloch, 1985, "Evaluating Tsunami Potential," Ziony, J. I., ed., "Evaluating Earthquake Hazards in the Los Angeles Region," *U.S. Geological Survey Professional Paper 1360*, p. 375-413.

Merz, H. A., and C. A. Cornell, December 1973, "Seismic Risk Analysis Based on a Quadratic Frequency Model," Bulletin of the Seismological Society of America, Vol. 63, No. 6, pp. 1999-2006.

Mononobe, M, and H. Matsuo, 1929, "On the Determination of Earth Pressures During Earthquakes," In *Proceedings World Engineering Congress*, 9.

Nadim, F. and R. V. Whitman, July 1983, "Seismically Induced Movement of Retaining Walls," *Journal of Geotechnical Civil Engineering* (ASCE) 109(7), 915-931.

Nadim, F., 1980, "Tilting and Sliding of Gravity Retaining Walls," S.M. Thesis, Res. Rpt. R82-33, Dept. of Civil Engineering, MIT, Cambridge, CA.

Nadim, F., and R. V. Whitman, 1984, "Coupled Sliding and Tilting of Gravity Retaining Walls During Earthquakes," In *Proceedings 8th World Conference on Earthquake Engineering*, San Francisco, III, 1984, 477-484.

National Research Council, Committee of the Alaska Earthquake of the Division of Earth Sciences, 1973, "The Great Alaska Earthquake of 1964," National Research Council, National Academy of Sciences, Washington, DC.

NEHRP, 1994, *NEHRP Recommended Provisions for the Development of Seismic Regulations for New Buildings*, National Earthquake Hazards Reduction Program, by the Building Seismic Safety Council for the Federal Emergency Management Agency, Washington, DC.

Newmark, N. W., and W. J. Hall, 1982, "Earthquake Spectra and Design," Earthquake Engineering Research Institute.

Nisar, A., and R. Golesorkhi, 1994, "Development of Vertical Design Response Spectrum for Use in the Near Field," Paper in Preparation for Fifth International Conference on Seismic Zonation to be held in Nice, France during October 117-19, 1995.

Nogami, T., H. W. Jones, and R. L. Mosher, 1991, "Seismic Response Analysis of Pile-Supported Structure: Assessment of Commonly Used Approximations," In *Proceedings, Second International Conference on Recent Advantages in Geotechnical Earthquake Engineering and Soil Dynamics*, S. Prakash (editor), St. Louis, MO.

Nogami, T., J. Otani, K. Konagai, and H. L. Chen, 1992, "Nonlinear Soil-Pile Interaction Model for Dynamic Lateral Motion," *Journal of Geotechnical Engineering*, ASCE, Vol. 118, No. 1, pp. 89-106.

Okabe, S., 1926, "General Theory of Earth Pressures," *J. Japan Soc. of Civil Engineering* 12(1).

OSHA, *29 CFR 1910, Occupational Safety and Health Administration Standards*, U.S. Department of Labor.

Peek, R., and M. El-Bkaily, October 1990, "Post-Buckling Behavior of Unanchored Steel Tanks Under Lateral Loading," *Journal of Pressure Vessel Technology.*

Prakash, S., 1992, "Piles Under Dynamic Loading," *Geotechnical Special Publication No. 34*, ASCE, NY.

Prakash, S., and Saran, S., 1966, "Static and Dynamic Earth Pressures Behind Retaining Walls," In *Proceedings, 3rd Symposium on Earthquake Engineering*, Roorkee, India, pp. 277-288.

Priestley, M. J. N. (Editor and Chairman), et al, December 1986, "*Seismic Design of Storage Tanks*," Study Group of the New Zealand National Society for Earthquake Engineering.

Reiter L., 1990, "Earthquake Hazard Analysis Issues and Insights," Published by Columbia University Press, New York.

Richter P.J., unpublished, "Nonlinear Analysis to Evaluate Distribution of Frictional Forces to Horizontal Vessel Support Piers," Fluor Daniel, Irvine, CA.

Richter, C. F. , 1958, "Elementary Seismology," W. H. Freeman, San Francisco, CA.

RMI, 1990, *Specification for the Design, Testing, and Utilization of Industrial Steel Storage Racks*, Rack Manufacturers Institute.

RMPP, June 1992, *Proposed Guidance for RMPP Seismic Assessments*, Prepared by the RMPP Seismic Guidance Committee for the RMPP Sub-committee of the Southern California Fire Chief Association.

SAC Joint Ventures, 1995, *Steel Moment Frame Structures - Interim Guidelines*, Report No. SAC-95-02.

SBC, 1994, *Standard Building Code*, Southern Building Code Congress International, Birmingham, AL.

Schnabel, P. N., J. Lysmer, and H. B. Seed, December 1972, "SHAKE, A computer Program for Earthquake Response Analysis of Horizontally Layered Sites," EERC Report No. 72-12, Earthquake Engineering Research Center, University of California, Berkeley.

SEAOC, 1990, *Recommended Lateral Force Requirements and Commentary*, Seismology Committee of the Structural Engineers Association of California, Sacramento, CA.

Seed, H. B., and I. M. Idriss, 1982, "Ground Motions and Soil Liquefaction During Earthquakes," Earthquake Engineering Research Institute.

Seed, H. B., and R. V. Whitman, 1970, "Design of Earth Retaining Structures for Dynamic Loads," ASCE Specialty Conf., Lateral Stresses in the Ground and Design of Earth Retaining Structures, 103-147.

Seed, H. B., R. C. Chaney, and P Sibel, 1991, "Chapter 16 - Earthquake Effects on Soil-Foundation Systems," *Foundation Engineering Handbook*, 2nd Edition, H. Y. Fang (editor), Van Nostrand Reinhold.

SJI, 1990, *Standard Specification Load Tables and Weight Tables for Steel Joists and Joist Girders*, Steel Joist Institute.

Summers, P. B., and P. A. Hults, 1994, "Seismic Evaluation of Existing Tanks at Grade," American Power Conference, Chicago, IL, April 24-27, 1994.

U.S. Nuclear Regulatory Commission, 1973, "Regulatory Guide 1.60 - Deisgn Response Spectra for Seismic Design of Nuclear Power Plants," Nuclear Regulatory Commission, Washington, DC.

UBC, 1994, *Uniform Building Code*, International Conference of Building Officials, Whittier, CA.

Whitman , R. V., 1990, "Seismic Design and Behavior of Gravity Retaining Walls: Design and Performance of Earth Retaining Structures," ASCE Geotechnical Special Publication 25, 817-842.

Wolf, J. P., 1985, "Dynamic Soil-Structure Interaction," Prentice-Hall, Inc., Englewood Cliffs, NJ 07632.

Wozniak, R. S., and Mitchell, W. W., May 1978, "Basis of Seismic Design Provisions for Welded Steel Oil Storage Tanks," Presented at the Session on Advances in Storage Tank Design, API Refining, 43rd Midyear Meeting, Toronto, Canada.

Youngs, R. R. and K. J. Coppersmith, 1985, "Implications of Fault Slip Rates and Earthquake Recurrence Models to Probabilistic Seismic Hazard Estimates," *Bulletin of Seismological Society of America*, Vol. 75, No. 4.

Zarrabi, **K.**, 1973, "Sliding of Gravity Retaining Wall During Earthquakes Considering Vertical Acceleration and Changing Inclination of Failure Surface," SM Thesis, Dept. of Civil Engineering, MIT, Cambridge, MA.

INDEX

F

G

H

P

Q

R

S

Z